A NEW COURSE IN GEOMETRY

A NEW COURSE IN GEOMETRY

by

A. Walker, M.A., B.Sc.(Lond.)
and
J. Millar, M.A.(Hons.)

Complete Edition
(with answers)

Part 1 (without answers)

Part 2 (without answers)

A NEW COURSE IN ARITHMETIC

Complete Edition
(with or without answers)

Part 1 (without answers)

Part 2 (without answers)

A NEW COURSE IN ALGEBRA

Complete Edition
(with answers)

Part 1 (with answers)

Part 1 (without answers)

Part 2 (with answers)

Part 2 (without answers)

A NEW COURSE IN GEOMETRY

BY

A. WALKER, M.A., B.Sc.(Lond.)

Formerly Headmaster, Jordanhill College School, Glasgow

AND

J. MILLAR, M.A.(Hons.)

Principal Teacher of Mathematics,
Dollar Academy

WITH ANSWERS

1724

LONGMANS

LONGMANS, GREEN AND CO LTD
48 Grosvenor Street, London W1

*Associated companies, branches and representatives
throughout the world*

First published 1954
Eighth impression 1964

Made and Printed in Great Britain by Butler & Tanner Ltd, Frome and London

GENERAL PREFACE

This book has been written in accordance with the modern trend in the teaching of Geometry, as shown, for example, in the recent booklet issued by the Scottish Education Department. The number of propositions with formal proofs has been reduced and stress laid on the solution of problems, attention being directed to the methodical arrangement of such solutions. In addition reference to Solid Geometry is made throughout the course.

The fundamental trigonometrical ratios have been introduced and use made of the methods of both Algebra and Trigonometry.

The Introduction is designed to acquaint the pupil with the basic facts of Geometry and to train him in the use of geometrical instruments.

The large number of Examples together with Revision Papers and Examination Papers should provide sufficient practice at all stages.

The book covers the work in Geometry for the Scottish Leaving Certificate, for the English Certificate of Education (Ordinary Level), and for the Preliminary Examinations of the Universities.

We gratefully acknowledge the permission granted by the following examining bodies to include questions set by them at various examinations :

H.M. Stationery Office ; Senate of Glasgow University ; Senate of London University ; Local Examinations Syndicate, University of Cambridge ; Local Examinations Syndicate, University of Oxford ; Joint Matriculation Board of the Northern Universities of England ; Examination Board of the University of Bristol.

CONTENTS

Book II

Book III

SYMBOLS

≡ stands for is congruent to.   ∠, ⌒ stands for angle.

\>   ,,   ,, is greater than.   △   ,,   ,, triangle.

\<   ,,   ,, is less than.   ⊙   ,,   ,, circle.

∴   ,,   ,, therefore.

ABBREVIATIONS

adj.	stands for	adjacent.
alt.	,, ,,	alternate.
bet.	,, ,,	between.
coint.	,, ,,	cointerior.
constr.	,, ,,	construction.
cor.	,, ,,	corollary.
corresp.	,, ,,	corresponding.
diag.	,, ,,	diagonal.
eq.	,, ,,	equal.
ext.	,, ,,	exterior.
fig.	,, ,,	figure.
hyp.	,, ,,	hypotenuse.
incl.	,, ,,	included.
int.	,, ,,	interior.
isos.	,, ,,	isosceles.
opp.	,, ,,	opposite.
parl.	,, ,,	parallel.
parm.	stands for	parallelogram.
perp.	,, ,,	perpendicular.
pt.	,, ,,	point.
prop.	,, ,,	proportional.
quad.	,, ,,	quadrilateral.
rad.	,, ,,	radius.
rect.	,, ,,	rectangle.
resp.	,, ,,	respectively.
rt.	,, ,,	right.
seg.	,, ,,	segment.
sim.	,, ,,	similar.
supp.	,, ,,	supplementary.
sq.	,, ,,	square.
str.	,, ,,	straight.
th.	,, ,,	theorem.
vert.	,, ,,	vertically.

INTRODUCTION

The word Geometry comes from two Greek words, ge—the earth, metron—a measure, and thus means earth measurement. Triangles and parallel lines are mentioned in early Babylonian records, as is also the division of a circle into 360 parts. More attention was given to the subject in ancient Egypt, because of the necessity to re-establish land boundaries, obliterated from time to time when the river Nile overflowed its banks. The land surveys, by which these boundaries were fixed, involved the measurement of certain geometrical figures and the construction of certain angles. The development of Geometry as it is studied to-day owed more to the Greeks, however, the most famous man in this connection being Euclid, who lived about 300 B.C. His book on Geometry was the textbook studied in schools until the beginning of this century, that is, for over 2,000 years, and it is still the foundation of the elementary work in the subject.

FUNDAMENTAL IDEAS

Solids.—In our everyday lives we are constantly coming into contact with an endless variety of things, whether it be in our homes, in our journeys to and from school, at work, or at play —books, pencils, marbles, cricket bats, cars, the air we breathe and the food we eat, and the list can be added to indefinitely. We can classify them in any way we please, by weight, by colour, or by age, but in spite of the endless diversity of the objects we have listed, there is an important property that they all possess. Each takes up a certain amount of room or space.

Anything which takes up space is spoken of as a Solid.

Thus each page of our books is a solid, however thin the paper may be. The air we breathe and the water we use have also this property of occupying space and are therefore solids. The word "solid" as used here must not be confused with the word "solid" which is used as opposed to "liquid" and "gas."

Most solids are irregular in shape, e.g. a pebble in the bed of a stream, a cloud in the sky. Geometry deals with the shape, size, and position of solids which are regular in shape, e.g. a ball, a matchbox, an unsharpened pencil . . .

The following sketches show some of the more common regular solids :

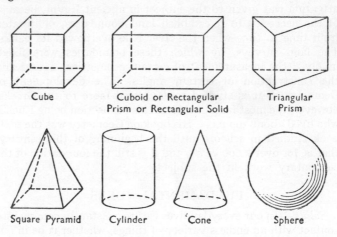

Cube

Cuboid or Rectangular
Prism or Rectangular Solid

Triangular
Prism

Square Pyramid

Cylinder

Cone

Sphere

EXERCISES 1

Nets.—If a cuboid were made of paper we could cut along some of the edges and lay the paper out as shown below. Such a figure is called a **net**.

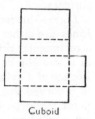

Cuboid

1. Draw the net on stiff paper, say four times the size shown, cut it out, fold along the dotted lines and bind the edges to form a cuboid.

2. Repeat Exercise 1 with the net for a triangular pyramid as shown and make the model.

Triangular Pyramid

3. Draw nets for the following solids and make the models : (*a*) Cube, (*b*) Triangular Prism, (*c*) Square Pyramid, (*d*) Cone, (*e*) Cylinder.

Surfaces.—Solids are bounded by surfaces. These surfaces separate the solids from the surrounding space. Surfaces are of two kinds, **plane** and **curved**.

The surfaces of a cube, rectangular prism, pyramid, are plane surfaces, while the surface of a sphere is curved. The nature of a surface may be tested as follows. Place a straight edge on the surface in several positions. If the straight edge is in contact with the surface throughout its whole length in all positions, then the surface is plane, and is referred to as a **plane surface** or simply as a **plane**. If the surface is not in contact with the straight edge in all positions, then the surface is a curved surface. Some surfaces, as for instance the curved surface of a cylinder or cone, answer to the test in some positions but not in all positions.

A sheet of paper, e.g. a leaf of this book, might be taken to represent a surface, but even the thinnest sheet of paper will be a geometrical solid, since it has length, breadth, and thickness, and a surface has length and breadth but no thickness. Each leaf of this book is a geometrical solid, the words being printed on the pages, which are two of its bounding surfaces.

Lines.—Surfaces intersect in lines and are bounded by lines. Lines are either **straight** or **curved.** Examine the model of a rectangular prism. When two surfaces intersect they do so in a straight line, called an edge of the prism. The curved surface of a cylinder and either of the plane surfaces intersect in a curved line. The trace made on paper by a fine pencil point might be taken to represent a line, but even the finest trace will be a geometrical solid, since it has length, breadth, and thickness, and a line has length, but no breadth and no thickness.

Points.—Lines intersect in points. Examine any face of a rectangular prism. The meeting place of two edges is called a point (a vertex of the prism). At each of the eight vertices it will be seen that three lines meet. The dot made on paper by a fine pencil point might be taken to represent a point. No matter how fine the pencil point is, however, the dot is a geometrical solid since it has length, breadth, and thickness, and a point has no length, no breadth, and no thickness. A point indicates position but has no size.

Naming of Points and Lines

A point is named by one letter, thus: •A

A line is named by two letters, thus: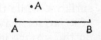

Exercises 2

The figure shown is the net of a solid.

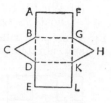

1. Name the lines of equal length.
2. What points will coincide with C when the solid is made?
3. What points will coincide with L?
4. What line will coincide with AF?
5. How many faces has the solid?
6. How many edges has it?
7. How many vertices has it?
8. What is the name of the solid?
9. Complete the following table:

Solid.	No. of Faces.	No. of Edges.	No. of Vertices.
Cube			
Square Pyramid .			
Cone			
Cylinder . . .			

10. Name a solid figure bounded by
    (a) One surface,
    (b) Two surfaces,
    (c) Three surfaces,
    (d) Four surfaces.

11. How many straight lines can be drawn through one point? How many curved lines can be drawn through two points? How many straight lines can be drawn through two points? Mark three points. How many (1) straight, (2) curved lines can be drawn through the three points?
    [*Note:* (1) Only one straight line can be drawn through two points.
    (2) If three or more points are in a straight line they are said to be **collinear**.]

12. What is (1) the greatest, (2) the least number of faces of (a) a cube, (b) a cylinder, (c) a square pyramid, that it is possible to see at one time?

13. (1) What is the shape of the water line if a wooden ball floats in water?

   (2) What is the shape of the water line if a wooden pencil floats in water?

14. Using your ruler copy carefully the following diagrams to any suitable scale:

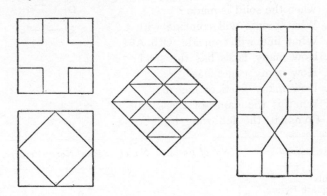

Measurement of Length

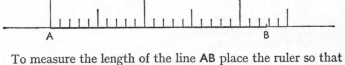

To measure the length of the line **AB** place the ruler so that the edge graduated in inches touches the line, and so that the point **A** is exactly opposite one of the inch marks on the ruler. Now count the number of complete inches and tenths of an inch between **A** and **B**. We might find that the point **B** lies between 2·2 and 2·3 in. from **A**. Mentally we divide the tenth of an inch between 2·2 and 2·3 into ten equal parts, and estimate how many of these parts lie between 2·2 and **B**. If there are seven such parts, then the length of AB is 2·27 in. It is essential to state the unit which is being used, i.e. inches or centimetres, which are written in. and cm.

A line is said to be **bisected** when it is divided into two parts of equal length.

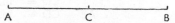

A   C   B

Thus if the line **AB** is bisected at the point **C** the parts **AC** and **CB** are equal in length and we write **AC = CB**.

Exercises 3

1. Draw a line **AB** 5 in. long. Measure its length in centimetres and hence find the number of centimetres in 1 in. Answer correct to 2 dec. pl.

2. Draw a line **AB** 10 cm. long. Measure its length in inches and hence find the number of inches in 1 cm. Answer correct to 2 dec. pl.

3.

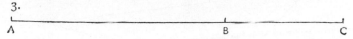

A   B   C

Measure in inches the lines **AB** and **BC** and find their sum. Write down the results as follows:

$$
\begin{aligned}
\mathbf{AB} &= \text{ in.} \\
\mathbf{BC} &= \text{ in.} \\
\mathbf{AB + BC} &= \text{ in.} \\
\text{i.e. } \mathbf{AC} &= \text{ in.}
\end{aligned}
$$

Check by measuring the length of **AC**.

4.

A   C   B

Measure in centimetres the lines **AB** and **CB** and find their difference. Write down the results as follows:

$$
\begin{aligned}
\mathbf{AB} &= \text{ cm.} \\
\mathbf{CB} &= \text{ cm.} \\
\mathbf{AB - CB} &= \text{ cm.} \\
\text{i.e. } \mathbf{AC} &= \text{ cm.}
\end{aligned}
$$

Check by measuring the length of **AC**.

5. Draw any two straight lines **AB** and **CD**. Now draw a third straight line **XY**, whose length you estimate to be equal to the sum of the lengths of **AB** and **CD**. Check your estimate by measurement and find your error.

Write down the results as follows:

$$\begin{aligned} \text{By measurement } AB &= \quad \text{in.} \\ CD &= \quad \text{in.} \\ AB + CD &= \quad \text{in.} \\ XY &= \quad \text{in.} \\ \text{Error} &= \quad \text{in.} \end{aligned}$$

6. Estimate and check by measurement the lengths of the lines named in the following figure:

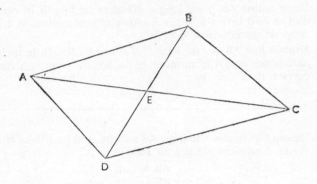

Complete the following table:

Line.	Estimated Length.	Actual Length.	Error.
AB			
BC			
CD			
DA			
AC			
BD			
AE			
EC			
BE			
ED			

Check that $AE + EC = AC$, and that $BE + ED = BD$.

7. The figure ABC is called a **tri-angle.** Draw any triangle ABC. Find by measurement the mid-points E and F of the sides AC and AB respectively. Draw the lines BE and CF and name the point, in which they intersect, G. Draw a straight line through A and G to meet BC at D. Measure BD and DC. What do you notice about them? Measure AD and GD. What do you notice about them? Find two other straight lines related in the same way as AD and GD.

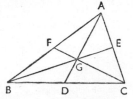

[*Note:* The straight line joining any vertex of a triangle to the mid-point of the opposite side is called a **median.** In the figure above AD, BE, CF are medians of the triangle ABC.]

8. Estimate the lengths of CA and CB. Measure them with your ruler and show that they are equal. (The point C is said to be **equidistant** from A and B.) Mark another

point which you think is equidistant from A and B and check by measurement. Find several points which you consider to be equidistant from A and B. Where do they all lie?

9. Mark a point A on your paper. Find a point which is 2 in. from A. Find two more points also 2 in. from A. Now mark by sight several points 2 in. from A. Where do they all lie?

✕ A

✕   ✕
B   C

10. **A, B, C** are three villages on a map on which every inch represents a mile. Estimate the distances from **A** to **B**, **B** to **C**, **C** to **A** and check by measurement. Try to mark on the map the point at which you would build a school so that it would be the same distance from all three villages. Check by measurement.

Horizontal, Vertical, and Oblique Lines and Planes

When a stone hangs freely from the end of a string, we say that the string is **vertical.** The string represents a line in a vertical direction. When a stone held in the hand is released, it falls directly to the ground. We say it falls vertically.

A builder uses a plumb-line to ensure that the walls of buildings are vertical. The surface of the wall is then said to be a **vertical plane.**

The floor of a room forms a **horizontal plane** and is tested by a spirit-level.

Two walls of a room thus meet in a vertical line and the floor or ceiling meets each of the walls in horizontal lines. Planes and straight lines which are neither vertical nor horizontal are said to be **oblique.**

EXERCISES 4

1. Point (1) vertically upwards, (2) vertically downwards.
2. How many (1) horizontal, (2) vertical lines can be drawn through a given point ?
3. Point in a horizontal direction. Turn once completely round while still pointing. Does this direction remain horizontal ?
4. What kind of plane is formed by the surface of the water in a water-tank ?
5. Tilt the water-tank in any direction. Does the nature of the surface change ?
6. Float a match in a basin filled with water. Is the match horizontal ? If all the matches in a box were emptied into the water in the basin would the matches all point in the same direction? Would all the matches be horizontal?
7. How many horizontal lines can be drawn on a horizontal plane ?
8. What kind of line is represented by the wire which supports the electric light in your room ?
9. In a large room, lit by many such lights, do the wires all run in the same direction ? Are they all vertical ?
10. (a) Do all horizontal lines run in the same direction ? (b) Do all vertical lines run in the same direction ?
11. How many vertical lines can be drawn on a horizontal plane ?
12. How many horizontal lines can be drawn on a vertical plane ?
13. Fix a point in a vertical plane. How many (1) horizontal, (2) vertical, lines lying in the plane can be drawn through the point ?
14. Fix a point in a horizontal plane. How many (1) horizontal, (2) vertical, lines lying in the plane can be drawn through the point ?
15. How many (1) horizontal, (2) vertical, lines can be drawn on an oblique plane ?
16. How many (1) horizontal, (2) vertical, lines can be drawn through a given point on an oblique plane ?

17. " If a vertical line can be drawn on a plane, then the plane must be a vertical plane." Is this correct ?

18. " If a horizontal line can be drawn on a plane, then the plane must be a horizontal plane." Is this correct ?

19. Place a cube on a horizontal plane. How many edges are horizontal ? How many are vertical ? How many faces are horizontal ? How many are vertical ?

20. Tilt the cube about one of its edges on the horizontal plane. How many edges are now horizontal ? How many are vertical ? How many faces are now horizontal ? How many faces are now vertical ?

21. If one edge of a cube is vertical, how many more must be vertical ? How many edges must be horizontal ?

22. The figure shows a square pyramid standing on a horizontal plane. Name any (1) horizontal lines, (2) vertical lines, (3) oblique lines.

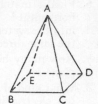

23. The figure shows a cuboid resting on a horizontal plane. What kind of lines are AE, HG, GC, EH, BH, FG, AG, EB ? If the cuboid is turned about the edge EH, which remains touching the table, what kind of lines do the above lines become ?

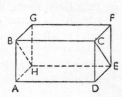

ANGLES

Angle.—When two straight lines meet they are said to form an angle. The straight lines OA and OB meet at O and they are said to form the angle AOB, written AÔB. The lines OA and OB are called the **arms** of the angle, and the point O is called the **vertex** of the angle.

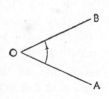

Three letters are generally necessary to name an angle and the middle one of the three is the vertex of the angle. When there is no doubt as to which angle is intended, one letter only may be used. Thus, in the figure above, we can name the angle AÔB or simply Ô.

Sometimes the symbol ∠ is used for the word angle. The size of the angle may be regarded as the amount of turning necessary to bring a straight line, rotating about O in a counter-clockwise direction, from the position OA to the position OB.

Two angles ABC and DEF are said to be equal when the one can be made to fit exactly on to the other. Imagine the figures cut out of the paper. Place the vertex B on the vertex E, so that the arm BA lies along the arm ED. Then if the arm BC can be made to lie exactly

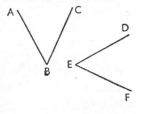

along the arm EF, the angles are equal in size. It is not necessary for the point A to lie on the point D or for the point C to lie on the point F. The size of an angle does not depend on the lengths of its arms. The size of an angle is not altered by lengthening or shortening its arms. The size depends only on the amount of turning from the position BC to the position BA or from the position EF to the position ED.

Adjacent Angles.—When two angles have a common vertex and lie on opposite sides of a common arm, they are said to be **adjacent** angles. Thus in the figure AÔB and BÔC are adjacent angles because

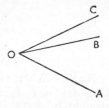

(1) they have a common vertex O,
(2) they have a common arm OB,
(3) they lie on opposite sides of OB.

Notice that all three conditions must be fulfilled. In the figure AÔB and AÔC have a common vertex O and a common arm OA, and, therefore, the first two conditions are fulfilled. Both angles lie on the same side of OA, so the third condition is not fulfilled, and so these angles are not adjacent angles.

Vertically Opposite Angles.—When two straight lines intersect vertically opposite angles are formed.

Thus in the figure the straight lines AB and CD intersect at O and form two pairs of vertically opposite angles.

AÔC and BÔD are vertically opposite angles.

AÔD and BÔC are vertically opposite angles.

Measurement of Angles

When a straight line starts turning about a point, and continues to turn in the same direction, until it returns to its original position, the line is said to have turned through a **complete rotation**.

A **straight angle** is an angle whose arms lie in one straight line. In the figure AÔB is a straight angle, the arm OA having turned about the point O until it has reached the position OB, such that BO and OA are in one straight line.

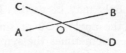

If the arm OB were to continue turning in the same direction until it had reached the original position OA, it would turn through another straight angle BOA. Since it would then have turned through one complete rotation, it follows that

2 straight angles = 1 complete rotation.

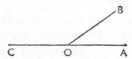

In the above figure COA is a straight line, and the sum of the adjacent angles AOB and BOC is one straight angle. If now we rotate the common arm OB about O, in the direction towards OC, the angle AOB will increase and the angle BOC will decrease. In one position the two adjacent angles will be equal and each is then called a **right angle**. AÔB and BÔC are then both right angles. We therefore define a right angle as follows:

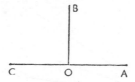

When one straight line stands on another straight line in such a way as to make the adjacent angles equal, each angle is a right angle.

It is clear that, since the two equal angles AOB and BOC are together equal to one straight angle,

2 right angles = 1 straight angle.

The complete rotation is divided into 360 equal angles, each of which is called one degree, written 1°.

We therefore get the following table:

I complete rotation = 360°
I straight angle = 180°
I right angle = 90°

The degree is further divided into 60 equal parts, called minutes, and each minute is divided into 60 equal parts, called seconds.

I degree = 60 minutes, written 60′
I minute = 60 seconds, written 60″

Supplementary Angles.—Two angles are said to be supplementary when their sum is two right angles. Each is called the supplement of the other. Thus angles of 30° and 150° are supplementary, as are also angles of 87° 13′ and 92° 47′.

Complementary Angles.—Two angles are said to be complementary when their sum is one right angle. Each is called the complement of the other. Thus angles of 20° and 70° are complementary, as are also angles of 41° 37′ and 48° 23′.

EXERCISES 5

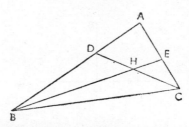

1. In the figure name
   (1) 3 angles with vertex H,
   (2) 2 angles with vertex C,
   (3) the vertex and the arms of HÊC and of AD̂C.
2. Through what angle does the minute hand of a clock turn between 6 p.m. and 7 p.m.?
3. Through what angle does the hour hand turn between 6 p.m. and 7 p.m.?

4. Through what angle does the minute hand of a clock turn between 2.15 a.m. and 4.15 a.m. ?

5. What is the size of the angle between the hands of a clock at (1) 3 o'clock, (2) 6 o'clock, (3) 8 o'clock ?

6. Through what angle does the minute hand turn between 5.10 p.m. and 5.25 p.m. ? Through what angle does the hour hand turn in the same time ?

7. It is 12 o'clock midday. The minute hand turns through 270°. What is the time now ?

8. At what hours is there a right angle between the hands of a clock ?

9. What is the hour when the angle between the hands of a clock is (1) 60°, (2) 120°, (3) 150° ?

10. About turn ! Through what angle must you turn ?

11. Left turn ! Through what angle must you turn ?

12. Half right turn ! Through what angle must you turn ?

13. You are facing north and turn to face east. Through what angle must you turn ?

14. You are walking north and change to walk north-east. Through what angle must you turn ?

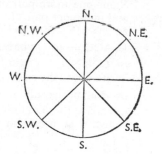

15. What is the size of the angle between the following pairs of directions :

    (1) N. and S.   (2) E. and N.
    (3) E. and S.E.   (4) S.E. and S.W.
    (5) N. and S.E.   (6) S. and N.E.

16. Write down the supplement of 20°, 70°, 79° 14′, 90°, 108° 37′, 120°, 179°.

17. Write down the complements of 10°, 30°, 45°, 51° 15′, 60°, 67° 47′, 87°, 37° 14′.

18. The angle formed at a bend in a road is 110°. Walking in either direction, through what angle must you turn at the bend?

19. A man walks east and then turns to walk south. Through what angle has he turned?

20. What angle is the same size as its supplement?

21. What angle is the same size as its complement?

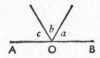

22. The angles marked *a*, *b*, *c* in the figure are all equal and AB is a straight line. What is the size of each angle?
    What kind of angles are (1) *a* and *b*, (2) *b* and *c*, (3) (*a* + *b*) and *c*, (3) *a* and (*b* + *c*)?

23. In the figure AB and CD are straight lines. What kind of angles are (1) AÔC and CÔB, (2) AÔC and BÔD? Name one more pair of adjacent angles and one more pair of vertically opposite angles.
    If AÔC = 40°, what must be the size of CÔB?
    Write down the sizes of all the angles in the figure. What do you notice about AÔC and BÔD?

24. Calculate the remaining angles in the following figure (not drawn accurately) in which two straight lines intersect.

25. In the figure AÔC is *x*°. Write down the sizes of all the angles in the figure. Can you give a reason why vertically opposite angles are always equal?

26. In the figure **AB** and **CD** are two straight lines. What kind of angles are **AOC** and **AOD**? What is their sum? Write down their sum in two different ways and find the value of x. Hence write down the sizes of all the angles in the figure.

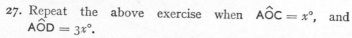

27. Repeat the above exercise when $A\hat{O}C = x°$, and $A\hat{O}D = 3x°$.

28. The figure represents a cuboid. What is the size of $A\hat{H}E$ and of $A\hat{H}G$? Name the complement of $E\hat{F}H$, and the supplement of $G\hat{O}\Gamma$. Name a pair of adjacent angles. Name a pair of vertically opposite angles.

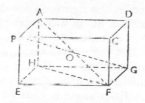

[*Note:* **AH** is at right angles to the straight lines **HE** and **HG** which intersect at **H** and are in the plane **HEFG**. **HF** is also a line in this plane, drawn from **H**. $A\hat{H}F$ is a right angle, and **AH** would be at right angles to any line drawn from **H** in the plane **HEFG**. This fact will be used from now on.]

The Protractor

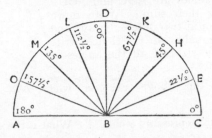

Take a circular piece of paper and halve it. Take one half and fold it in two. Open it out and mark the crease. Repeat the process of folding until the paper, when opened out, shows the creases indicated in the figure. Consider a straight line turning from the postion **BC** in a counter-clockwise direction into the position **BA**. The arms **BC** and **BA** are in one straight line, so the moving arm has turned through 180°. Hence we can mark 0° at **C** and 180° at **A**. By the construction of the figure there are eight equal angles whose sum is 180°, all with their vertices at **B**. Each angle is thus $22\frac{1}{2}$°, and hence the points **E**, **H**, **K**, etc., are marked as in the figure. This paper could be used to measure angles approximately. Such an instrument is called **a protractor**. The best type of protractor is made of celluloid. A diagram of such a protractor is shown below:

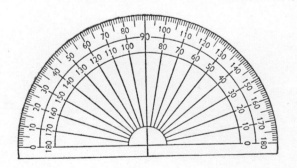

There are two sets of numbers on the protractor. One set is obtained by considering a line turning, as in the previous figure, from the position **BC** through the successive positions **BE**, **BH**, **BK**, etc., the other set by considering a line turning from the position **BA**, through the successive positions **BO**, **BM**, **BL**, etc. In the first case the line is turning in a counter-clockwise direction, in the second case the line is turning in a clockwise direction.

Care must be taken to use the correct set of numbers. Mistakes can usually be avoided by judging the size of the angle, noting particularly whether it is greater or less than 90°.

To Measure an Angle with a Protractor

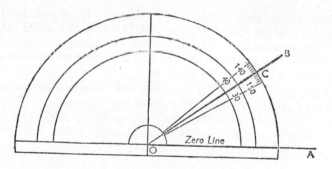

Suppose A$\hat{O}$B is the angle to be measured. Place the protractor so that the zero line lies along one arm of the angle, say **OA**, and the mid-point of the zero line lies on the vertex **O**. Note the position at which the other arm of the angle cuts the scale of the protractor. Reading on the correct set of figures, A$\hat{O}$B is seen to be 35°.

If we wish to find the size of the angle **AOB**, marked $x°$ in the figure, we measure the angle **AOB**, marked $y°$, and subtract this from 360°. (A line starting from **OA** and turning through the angles marked $x°$ and $y°$ has turned through a complete rotation or 360°.)

To Draw an Angle with a Protractor

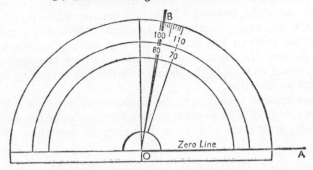

Suppose an angle of 79° is to be drawn. Draw a straight line **OA**. Place the protractor with the zero line along **OA** and the mid-point of the zero line on **O**. Using the correct scale on the protractor mark the point **B** on the paper opposite the mark for 79° on the protractor.

Remove the protractor and join **OB**. Then AÔB is the required angle. To draw an angle of 263°, first subtract 263° from 360°, and, having obtained 97°, make an angle of 97°. The angle of 263° is thus the adjacent angle which, with the angle of 97°, makes up the complete rotation.

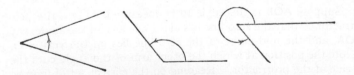

Angles are classified according to size as follows:

(1) An **acute** angle is an angle less than a right angle.

(2) An **obtuse** angle is an angle greater than a right angle, but less than a straight angle.

(3) A **reflex** angle is an angle greater than a straight angle, but less than a complete rotation.

In the figure the straight line **OA** drawn from the vertex **O** of BÔC divides BÔC into two equal parts. The angle **BOC** is said to be **bisected** by **OA**.

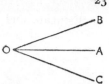

When measuring an angle always estimate its size before using the protractor.

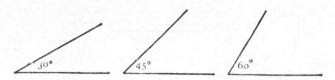

Draw angles of 30°, 45°, 60°, as above, in your jotter. Draw them in a number of different positions, and this should help you to estimate more accurately the sizes of other angles.

The two set-squares commonly used have angles of 45°, 45°, 90° and 30°, 60°, 90°.

EXERCISES 6

1. Draw angles of 33°, 67°, 127°, 218°, 321°.
2. Place the following angles in ascending order of magnitude without using a protractor :

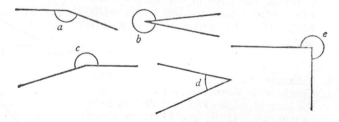

3. Why are there two readings opposite any mark on the protractor ? What do you notice about these readings ? If one reading is 65° what is the other ?

4. Estimate and then measure the angles shown below:

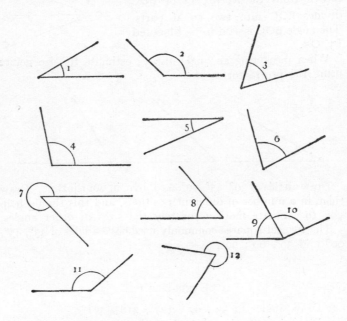

5. Estimate the sizes of the angles AOB, BOC, AOC. Measure the angles AOB, BOC. How far wrong were your estimates?

6. Estimate the sizes of $\widehat{PRS}$ and $\widehat{PRT}$. Check with your protractor. Describe the pair of angles PRS and PRT as fully as you can. If the line RP turns about R in a direction towards T draw the figure when the angle PRS ceases to be an acute angle. What then is the size of $\widehat{PRS}$?

7. Draw a figure bounded by three straight lines. The figure is called a **triangle**. Measure the three angles and find their sum. From the class results what can you say about the sum of the angles of any triangle?

8. Draw a figure bounded by four straight lines. This figure is called a **quadrilateral.** Measure the four angles and find their sum. From the class results what can you say about the sum of the angles of any quadrilateral?

> [*Note :* (1) **The sum of the angles of any triangle is two right angles.**
> (2) **The sum of the angles of any quadrilateral is four right angles.**]

9. How many obtuse angles can a triangle have?

10. How many right angles can a triangle have?

11. How many acute angles can a triangle have?

12. If all three angles of a triangle are equal, what is the size of each?

13. If one angle of a triangle is 42°, and the remaining angles are equal, what is the size of each?

14. Make an angle AOB equal to a right angle. Mark a point C on AO about 2 in. from O and from C draw a straight line CD to meet OB in D, making $D\hat{C}O = 30°$. Measure $C\hat{D}O$. How would you describe $C\hat{D}O$ and $D\hat{C}O$. Can you state, without measurement, the sizes of $A\hat{C}D$ and $B\hat{D}C$? Find the mid-point E of CD, and join EO. Measure $E\hat{O}D$ and $E\hat{O}C$ and name any pairs of angles which are equal.

15. Classify the following angles as being acute, obtuse, or reflex :

   12°, 78°, 325°, 168°, 1°, 179°, 258°, 91°.

16. You are thinking of an acute angle. What kind of angle is (1) its complement, (2) its supplement?

17. You are thinking of an obtuse angle. What kind of angle is its supplement?

18. In the figure for Exercise 14, state which angles are acute and which obtuse.

19.

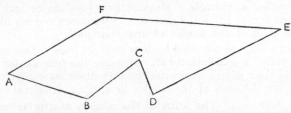

A man walks from **A** to **B**, and then from **B** to **C**, and so on until he returns to **A**. Mark the angles through which he must turn at each of the points **B, C, D, E, F** and state what kind of angle each is.

20. In the figure for Exercise 19, if the man turns to his left at **C** instead of to his right, through what kind of angle must he turn to face towards **D**?

Angles at a Point

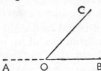

Exercise 1.—Draw an acute angle **BOC** and produce **BO** to a point **A**.

What kind of angle is **AOC**?

What is the sum of the angles **AOC** and **COB**? Give a reason for the answer in each case.

Exercise 2.—Draw an obtuse angle **BOC** and produce **BO** to a point **A**.

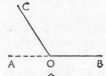

What kind of angle is **AÔC**?

What is the sum of the angles **AOC** and **COB**? Give a reason for your answer in each case.

Exercise 3.—Draw a straight line **AB** and mark a point **O** in the line. From **O**, draw any straight line **OC**.
What is the sum of the angles **AOC** and **COB**?

In the above exercises nothing has been said about the size of the angle **COB**, nor has it been necessary to measure the angles **AOC** and **COB** to find their sum. The result is true no matter what the sizes of the angles happen to be. It may be stated thus:

When one straight line stands on another straight line, the adjacent angles so formed are together equal to two right angles, or are supplementary.

Exercise 4.—Draw angle **BOC** = 65°.

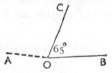

At **O** make angle **COA** equal to the supplement of 65°. What do you notice about the arms **OB** and **OA** of these adjacent angles?

Exercise 5.—Draw angle **BOC** = 146°.

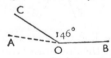

At **O** make angle **COA** equal to the supplement of 146°. What do you notice about the arms **OB** and **OA** of these adjacent angles?

The results of Exercises 4 and 5 may be stated thus:
If two adjacent angles are supplementary, their outer arms are in one straight line.

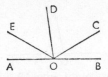

Exercise 6.—Draw a straight line AB and mark a point O in it. From O draw lines OC, OD, OE all on the same side of the straight line AB. Measure the angles BOC, COD, DOE, EOA and find their sum.

Would the answer be different if, instead of drawing three lines OC, OD, OE from O, we had drawn four or five or more lines from O ? Can you give a reason why the answer is always the same no matter how many lines are drawn from O, provided they are all drawn on the same side of AB ?

The result may be stated thus :

If from a point in a straight line any number of straight lines are drawn on one side of the line, the sum of the consecutive angles so formed is two right angles.

Exercise 7.—Draw a straight line AB and mark a point O in it.

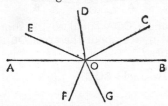

On one side of the line draw straight lines OC, OD, OE. On the other side of the line draw straight lines OF and OG. Give reasons for each of the answers to the following questions :

(1) What is the sum of the four angles BOC, COD, DOE, EOA ?

(2) What is the sum of the three angles AOF, FOG, GOB ?

(3) What is the sum of all seven angles ?

Will these results still be true if we change the number of angles on one or both sides of AB ?

If the arm OA were omitted from the figure, what will then be the sum of the six angles formed by the lines radiating from O ?

Can you give a reason why the sum of the angles so formed will always be the same ?

The result may be stated thus :

If any number of straight lines is drawn from a point, the sum of the consecutive angles so formed is four right angles.

Exercise 8. Draw any two straight lines AB and CD intersecting at O.

AÔC and BÔD are vertically opposite angles.

AÔD and BÔC are vertically opposite angles.

What is the sum of AÔC and CÔB ?

What is the sum of DÔB and BÔC ?

What can you state about the angles AOC and BOD ?

Try to prove the same fact about the angles AOD and BOC.

The result may be stated thus :

If two straight lines intersect, the vertically opposite angles are equal.

EXERCISES 7

1. ABC is a straight line. Find x.

2. DEF is a straight line. Find y.

3. XYZ is a straight line. Find a.

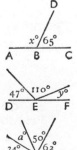

4. **ABC** is a straight line. In each case find x.

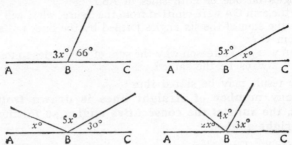

5. **AOB** is a straight line. **AÔD = DÔC.**
Find the size of each.

6. **AOB** is a straight line. **AÔE and BÔC**
are complementary and **OD** bisects
EÔC. Find x and the size of **EÔD.**

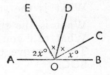

7. **AB** and **CD** are two straight lines.
Find the sizes of all the angles.

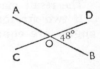

8. **AB, CD, EF** are three straight lines.
Find the sizes of all the angles.

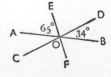

9. **AB, CD, EF** are three straight lines.
Find the sizes of all the angles.

10. Two straight lines **AB** and **CD** intersect at **O**, making AÔC a right angle. Prove that all the angles at **O** are right angles.

11. Find the values of x and y, and the size of AÔC.

12. BÔD is bisected by **OE**. Find the size of CÔB.

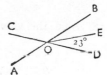

13. **OE** bisects BÔD and **OF** bisects CÔB. Find the size of CÔF, and show that EÔF = 1 right angle.

14. **OE** bisects BÔD and EÔF = 1 right angle. Show that **OF** bisects BÔC, and hence find the size of CÔF.

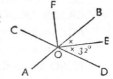

15. **OE** bisects BÔD and **OF** bisects AÔD. Prove that EÔF = 1 right angle. If **EO** is produced to **G**, prove that **OG** bisects AÔC. What is the size of FÔG?

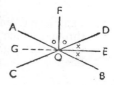

16. Find the value of x.

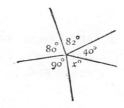

17. Find the value of x.

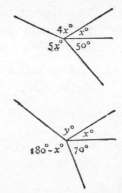

18. Find the value of y.

19. The straight lines **OC** and **AB** meet at **O** and $A\hat{O}C = C\hat{O}B$.
    The straight line **OD** makes $C\hat{O}D = 15°$.
    What is the difference between $A\hat{O}D$ and $D\hat{O}B$?
    What is their sum?

20. $A\hat{O}B$ is $42°$ and **AO** is produced to **C**. $B\hat{O}C$ is bisected by
    OD. Find the size of the reflex angle $A\hat{O}D$.

21. **OA, OB, OC, OD** are four straight lines in order such that
    $A\hat{O}C = B\hat{O}D = 90°$.
    If $B\hat{O}C = x°$, calculate the size of $A\hat{O}D$.
    If **AO** is produced to **E**, find the size of $D\hat{O}E$.

22. The dotted lines bisect the angles
    through which they pass. Find the
    size of the angle between the dotted
    lines.

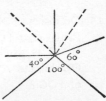

23. **AD** bisects $B\hat{A}C$ and
    $D\hat{A}E = 90°$. Find the
    size of $A\hat{E}C$.

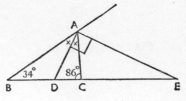

24. Find *x, y, z*.

25. **ABCD is a quadrilateral. Calculate BĈD.**

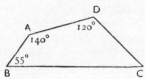

26. ABCD is a quadrilateral.   Calculate *x*.

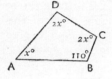

27. ABCD is a quadrilateral.   Calculate *x*.

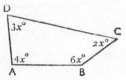

28. ABCD is a quadrilateral.   Calculate AB̂D and then AD̂B

PERPENDICULARS

When one straight line stands on another straight line in such a way as to make the adjacent angles equal, the straight lines are said to be at **right angles to,** or **perpendicular to,** each other. In the figure the angles ABC and ABD are equal, and each is, therefore, one right angle. AB and CD are at right angles to each other, or AB is perpendicular to CD.

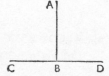

Lines at right angles to each other, or perpendicular lines, are of frequent occurrence in everyday life, e.g. the top and side edges of this page meet at right angles.

To draw a perpendicular to a given straight line XY *through a given point* O, *using a ruler and set-square.*

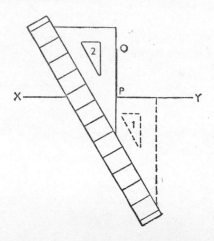

Place the set-square so that one of the short edges lies along XY [position 1 in the figure above], and place the ruler against the longest edge of the set-square. Hold the ruler firmly, and slide the set-square along till the other short edge passes through O [position 2 in the figure]. Draw the perpendicular OP.

Distance of a Point from a Line

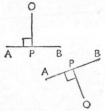

The distance of the point **O** from the line **AB** is measured by the length of the perpendicular **OP** drawn from the point **O** to the line **AB**.

From a point **O** any number of straight lines can be drawn to points in **AB**, e.g. **OQ**, **OR**, **OS**, **OT**. It will be shown later

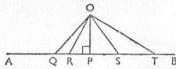

that **OP**, the perpendicular from **O** to **AB**, is the shortest of all such lines.

Parallels

Parallel straight lines are straight lines which lie in the same plane, and which do not meet however far they are produced beyond both ends.

The words " lie in the same plane " must be carefully noted. Two straight lines might not meet however far they were produced beyond both ends, and yet not be parallel, because they did not lie in the same plane. Such lines are called **skew** lines.

The figure represents a rectangular prism. **AB** and **DC** are parallel because they lie in the same plane **ABCD** and do not meet however far they are produced beyond both ends. Similarly **BC** and **HE** are parallel. They lie in the plane **BEHC**. But **GF** and **CD** are not parallel, because, although they do not meet however far they are produced beyond both ends, they do not lie in the same plane.

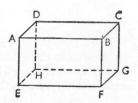

GF and **CD** are skew lines.

. The figure represents a triangular pyramid.   **AB** and **CD** are skew lines.

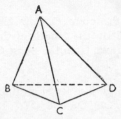

We might have said that parallel straight lines are straight lines which are in the same direction.   Thus two lines each running due East and West are parallel.   Are any two vertical lines parallel ?   Are any two horizontal lines parallel ?

To draw a parallel to a given straight line **XY**, *through a given point* **O**, *using ruler and set-square.*

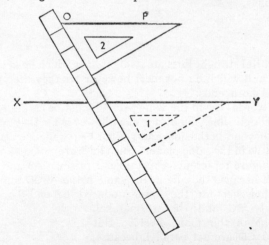

Place the set-square so that the longest edge lies along **XY** [position 1 in the figure above], and place the ruler against one of the short edges.   Hold the ruler firmly, and slide the set-square along it till the longest edge passes through **O** [position 2 in the figure].   Draw the parallel **OP**.

Transversal Diagram

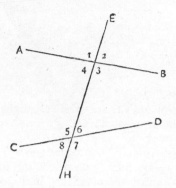

AB and CD are two straight lines, each of which is cut by a third straight line EH. This line EH is called a **transversal**. The transversal forms with the other two lines eight angles, numbered 1 to 8 in the figure.

The eight angles are classified thus :

(1) 1, 2, 7, 8 are **exterior** angles.

(2) 3, 4, 5, 6 are **interior** angles.

(3) The pairs of angles, 1, 5 ; 2, 6 ; 3, 7 ; 4, 8 are called **corresponding** angles (or sometimes F angles).

(4) The pairs of angles 3, 5 ; 4, 6 are called **alternate** angles (or sometimes Z angles).

(5) The pairs of angles, 4, 5 ; 3, 6 are called **co-interior** angles.

If now we make the lines AB and CD parallel, and draw the transversal EH, we can show that

(1) corresponding angles are equal,

(2) alternate angles are equal,

(3) co-interior angles are supplementary.

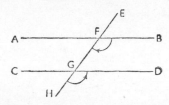

(1) *Corresponding Angles*

In the figure **AB** and **CD** are parallel straight lines, crossed at **F** and **G** by the transversal **EH**.

Suppose we wish to walk from **A** to **D** along the path **AFGD**. We have to make two turns, one at **F**, the other at **G**. On reaching **F** we are facing towards **B** and must turn to face towards **G**. We must therefore turn in a clockwise direction through the angle **BFG**. On reaching **G** we are facing towards **H** and must turn to face towards **D**. We must therefore turn in a counter-clockwise direction through the angle **DGH**. But since **AB** and **CD** are parallel, i.e. drawn in the same direction, we are now facing in the same direction as we were originally.

Having made one clockwise turn and one counter-clockwise turn on the journey, these turns must have been the same size.

$\therefore$ B$\hat{\text{F}}$G $=$ D$\hat{\text{G}}$H and these are corresponding angles.

The same result could be found for the other pairs of corresponding angles.

Hence, when two parallel straight lines are crossed by a transversal, corresponding angles are equal.

(2) *Alternate Angles*

$$\text{B}\hat{\text{F}}\text{G} = \text{D}\hat{\text{G}}\text{H} \text{ (proved above).}$$

But $\quad$ D$\hat{\text{G}}$H $=$ F$\hat{\text{G}}$C (vertically opposite angles)

$\therefore$ B$\hat{\text{F}}$G $=$ F$\hat{\text{G}}$C (each is equal to D$\hat{\text{G}}$H)

and these are alternate angles.

The same result could be proved for the other pair of alternate angles.

Hence, when two parallel straight lines are crossed by a transversal, alternate angles are equal.

(3) *Co-interior Angles*

$$B\widehat{F}G = D\widehat{G}H \text{ (proved)}.$$

But $F\widehat{G}D$ and $D\widehat{G}H$ are the adjacent angles made by the straight line DG standing on the straight line FH

$$\therefore\ D\widehat{G}H + F\widehat{G}D = 2 \text{ rt. angles}$$
$$\therefore\ B\widehat{F}G + F\widehat{G}D = 2 \text{ rt. angles}$$

and these are co-interior angles.

The same result could be proved for the other pair of co-interior angles.

Hence when two parallel straight lines are crossed by a transversal, co-interior angles are supplementary.

These facts provide us with a means of testing whether or not two straight lines are parallel. We can show that **if two straight lines are crossed by a transversal and**

(1) **corresponding angles are equal,**

or (2) **alternate angles are equal,**

or (3) **co-interior angles are supplementary,**

      then the two straight lines are parallel.

(1) *Corresponding Angles Equal*

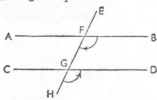

In the figure the straight lines **AB** and **CD** are crossed by the transversal **EH** at **F** and **G**, and the corresponding angles **BFG** and **DGH** are equal. Suppose we walk from **A** to **D** along the path **AFGD**. We have to make two turns, one at **F**, the other at **G**. On reaching **F** we are facing towards **B**, and must turn to face towards **G**. We must, therefore, turn in a clockwise direction through the angle **BFG**. On reaching **G** we are facing towards **H**, and must turn to face towards **D**. We must, therefore, turn in a counter-clockwise direction through the angle **DGH**.

But the two angles BFG and DGH through which we have turned are equal.

At F we turned through an angle, and at G we turned back through the same angle. We must, therefore, be facing in exactly the same direction as before.

∴ The straight lines AB and CD are parallel.

The same result would follow for any pair of corresponding angles.

Hence, if two straight lines are crossed by a transversal, and a pair of corresponding angles are equal, the two straight lines are parallel.

(2) *Alternate Angles Equal*

In the figure the alternate angles BFG and FGC are given equal.

Then $B\hat{F}G = F\hat{G}C$.

But $F\hat{G}C = D\hat{G}H$ (vertically opposite angles)

∴ $B\hat{F}G = D\hat{G}H$.

But these are corresponding angles.

∴ By the previous section, the straight lines AB and CD are parallel.

The same result would follow if the other pair of alternate angles were given equal.

Hence, if two straight lines are crossed by a transversal, and a pair of alternate angles are equal, the two straight lines are parallel.

(3) *Co-interior Angles Supplementary*

In the figure we are given that the co-interior angles BFG and FGD are supplementary.

Then $B\hat{F}G$ is the supplement of $F\hat{G}D$.

But $D\hat{G}H$ is the supplement of $F\hat{G}D$ (adj. ∠s, DG standing on str. line FH).

∴ $B\hat{F}G = D\hat{G}H$

But these are corresponding angles.

∴ By the first section the straight lines AB and CD are parallel.

The same result would follow if we were given that the other pair of co-interior angles were supplementary.

Hence, if two straight lines are crossed by a transversal and a pair of co-interior angles are supplementary, the two straight lines are parallel.

Worked Examples

The following worked examples indicate a method of setting down the solution. The various facts must be stated clearly, as must also the reasons for each step.

Example 1.—AB and CD are two parallel straight lines. A point E is taken on AB, and from E a straight line EF is drawn to meet CD in F, making $A\hat{E}F = 60°$. Also from E a straight line EG is drawn meeting CD in G, making $F\hat{E}G = 75°$. Calculate the size of $F\hat{G}E$.

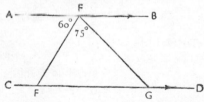

[Draw a figure from the information in the exercise and mark in the various facts that are known. The arrow heads indicate that AB and CD are parallel.]

To find the size of $F\hat{G}E$.

$A\hat{E}F = 60°$ and $F\hat{E}G = 75°$ (given).

$A\hat{E}F + F\hat{E}G + B\hat{E}G = 180°$ (sum of $\angle$s at point E on one side of str. line AB)

$\therefore 60° + 75° + B\hat{E}G = 180°$

$\therefore 135° + B\hat{E}G = 180°$

$\therefore B\hat{E}G = 180° - 135°$

$= 45°.$

But $\qquad F\hat{G}E = B\hat{E}G$ (alt. $\angle$s to parallel lines AB and

$\therefore F\hat{G}E = 45°.$ CD)

[*Note:* In later exercises the reasons will be stated more concisely; e.g. the last reason stated above will be given as " alt. ∠s, AB, CD parl."]

Example 2.—AB and CD are two parallel straight lines, crossed at F and G respectively by a transversal EH. FO bisects BF̂G and GO bisects FĜD, the two bisectors meeting at O. If EF̂B = 140°, find the size of FÔG.

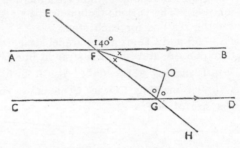

Required.—To find the size of FÔG.

$$EF̂B + BF̂G = 180° \text{ (adj. ∠s, BF standing on str. line EG).}$$

But
$$EF̂B = 140° \text{ (given)}$$
$$∴ BF̂G = 40°.$$
$$OF̂G = 20° \text{ (OF is the bisector of BF̂G).}$$
$$EF̂B = FĜD \text{ (corresp. ∠s AB, CD parl.)}$$
$$∴ FĜD = 140°$$
$$∴ OĜF = 70° \text{ (OG is the bisector of FĜD).}$$

But FOG is a triangle
$$∴ FÔG + OĜF + GF̂O = 180°$$
$$∴ FÔG + 70° + 20° = 180°$$
$$∴ FÔG = 90°.$$

FÔG will be a right angle no matter what size EF̂B is. This is proved as follows :

FO bisects BF̂G and GO bisects FĜD
$$∴ OF̂G = \tfrac{1}{2}BF̂G \text{ and } OĜF = \tfrac{1}{2}FĜD.$$

But $\qquad$ $B\hat{F}G + F\hat{G}D = 180°$ (co-int. $\angle$s, AB,
$\qquad\qquad\qquad\qquad$ CD parl.)

$\therefore \frac{1}{2}B\hat{F}G + \frac{1}{2}F\hat{G}D = 90°$

$\therefore O\hat{F}G + O\hat{G}F = 90°$.

But $O\hat{F}G$ and $O\hat{G}F$ are two angles of $\triangle$FOG and their sum is $90°$

$\therefore$ the third angle $F\hat{O}G = 90°$ (sum of $\angle$s of $\triangle = 180°$).

EXERCISES 8

Find all the angles in the following figures :

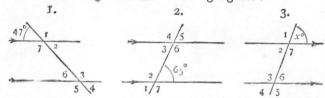

4. AB and CD are two parallel straight lines, crossed at F and G respectively by a transversal EH. If $E\hat{F}B = 58°$, find all the angles of the figure. If $E\hat{F}B = 90°$, what can be said about all the angles ?

5. AB and CD are parallel. What is the relation between x and y ?

6. AB and CD are parallel. FK bisects $A\hat{F}G$. Find $F\hat{K}G$.

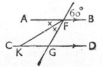

7. In the figure for Exercise 6, $B\hat{F}G$ is bisected by FM, which meets CD in M. Find the size of $F\hat{M}K$, and prove that $K\hat{F}M = 90°$.

8. In the figure **AB** is parallel to **CD**, and **EF** is parallel to **CD**. Mark the other angles in the figure which are equal to $x°$. Is **AB** parallel to **EF**? If so, why?

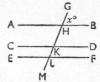

9. **AB** and **EF** are both parallel to **CD**. Find x.

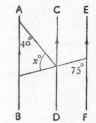

10. **AB** is parallel to **DC** and **BC** is parallel to **AD**. [The figure is called a **parallelogram**.] Find the sizes of the remaining angles in the figure. What do you notice about the opposite angles in the parallelogram?

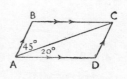

11. **ABCD** is a parallelogram in which $B\widehat{A}D = 90°$. Prove that the other angles of the figure are also right angles.

12. Draw an angle **BAC** = 80°. Divide it into any two parts by a straight line **AD**. Through **P**, any point in **AD**, draw **PQ** parallel to **BA** meeting **AC** in **Q**. Through **P** draw **PR** parallel to **CA** meeting **AB** in **R**. Find $Q\widehat{P}R$.

13. **BA** is parallel to **ED**. Find $C\widehat{D}E$. [*Hint.*—Through **C** draw **CX** parallel to **BA**.]

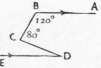

14. In the figure for Exercise 13, if $A\widehat{B}C = x°$, $B\widehat{C}D = y°$ and $C\widehat{D}E = z°$ find a relation between x, y and z.

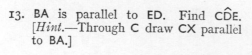

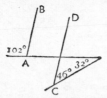

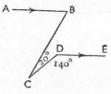

15. Prove that AB is parallel to CD.

16. AB is parallel to DE. Find A$\hat{B}$C.

17. AB is parallel to CD and CB is parallel to DE. Prove that A$\hat{B}$C + C$\hat{D}$E = 180°.

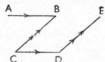

18. AB is parallel to CD and EH is parallel to KL. Prove that

    (1)   A$\hat{E}$H = K$\hat{L}$D.

    (2)   K$\hat{E}$H = K$\hat{L}$H.

    (3) A$\hat{E}$H + B$\hat{K}$L = 180°.

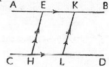

19. The figure represents a rectangular prism. What kind of lines are

    (1) AE and DL,

    (2) AE and CK,

    (3) AE and BC?

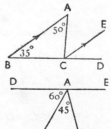

Write down the sizes of C$\hat{K}$H, C$\hat{K}$L, C$\hat{K}$E. Prove that AC and EK are parallel.

20. BA is parallel to CE. Find the size of A$\hat{C}$D.

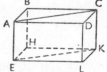

21. DE is parallel to BC. Find angles B and C.

22. **CB** and **ED** are parallel. Find angle **A**.

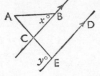

23. Draw a triangle **ABC** with $\hat{A} = 70°$, $\hat{B} = 60°$. Through the three vertices draw straight lines parallel to the opposite sides, forming the triangle **PQR**. Find the angles **P, Q, R**.

24. **AB** and **CD** are parallel. Find **ED̂K**.

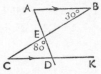

25. **ABC** is a triangle with **BC** produced to **D**. **CE** is parallel to **BA**. Find **AĈE**, **EĈD** and show that $A\hat{C}D = \hat{A} + \hat{B}$.

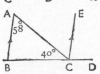

26. **AB** and **DC** are parallel. **DĈB** = 120°, **CÂB** = 30°. Find $\hat{B}$.

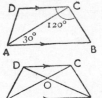

27. **AB** and **DC** are parallel. Prove that $A\hat{O}D = O\hat{C}D + O\hat{B}A$.

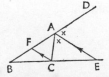

28.

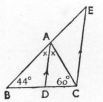

In △**ABC**, **AD** bisects **BÂC**. **CE** is parallel to **DA**. Calculate $\hat{E}$, **DĈE**.

29.

In △**ABC**, **BA** is produced to **D** and **AE** bisects **DÂC**. **CF** is parallel to **EA**. If **B** = 30°, **AĈE** = 80°, calculate **AÊC**, **AF̂C**.

THE CIRCLE

Definition.—A circle is a plane figure bounded by one line called the **circumference**, which is such that all points on the circumference are equidistant from a fixed point within it. The fixed point is called the **centre** of the circle.

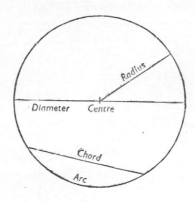

A **radius** of a circle is a straight line drawn from the centre to the circumference. All radii are equal.

A **chord** of a circle is a straight line joining any two points on the circumference.

A **diameter** of a circle is a chord which passes through the centre.

An **arc** of a circle is any part of the circumference.

By using a pair of compasses it is possible to draw a circle, having any given point as centre and any given length as radius.

Compasses may also be used to cut off from a given straight line any given length.

The Relation between the Circumference of a Circle and its Diameter

Wrap a strip of paper round a cylinder till the paper overlaps and pierce the paper at the overlapping part with a pin. Unwind the paper and measure the distance between the two marks made by the pin. This distance is the length of the circumference of the end of the cylinder. Measure the diameter of the cylinder. Repeat for different cylinders and record the results in a table as follows:

Length of Circumference.	Length of Diameter.	$\dfrac{Circumference}{Diameter}$

The relation, or ratio, of the length of the circumference to the length of the diameter is the same for all circles. It cannot be expressed by a terminating decimal and is represented by the Greek letter π.

$$\pi = 3 \cdot 1416 \text{ (correct to 4 decimal places)}$$
$$= \frac{22}{7} \text{ (approx.)}.$$

The ratio is often written thus:
$$\frac{\text{Circumference}}{\text{Diameter}} = \pi,$$

or in symbols, $\dfrac{c}{d} = \pi$

$\therefore\ c = \pi d = 2\pi r$, where r is the radius of the circle.

Example 1.—The diameter of a bicycle wheel is 28 in.   If a cyclist's speed is such that the wheels make 120 revolutions per minute, at what speed in miles per hour is he travelling?

Distance travelled in 1 revolution $= \pi d$

$\qquad\qquad\qquad\qquad\qquad\qquad\quad = \pi . 28$ in.

$\therefore$ Distance travelled in 120 revolutions $= 28\pi \times 120$ in.

$\therefore$ Distance travelled in 1 hour $\quad = 28\pi \times 120 \times 60$ in.

$$= \frac{28\pi \times 120 \times 60}{12 \times 5280}\,\text{ml.}$$

$$= \frac{35\pi}{11}\,\text{ml.}$$

$$= \frac{35}{11} \times \frac{22}{7}\,\text{ml.}$$

$$= 10\,\text{ml.}$$

$$\text{Speed} = 10\ \text{m.p.h.}$$

Example 2.—The diameter of a bicycle wheel is 28 in. How many revolutions does it make in travelling 1 mile?

Distance travelled in 1 revolution $\quad = \pi d$

$\qquad\qquad\qquad\qquad\qquad\qquad\qquad = 28\pi$ in.

$\therefore$ No. of revolutions in travelling 1 mile $\quad = \dfrac{1\ \text{mile}}{28\pi\ \text{in.}}$

$$= \frac{5280 \times 12}{28 \times \pi}$$

$$= \frac{5280 \times 12}{28} \times \frac{7}{22}$$

$$= 720.$$

EXERCISES 9

$$\left(\text{Take } \pi = \frac{22}{7}\right)$$

1. Calculate the circumference of a circle, whose diameter is
   (1) $3\frac{1}{2}$ ft.   (2) 8·4 in.   (3) 35 yd.
2. Calculate the circumference of a circle, whose radius is
   (1) 5 in.   (2) 6·3 cm.   (3) $4\frac{1}{5}$ yd.
3. Find the diameter of a circle if its circumference is 15·4 in.

4. Find the radius of a circle if its circumference is 54 cm. Answer correct to 1 decimal place.

5. The diameter of a wheel is 28 in. How far does it travel in 1 revolution ? How far in 100 revolutions ?

6. A cyclist travels at 15 miles per hour. If the wheel makes 10,800 revolutions in an hour, find the diameter of the wheel in inches.

7. Draw a circle, radius $1\frac{1}{2}$ in. Draw two diameters, AB and CD, making the angle between them 45°. Join AC, BC, AD, BD and measure them.

8. Draw any circle and any diameter AB in it. Mark C any point on the circumference. Join AC, BC. Measure $A\widehat{C}B$.

9. Mark two points A and B $3\frac{1}{2}$ in. apart. Find a point which is 2 in. from A and $1\frac{1}{2}$ in. from B. How many such points are there ?

10. In the figure for Exercise 9, find a point which is 3 in. from A and 2 in. from B. How many such points are there ?

11. Mark two points A and B. Using compasses only, find several points, say 5, equidistant from A and B. What do you notice ?

12. Two forts A and B 4 miles apart have guns with a maximum range of 3 miles. Show by a diagram the ground covered by both guns.

13. Two places A and B are joined by a straight road. A gun is 3 miles distant from the road and has a maximum range of 4 miles. Show by a diagram the part of the road covered by the gun.

14. Draw two circles, cutting at A and B. Join AB and let the straight line joining the centres of the circles cut AB at O. Measure AO and BO.

15. Draw a circle of radius 2 in. Beginning at any point on the circumference, draw chords equal in length to the radius and placed end to end in the circle. How many such chords can you draw ? Measure the angle between any two chords.

16. Draw three circles each of which passes through the centres of the other two.

17. Copy the following diagrams to any suitable scale:

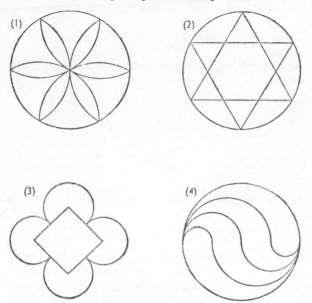

THE TRIANGLE

A **triangle** is a plane figure bounded by three straight lines. The triangle **ABC** has three sides, **AB, BC, CA,** and three angles, $\hat{A}, \hat{B}, \hat{C}$.

These are called the six **elements of** the triangle.

The sides are often denoted by the small letters a, b, c, the side a being opposite the vertex **A**, the side b being opposite the vertex **B**, and the side c opposite the vertex **C**. In the figure **BC** is usually taken to be the **base** of the triangle **ABC** but any side may be taken as the base.

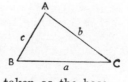

Triangles may be classified with reference to their sides thus :

An **equilateral** triangle is a triangle which has all its sides equal.

An **isosceles** triangle is a triangle which has any two of its sides equal.

A **scalene** triangle is a triangle which has all its sides unequal.

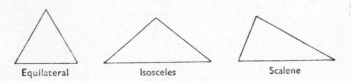

Equilateral   Isosceles   Scalene

Triangles may be classified with reference to their angles thus :

An **acute-angled** triangle is a triangle which has all its angles acute angles.

An **obtuse-angled** triangle is a triangle which has one of its angles an obtuse angle.

A **right-angled** triangle is a triangle which has one of its angles a right angle.

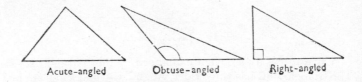

Acute-angled   Obtuse-angled   Right-angled

Construction of Triangle from Known Elements

How many of the six elements of a triangle must be known before a definite triangle can be constructed? If only one element is known, for example, a side, it can be shown easily that any number of different triangles can be constructed with this side as one of the sides. The same is true when only one angle is known.

If only two elements are known these may be (1) two sides, or (2) one side and one angle, or (3) two angles. You will find that in each case any number of different triangles can be constructed. Note that if two angles are known, the third angle is also known, and although any number of different triangles can be constructed these triangles have all the same shape. This is discussed more fully on pages 58 and 59.

If three elements are known these may be:

(1) three sides,

or (2) two sides and the angle included by those two sides,

or (3) two sides and an angle, not the angle included by the two sides,

or (4) one side and two angles,

or (5) three angles.

I. *Three sides*

Construct a triangle, with its three sides 6 cm., 5 cm., 4 cm. in length.

* Draw a straight line BC 6 cm. long. With centre B and radius 5 cm. draw an arc of a circle.

With centre C and radius 4 cm. draw an arc of another circle to cut the former arc at A and D.

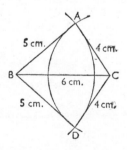

Join AB, AC, BD, CD, thus forming two triangles ABC and DBC. When the angles of triangle DBC are measured they are found to be equal to the angles of triangle ABC.

Thus the six elements of the two triangles are equal, each to each, so that the triangles are exact copies of each other.

Therefore, when the lengths of the three sides are known a definite triangle can be constructed.

* Throughout the book, when necessary, figures are drawn to scale.

II. *Two sides and the included angle*

Construct a triangle with two of its sides 2 in. and 3 in. in length, the angle included by these two sides being 40°.

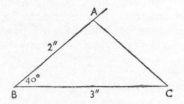

Draw a straight line BC 3 in. long.
At B make angle ABC = 40°, making BA 2 in. long.
Join AC.
One triangle ABC, and only one triangle, has been constructed. Therefore when the lengths of two sides and the size of the angle included by these sides are known a definite triangle can be constructed.

III. *Two sides and an angle, not the included angle*

Construct a triangle with two of its sides 2 in. and 3 in. in length, the angle opposite the side 2 in. long being 35°.

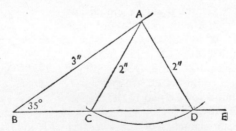

Draw a straight line BE of indefinite length.
At B make angle ABE = 35°, making BA = 3 in.
With centre A and radius 2 in. draw an arc to cut BE.
It will cut BE in two points, C and D.
Join AC and AD.

Two different triangles **ABC** and **ABD** have been constructed and in each of them there are two sides 2 in. and 3 in. long, the angle opposite the smaller side being 35°.

Therefore a definite triangle cannot be constructed in all cases when we know two sides and an angle, not the included angle.

IV. *One side and two angles*

Construct a triangle with two of its angles 50° and 60°, the side opposite the angle of 50° being 2 in. long.

[*Note:* Since two of the angles are known the third angle is also known, since the sum of the three angles of a triangle is 180°.]

In this case the third angle is 70°.

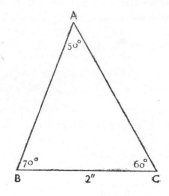

Draw a straight line **BC** 2 in. long.

At **B** make an angle of 70°.

At **C** make an angle of 60°.

Let the arms of these angles cut at **A**.

Then one triangle **ABC**, and only one triangle, has been constructed.

Therefore, when the length of one side and the sizes of two angles are known, a definite triangle can be constructed.

V. *Three angles*

[*Note:* If two angles are given the size of the third angle is known since the sum of the angles of any triangle is two right angles.]

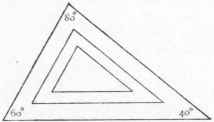

Construct a triangle with its three angles 60°, 40° and 80°.

The figure will show that any number of different triangles can be drawn having the angles of each 60°, 40°, 80°. Therefore a definite triangle cannot be constructed when the sizes of the three angles are known. Although, however, the triangles in the figure are different in size, they all have the same **shape.**

Special Case of Right-Angled Triangle

Construct a right-angled triangle with the side opposite the right angle (called the **hypotenuse**) 3 in. long, and one of the other sides 2 in. long.

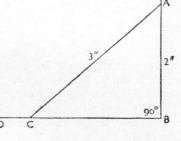

Draw $A\hat{B}D = 90°$, making $BA = 2$ in.

With centre A and radius 3 in. draw an arc, cutting DB in C. Join AC.

One triangle, and only one triangle, ACB has been constructed. Therefore, when the lengths of the hypotenuse and one other side of a right-angled triangle are known, a definite triangle can be constructed.

EXERCISES 10

Construct the following triangles from the given measurements, write out the constructions and measure the sides and angles indicated.

1. AB = 4 in., BC = 3 in., $A\hat{B}C = 64°$. Measure AC and $A\hat{C}B$.

2. $a = 8·2$ cm., $b = 5·4$ cm., $\hat{C} = 73°$. Measure c and $\hat{A}$.

3. BC = 4·3 in., $A\hat{B}C = 37°$, $A\hat{C}B = 42°$. Measure CA and AB.

4. $c = 9·4$ cm., $\hat{A} = 43°$, $\hat{C} = 72°$. Measure a and b.

5. AB = 3 in., BC = 4 in., CA = 5 in. Measure all the angles.

6. $a = 7·2$ cm., $b = 5·6$ cm., $c = 9·1$ cm. Measure all the angles.

7. $\hat{A} = 90°$, AB = 2·7 in., BC = 3·6 in. Measure AC and $\hat{B}$.

8. $b = 10$ cm., $\hat{B} = 90°$, $c = 6$ cm. Measure a and $\hat{C}$.

9. On a line BC of length 3·8 in. construct a triangle ABC in which AB and AC are each 3 in. long. Measure the angles ABC and ACB. Find by measurement the mid-point D of BC and join AD. Measure $B\hat{A}D$, $C\hat{A}D$, and the angles at D.

10. Construct a right-angled triangle LMN in which $\hat{L} = 90°$, MN = 4·8 in. and LM = 2·4 in.
    Find by measurement the mid-point P of MN and join PL. Measure PL and state what you notice about it. Measure the angles of $\triangle$LPM.

    [*Note:* P, the mid-point of the hypotenuse, is equidistant from the vertices. This fact about a right-angled triangle will be proved later and may be used in exercises.]

11. Construct $\triangle$ABC in which $\hat{B} = \hat{C} = 65°$ and BC = 2·9 in. Measure AB and AC.

12. Construct an equilateral triangle, each of whose sides is 2 in. long. Measure any two of its angles and calculate the third angle.

13. Draw a straight line BC = 4 cm. On opposite sides of BC draw two isosceles triangles ABC and DBC in which AB = AC = 3 cm. and DB = DC = 5 cm. Join AD, cutting BC at O. Measure BO, CO, $D\hat{A}B$, $C\hat{A}B$.

14. Construct $\triangle$ABC given $\widehat{B} = 40°$, $c = 8$ cm., $b = 6$ cm. How many solutions are there? Measure a and $\widehat{C}$.

15. Construct $\triangle$ABC given $\widehat{B} = 40°$, $c = 8$ cm., $b = 10$ cm. How many solutions are there? Measure a and $\widehat{C}$.

16. Construct isosceles triangle ABC in which AB = AC given that $\widehat{A} = 36°$ and that BC = 3 cm. Make $A\widehat{B}D = 36°$, D being on AC. Measure BD and $B\widehat{D}C$.

17. Construct a triangle ABC in which BC = 2·7 in., angle B = 42°, angle C = 104°. Draw through A a line parallel to BC and take a point E on it such that AE = AB (the angle EAB being acute). Measure the size of angle AEB.

18. A, B, C are three points in a straight line such that AB = BC = 4 cm. On AB, BC as bases construct two equilateral triangles, ADB and BEC, on the same side of ABC. Join DE and measure DE. Measure $E\widehat{D}B$.

19. Construct the triangle ABC in which AB = 10·5 cm., BC = 8·4 cm., CA = 6·3 cm. Measure $\widehat{C}$. Draw CD from C perpendicular to AB. Measure CD.

20. ABC is a right angle in which AB = BC = 5 cm. On AB and BC construct equilateral triangles APB, CQB, each triangle being within the arms of the angle. Measure $C\widehat{B}P$, $P\widehat{B}Q$, $Q\widehat{B}A$.

Similar Triangles

We have seen that any number of different triangles can be drawn having the angles of each say 60°, 40°, 80°. Two such triangles are shown below.

These triangles are all different in size, but they have the same shape. They are called **s i m i l a r** triangles. The following exercises will help us to find out certain facts about similar triangles :

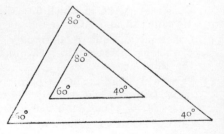

Exercise 1.—Construct △ABC with AB = 6 cm., BC = 8 cm., CA = 7 cm. Find by measurement the mid-point D of BC. Through D draw DF parallel to CA to meet BA in F. Why are the triangles ABC and FBD equiangular? Measure BF and compare its length with the length of AB. Measure FD and compare its length with the length of AC.

Exercise 2.—Construct △ABC with BC = 4 cm., $\widehat{B} = 60°$, $\widehat{C} = 50°$. Measure AB and AC.

Construct a second triangle DEF with EF = 12 cm., $\widehat{E} = \widehat{B}$ and $\widehat{F} = \widehat{C}$. Measure DE and DF. Compare the lengths of DE and AB and the lengths of DF and AC. What do you notice?

Exercise 3.—Construct △ABC with $a = 1\frac{1}{2}$ in., $b = 2$ in., $c = 2\frac{1}{2}$ in. Construct △DEF with $d = \frac{3}{4}$ in., $e = 1$ in., $f = 1\frac{1}{4}$ in. Measure the angles of △ABC and of △DEF. What do you notice?

[*Note:* In Exercise 1 the triangles are equiangular and it is found that each side of △FBD is one half of the corresponding side of △ABC.

In Exercise 2 the triangles ABC and DEF are equiangular and each side of △DEF is three times the length of the corresponding side of △ABC.

Hence, if two triangles are equiangular, each side of the one is the same fraction of the corresponding side of the other *or* **the sides of the two triangles are proportional.**

In Exercise 3 each side of △DEF has the same relation to the corresponding side of △ABC and it is found that the triangles are equiangular. It should be noticed that the relation of a to b in △ABC is the same as the relation of d to e in △DEF,

for $\dfrac{a}{b} = \dfrac{1\frac{1}{2}}{2} = \dfrac{3}{4}$ and $\dfrac{d}{e} = \dfrac{\frac{3}{4}}{1} = \dfrac{3}{4}$. In the same way it can be

shown that $\dfrac{b}{c} = \dfrac{e}{f}$ and that $\dfrac{c}{a} = \dfrac{f}{d}$.

Hence, if the sides of two triangles are proportional, then the triangles are equiangular.]

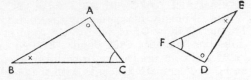

If △s **ABC** and **DEF** are similar

then   (1) $\hat{A} = \hat{D}$, $\hat{B} = \hat{E}$, $\hat{C} = \hat{F}$

and   (2) $\dfrac{AB}{DE} = \dfrac{BC}{EF} = \dfrac{CA}{FD}$

$\left[\text{or} \quad (2)\ \dfrac{AB}{BC} = \dfrac{DE}{EF}\ ;\ \dfrac{BC}{CA} = \dfrac{EF}{FD}\ ;\ \dfrac{CA}{AB} = \dfrac{FD}{DE}\right]$.

To prove two triangles **ABC** and **DEF** similar it is sufficient to prove either (1) or (2).

Example 1.—Prove that triangles **PQR** and **PYZ** are similar. Calculate the lengths of PY and ZY if PR = 8 cm., PQ = 6 cm., QR = 10 cm., PZ = 5 cm.

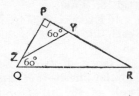

In △s PQR, PYZ

    1. $\hat{P}$ is common.

    2. $P\hat{Y}Z = \hat{Q}$ (each is 60°).

    3. $P\hat{Z}Y = \hat{R}$ (sum of ∠s of △ = 2 rt. angles).

∴ △s PQR and PYZ are equiangular

∴ Their corresponding sides are proportional, i.e. they are similar.

$$\frac{PZ}{PR} = \frac{PY}{PQ} = \frac{ZY}{QR}$$

$$\therefore \frac{5}{8} = \frac{PY}{6} = \frac{ZY}{10}$$

$$\therefore PY = \frac{6 \times 5}{8} = 3{\cdot}75 \text{ cm.}$$

$$ZY = \frac{10 \times 5}{8} = 6{\cdot}25 \text{ cm.}$$

EXERCISES 11

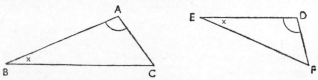

Why are the △s in the figure similar?

1. If AB = 3 cm., BC = 9 cm., DE = 2 cm., calculate the length of EF.

2. If BC = 6 in., CA = 2 in., FD = 1·5 in., calculate the length of EF.

3. If CA = 9 cm., EF = 7 cm., DF = 2·1 cm., calculate the length of BC.

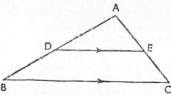

In the above figure DE and BC are parallel.

4. Name two similar triangles and prove that they are similar.

5. If AD = 5 in., DB = 3 in., AE = 1 in., find AC.

6. If AD = 4 cm., DE = 3 cm., AB = 9 cm., find BC.

7. If AD = 8 in., DE = 4 in., AE = 6 in., DB = 4 in., find BC and AC.

In the diagram AD and CB are parallel.

8. Prove △s ADO, BCO similar.

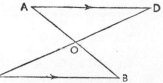

9. If AD = 6 cm., CB = 8·4 cm., OD = 5 cm., find OC.

10. If AO = 4 in., CO = 6 in., OB = 3 in., find OD.

11. If AD = 4·2 cm., DO = 6·4 cm., AO = 3·2 cm., OB = 4·8 cm., find OC and CB.

12. ABC is a triangle with $\widehat{A}$ a right angle. AD is perpendicular to BC and $\widehat{B} = 30°$.
Find $\widehat{C}$, $B\widehat{A}D$, $C\widehat{A}D$.
Prove that $\triangle$s ABC, ABD and ACD are all similar.

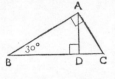

13. In the figure for Exercise 12 would the three triangles still be similar if $\widehat{B} = $ (1) 40°, (2) 50°, (3) any acute angle?

14. In the figure for Exercise 12 if AB = 4 cm., BD = 3·2 cm., AC = 3 cm., find AD and CD.

15. Draw a figure like the one shown in which two chords of a circle intersect. Measure the angles of $\triangle$s AOC and BOD. Are they similar triangles?

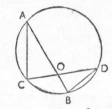

16. In the figure for Exercise 15, if AO = 4·8 cm., AB = 6 cm., CO = 2·4 cm., find OD.

17. Repeat Exercise 15 for the following diagram where the two chords meet when produced.
If OB = 6 cm., OC = 10 cm., OA = 12 cm., find OD.

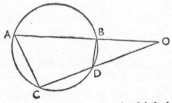

18. The length of the shadow of a vertical post 3 ft. high is 5 ft. The length of the shadow of a tree at the same time is 150 ft. How high is the tree?

19. The length of the shadow of a vertical post 6 ft. high is 8 ft. The lamp casting the shadow is 24 ft. high. How far is the post from the lamp?

20. On a map a triangular field is represented by a triangle, the longest side being 2 in. long. If the sides of the field are 300 yd., 400 yd., 500 yd., find the lengths of the other two sides of the triangle on the map.

BOOK I

CONGRUENCE OF TRIANGLES

We have shown that if we know certain sets of elements, one, and only one, definite triangle can be constructed. All triangles having for their elements one of these sets of elements will be exactly alike in every respect, i.e. the six elements of any one will be equal to the six elements of any other, each to each, and the triangles will be equal in area. Such triangles are said to be **congruent** triangles.

I. *Three sides*

Suppose, for example, that the two triangles shown below have the three sides of the one equal to the three sides of the other, each to each, then the triangles are congruent.

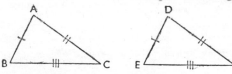

The triangles **ABC** and **DEF** have

$$AB = DE,$$
$$BC = EF,$$
$$CA = FD.$$

We know that each angle of $\triangle ABC$ is equal to the corresponding * angle of $\triangle DEF$, i.e.

$$\hat{A} = \hat{D}, \ \hat{B} = \hat{E}, \ \hat{C} = \hat{F}$$

and the triangles are equal in area, i.e. the triangles are congruent. We write it thus

$$\triangle ABC \equiv \triangle DEF \text{ (three sides).}$$

The statement in brackets is referred to as the case of congruence.

* [Corresponding sides of two congruent triangles are sides which lie opposite equal angles. Corresponding angles in two congruent triangles are angles which lie opposite equal sides.]

63

II. *Two sides and the included angle*

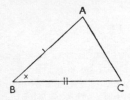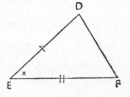

In triangles ABC and DEF

    1. AB = DE.

    2. BC = EF.

    3. $\widehat{B} = \widehat{E}$.

∴ △ABC ≡ △DEF (two sides and incl. ∠).

∴ The remaining elements of △ABC will be equal to the corresponding elements of △DEF

$$∴ AC = DF, \widehat{C} = \widehat{F}, \widehat{A} = \widehat{D}.$$

III. *Two angles and a corresponding side*

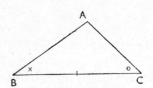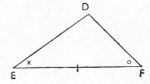

In triangles ABC and DEF

    1. BC = EF.

    2. $\widehat{B} = \widehat{E}$.

    3. $\widehat{C} = \widehat{F}$.

∴ △ABC ≡ △DEF (two ∠s and corresp. side).

∴ The remaining elements of △ABC are equal to the corresponding elements of △DEF

$$∴ AB = DE, AC = DF, \widehat{A} = \widehat{D}.$$

IV. *Right angle, hypotenuse and one side*

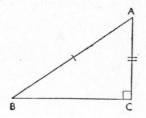 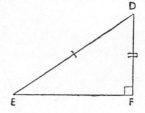

In triangles ABC and DEF

1. rt. $\angle$ C = rt. $\angle$ F.
2. AC = DF.
3. hyp. AB = hyp. DE.

∴ $\triangle$ABC ≡ $\triangle$DEF (rt. angle, hyp. and side).

∴ The remaining elements of $\triangle$ABC are equal to the corresponding elements of $\triangle$DEF

∴ BC = EF, $\hat{B}$ = $\hat{E}$, $\hat{A}$ = $\hat{D}$.

In trying to prove that two triangles are congruent, we must first of all show that three elements of the one triangle are equal to three elements of the other, and then we must check that these three elements form one of the four groups called cases of congruence :

(1) Three sides.
(2) Two sides and the included angle.
(3) Two angles and a corresponding side.
(4) Right angle, hypotenuse and one side.

The following examples will illustrate how to set down the facts :

N.C.G.—3

Example 1.—ABC is an isosceles triangle in which AB = AC. The angle A is bisected by a straight line which meets BC in D. Prove that BD = DC, and that AD is perpendicular to BC.

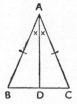

Given: △ABC with AB = AC, AD bisecting $\hat{A}$ and meeting BC in D.

Required: To prove that (1) BD = DC, (2) AD is perpendicular to BC.

Proof: In △s ABD and ACD
    1. AB = AC (given).
    2. AD is common.
    3. $B\hat{A}D = C\hat{A}D$ ($\hat{A}$ is bisected).
    ∴ △ABD ≡ △ACD (two sides and incl. ∠)
      ∴ BD = DC.
    Also $A\hat{D}B = A\hat{D}C$.

But these two angles are adjacent angles on the straight line BC

        ∴ AD is perp. to BC.

Example 2.—$B\hat{A}C$ is bisected by the straight line AD. P is any point on AD, PX is the perpendicular from P to AB, PY is the perpendicular from P to AC. Prove that PX = PY.

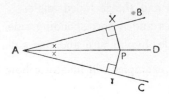

Given: BÂC bisected by AD. P is any point on AD and PX and PY are drawn perpendicular to AB and AC respectively.

Required: To prove that PX = PY.

Proof: In △s XAP and YAP

    1. $\hat{X} = \hat{Y}$ (rt. angles).

    2. XÂP = YÂP (Â is bisected).

    3. AP is common.

∴ △XAP ≡ △YAP (two ∠s and corresp. side)

    ∴ PX = PY.

Example 3.—AB and CD are equal chords of a circle with centre O. Prove that AÔB = CÔD.

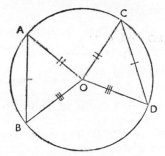

Given: Circle with centre O and AB and CD two equal chords.

Required: To prove that AÔB = CÔD.

Construction: Join AO, BO, CO, DO.

Proof: In △s AOB and COD

    1. AB = CD (given).

    2. AO = CO (radii of same ⊙).

    3. BO = DO (radii of same ⊙).

∴ △AOB ≡ △COD (three sides)

    ∴ AÔB = CÔD.

[Draw the figure when the two equal chords intersect, and check the above proof in this case.]

Example 4.—O is the centre of a circle of which AB is a chord. OD meets the chord AB at right angles at D. Prove that D is the mid-point of the chord AB.

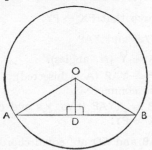

Given : Circle with centre O and chord **AB ;** OD meets **AB** at right angles at **D.**

Required : To prove that **D** is the mid-point of **AB.**

Construction : Join **OA** and **OB.**

Proof : In △s **AOD** and **BOD**

    1.　A$\hat{\text{D}}$O = B$\hat{\text{D}}$O (each is a rt. angle).

    2.　OA = OB (radii of same ⊙).

    3.　OD is common.

  ∴　△AOD ≡ △BOD (rt. angle, hyp. and side)

    ∴　AD = DB,

      i.e. **D** is the mid-point of **AB.**

EXERCISES 12

1. State which of the following groups of elements will make the triangles **LMN** and **PQR** congruent and state the case of congruence :

    (i) LM = PQ, MN = QR, LN = PR.

    (ii) LM = PQ, MN = QR, L$\hat{\text{N}}$M = P$\hat{\text{R}}$Q.

    (iii) MN = QR, $\hat{\text{L}}$ = $\hat{\text{P}}$, LN = PR.

    (iv) $\hat{\text{M}}$ = $\hat{\text{Q}}$, $\hat{\text{N}}$ = $\hat{\text{R}}$, LM = PQ.

    (v) $\hat{\text{L}}$ = $\hat{\text{P}}$, $\hat{\text{M}}$ = $\hat{\text{Q}}$, LM = QR.

    (vi) MN = QR, $\hat{\text{M}}$ = $\hat{\text{Q}}$, $\hat{\text{L}}$ = $\hat{\text{R}}$.

  (vii) LN = PR, MN = QR, LM̂N = PR̂Q.

(viii) L̂ = P̂ = 90°, MN = QR, LM = PQ.

  (ix) L̂ = P̂ = 90°, MN = QR, LM = PR.

   (x) LM = QR, MN = PR, LN = PQ.

2. In the triangles ABC and XYZ the following elements are known to be equal. In each case, state the additional information necessary to prove the triangles congruent. Give as many alternatives as you can and state the case of congruence :

  (1) AB = XY, BC = YZ.

  (2) AC = XZ, BÂC = YX̂Z.

  (3) BC = YZ, BÂC = YX̂Z.

  (4) Ĉ = Ẑ = 1 rt. angle, BC = YZ.

  (5) Ĉ = Ẑ = 1 rt. angle, B̂ = Ŷ.

  (6) B̂ = Ŷ ; Â = X̂.

In Exercises 3 to 18 the case of congruence to be used is stated at the end of the exercise. It may be helpful to mark the equal elements in the various figures.

3. Two circles intersect at A and B. Their centres are C and

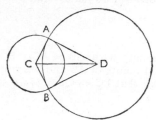

D. Prove that CÂD = CB̂D, and that CD bisects AĈB. (Three sides.)

4. ABC is a triangle with AB = AC. D is the mid-point of

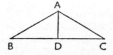

BC. Prove that AD̂B is a right angle. (Three sides.)

5. **ABC** and **DBC** are two isosceles triangles on opposite sides of the same base. Prove that **AD** bisects the angles at **A** and **D**. (Three sides.)

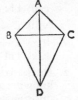

6. Three points **A, B, C** are taken on the circumference of a circle, centre **O**, so that **AB = BC**. Prove that **OB** bisects **AB̂C**. (Three sides.)

7. **O** is the mid-point of a straight line **AB**, and through **O** a straight line **XOY** is drawn at right angles to **AB**. **P** is a point on **XOY**. Prove that **PA = PB**. (Two sides and incl. ∠.)

8. Two straight lines **AB** and **CD** bisect each other at **O**. Prove that **AC = BD**. (Two sides and incl. ∠.)

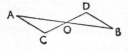

9. **ABC** is a triangle with **AB = AC**. **P** and **Q** are the mid-points of **AB** and **AC** respectively. Prove that **PC = QB**. (Two sides and incl. ∠.)

10. **AB̂C** is an angle with **AB = BC**. **BX** bisects **AB̂C**. Prove that any point on **BX** is equidistant from **A** and **C**. (Two sides and incl. ∠.)

11. **AB** and **CD** are two equal and parallel straight lines. **AD** and **BC** when joined meet at **O**. Prove that **AO = OD** and **BO = OC**. (Two ∠s and corresp. side.)

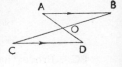

12. A$\widehat{B}$C is bisected by BD. E is any point in BD and HEK

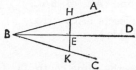

is perpendicular to BD. Prove that HE = EK. (Two ∠s and corresp. side.)

13. In △ABC, BI bisects $\widehat{B}$ and CI bisects $\widehat{C}$. ID, IE, IF are

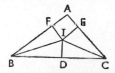

perpendicular to BC, CA, AB respectively. Prove that
(1) ID = IE,
(2) ID = IF. (Two ∠s and corresp. side.)

14. ABC is a triangle with D the mid-point of BC. Through C

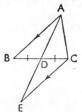

a line CE is drawn parallel to AB to meet AD produced in E. Prove that AD = DE. (Two ∠s and corresp. side.)

15. From the vertex A of an isosceles triangle ABC a straight

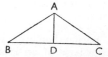

line AD is drawn meeting the base BC at right angles at D. Prove that $\widehat{B}$ = $\widehat{C}$. (Rt. angle, hyp. and side.)

16. **P** is any point equidistant from the arms **AB** and **AC** of BÂC. Prove that **PA** bisects BÂC. (Rt. angle, hyp. and side.)

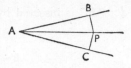

17. The circles have the same centre **O**. **A** and **B** are any two points on the inner circle. **AX** is perpendicular to **OA** and **BY** is perpendicular to **OB**. Prove that **AX = BY**. (Rt. angle, hyp. and side.)

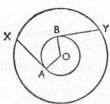

18. **ABCD** is a square. A circle, centre **A**, and with radius less than **AC**, cuts **BC** at **X** and **CD** at **Y**. Prove that **DY = BX**. (Rt. angle, hyp. and side.)

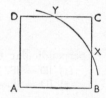

19. In the figure **ABCD**, the opposite sides are equal and the angles are all right angles. **BP = RD** and **AS = QC**. Find two pairs of congruent triangles and prove that the opposite sides of **PQRS** are equal.

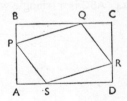

20. In the figure **ABCD**, **AB** is parallel to **DC** and **BC** is parallel to **AD**. Name the triangle which is congruent to (1) △ABC, (2) △BCD, (3) △AOB, (4) △AOD. In each case state the case of congruence.

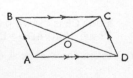

21. Prove that the perpendiculars drawn from the ends of the base of an isosceles triangle to the opposite sides are equal.

22. Prove that if the perpendicular drawn from a vertex of a triangle to the opposite side bisects that side, then the triangle is isosceles.

23. AB is a straight line, and O is its mid-point. Through A and B are drawn two parallel straight lines. Prove that any other straight line through O, and terminated by the parallels, is bisected at O.

24. ABC is a triangle with D the mid-point of BC. DE and DH are drawn perpendicular to AB and AC respectively. If DE = DH prove that

    (1) BE = CH,
    (2) AE = AH,

and hence that △ABC is isosceles.

25. In △ABC the sides AB and AC are produced to D and E respectively and the exterior angles DB̂C and EĈB are bisected by straight lines meeting at R. From R perpendiculars are drawn to BD, to BC and to CE. Prove that these perpendiculars are equal.

26. On the arm OA of an angle AOB, any two points P, S are taken, and on OB two points Q, T are taken such that OQ = OP ; OT = OS. PT and QS cut at X. Prove that

    (1) △OQS ≡ △OPT,
    (2) △PXS ≡ △QXT,
    (3) OX bisects AÔB.

27. D is the mid-point of the side BC of △ABC. BH and CK are drawn perpendicular to AD or AD produced. Prove that BH = CK.

28. ABC is a triangle and through C a straight line CD is drawn parallel to BA, to meet in D, a straight line drawn through A, parallel to BC. Prove that B̂ = D̂.

29. ABCD is a quadrilateral in which all the sides are equal and all the angles are right angles. AP, AQ are drawn inside the quadrilateral, each equal to AD, making angles of 30° and 60° respectively with AD. Prove that

$$BQ = QP = PD.$$

30. ABCD is a quadrilateral with its opposite sides equal and parallel. AH is drawn perpendicular to AD and equal to AD, H being on the side of AD opposite to B. AF is drawn perpendicular to AB and equal to AB, F being on the side of AB opposite to D. Prove that FH = AC.

31. The figure represents a cuboid.
X is the mid-point of DC.
Y is the mid-point of EF.
Prove that

(1) AX = GY.
(2) HX = AY.

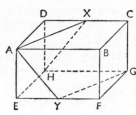

32. The figure represents a cube.
O is the mid-point of EG.
Prove that AO = CO and that AFC is an equilateral triangle.

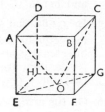

33. The figure represents a solid bounded by 4 equilateral triangular faces. X and Y are points on BD and CD respectively so that BX = CY. Prove that AX = AY.

THEOREMS

A **theorem** is a statement of a geometrical truth which has to be proved from facts already proved or assumed.

A **corollary** is a statement the truth of which may readily be inferred from a theorem.

The parts of a theorem are :

(1) *The General Enunciation.*—This states in general terms the truth which has to be proved.

(2) *The Particular Enunciation.*—This restates with reference to a particular figure the truth which has to be proved. It has two parts : (i) a statement of what is given, (ii) a statement of what has to be proved.

(3) *The Construction.*—This states any lines or figures which are required for the proof.

(4) *The Proof.*—This proves the truth by facts already established or assumed.

The **converse** of a theorem proves what the theorem assumes and assumes what the theorem proves.

For example :

Theorem—If a triangle is equilateral, it is equiangular.
Converse—If a triangle is equiangular, it is equilateral.

If a theorem is true it must not be assumed that its converse must be true. For example, consider the theorem : If two straight lines are parallel, they lie in the same plane. The converse of this is : If two straight lines are in the same plane they are parallel, which is not true. Hence the converse of a theorem must be proved separately.

THEOREM 1

The angles at the base of an isosceles triangle are equal.

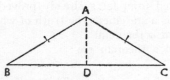

Given: △ABC with AB = AC.

Required: To prove that $\hat{B} = \hat{C}$.

Construction: Let the bisector of $\hat{A}$ meet BC at D.

Proof: In △s ABD, ACD

    1. AB = AC (given).

    2. AD is common.

    3. $B\hat{A}D = C\hat{A}D$ (constr.).

∴ △ABD ≡ △ACD (two sides and incl. ∠)

∴ $\hat{B} = \hat{C}$.

Cor.—If a triangle is equilateral, it is equiangular.

This theorem may also be stated thus: If two sides of a triangle are equal, the angles opposite these sides are equal.

THEOREM 2

If two angles of a triangle are equal, the sides opposite these angles are equal.

Given: △ABC with $\hat{B} = \hat{C}$.

Required: To prove that AB = AC.

Construction: Let the bisector of $\hat{A}$ meet BC in D.

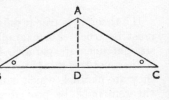

Proof: In △s ABD and ACD

 1. $\hat{B} = \hat{C}$ (given).
 2. $B\hat{A}D = C\hat{A}D$ (constr.).
 3. AD is common.

∴ △ABD ≡ △ACD (two ∠s and corresp. side)
 ∴ AB = AC.

Cor.—If a triangle is equiangular, it is equilateral.

EXERCISES 13

1. In a right-angled isosceles triangle what is the size of each angle ?

2. In an isosceles triangle each of the base angles is double the vertical angle. What is the size of each angle ?

3. Find D$\hat{A}$E.

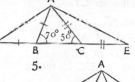

4.

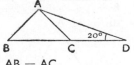

 AB = AC.
 CD = CA.
 Find $\hat{B}$.

5.

AB = AC.
BD = EC.

Prove that △ADE is isosceles.

6.

 AB = AC.
 B$\hat{A}$C = 100°.
 CA = AD.
Find $\hat{C}$, $\hat{D}$, D$\hat{B}$C.

7.

AE = BE.
Find $\hat{C}$.

8. ABC and DBC are two isosceles triangles on opposite sides of the base BC. Prove that $A\hat{B}D = A\hat{C}D$.

9. ABC and DBC are two isosceles triangles on the same side of the base BC. Prove that $A\hat{B}D = A\hat{C}D$.

10. Draw AB the diameter of any circle, centre O. Draw OC any radius. Join AC, CB. Prove that $A\hat{C}B = \hat{A} + \hat{B}$. What is the size of $A\hat{C}B$?

11. ABCD is a quadrilateral with all its sides equal. Without using cases of congruence prove $\hat{A} = \hat{C}$, $\hat{B} = \hat{D}$.

12. ABC is an equilateral triangle with D, E, F respectively the mid-points of AB, BC, CA. Prove that $\triangle$DEF is equilateral.

13. In $\triangle$ABC, BA is produced to Y so that AY = AC. CA is produced to X so that AX = AB. Prove that BX is parallel to CY.

14. AB = AC.
BD bisects $A\hat{B}C$.
CD bisects $A\hat{C}B$.
Prove $\triangle$BDC isosceles.

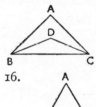

15.

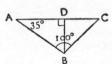

$\hat{A} = 35°$. $A\hat{B}C = 100°$.
BD is perp. to AC.
Prove $\triangle$BDC isosceles.

16.

AB = AC.
DE is parallel to BC.
Prove that AD = AE.

17.

AB = AC.
$\hat{A} = 32°$.
$B\hat{C}E = 42°$.
$C\hat{B}D = 53°$.

Prove (1) AE = CE
(2) CD = BC.

18.

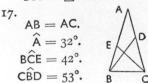

AD bisects $B\hat{A}C$.
CE and DA are parallel.
Prove that AC = AE.

19. ABC is a triangle with $\hat{A} = 90°$. O is a point in BC such that OA = OB. Prove that OA = OC.

20. ABCD is a quadrilateral with AB = AD and $\hat{B} = \hat{D}$. Prove that BC = CD.

21. From the vertex A of a right-angled triangle a perpendicular is drawn to the hypotenuse BC. The bisector of the angle B meets the perpendicular at R and meets AC at S. Prove that the triangle ARS is isosceles.

22. ABC is an isosceles triangle with AB = AC. From B and C, BX and CY are drawn perpendicular to AC and AB respectively. BX and CY intersect in O. Prove that $\triangle$OBC is isosceles.

23. In triangle ABC, AB = AC. BC is produced to E and CB is produced to D. The bisectors of angles ACE and ABD meet, when produced, in X. Prove that $\triangle$BXC is isosceles and that XA is the bisector of angle BAC.

24. ABC is a triangle having AB greater than AC. BC is produced to E. The bisectors of the angles ABC, ACE meet at D, and DLM is drawn parallel to BC, cutting AC at L and AB at M. Prove that BM = ML + LC.

25. ABC is a right-angled triangle with hypotenuse AB. AX, the bisector of $\hat{A}$, meets BC in X. BD is drawn perpendicular to AB to meet AX produced. Prove that BX = BD.

26. PQRS is a quadrilateral with its opposite sides parallel and equal. The internal bisectors of the angles SPQ, PSR meet QR (produced if necessary) at X and Y respectively. Prove that $\triangle$PQX is isosceles and that QY = RX.

27. The figure represents a cuboid on a square base. Prove that $\hat{FAC} = \hat{FCA}$ and $\hat{AHF} = \hat{AFH}$.

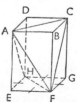

28. The figure represents a cuboid. Prove that $\hat{XEF} = \hat{XFE}$.

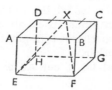

SYMMETRY

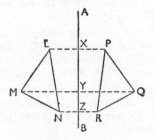

Fold a sheet of paper along a line **AB**. Prick with a pin through both parts of the paper at 3 points **L, M, N.** Open the paper and join up the points to form the triangles **LMN** and **PQR.**

L and **P** are called **corresponding** points. So also are **M, Q** and **N, R.**

We may say that **P** is the image of **L** and that △PQR is the image of △LMN, since, when the paper is folded about **AB,** the △PQR fits exactly the △LMN.

Hence
$$LM = PQ$$
$$MN = QR$$
$$NL = RP$$
i.e. corresponding lines are equal.

$$\hat{L} = \hat{P}$$
$$\hat{M} = \hat{Q}$$
$$\hat{N} = \hat{R}$$
i.e. corresponding angles are equal.

The triangles **LMN** and **PQR** are said to be **symmetrical** about the line **AB** which is called the **axis of symmetry.** Thus when two figures are symmetrical about an axis, every feature of the one figure, whether it be a point, a line, or an angle, has its image in the other.

Now join **LP** and let it cut **AB** at **X.**

LX and PX are now corresponding lines

$$\therefore LX = PX.$$

Also AX̂L and AX̂P are corresponding angles

$$\therefore A\hat{X}L = A\hat{X}P,$$

and since these are adjacent angles standing on a straight line, each is a right angle.

Hence the straight line joining corresponding points in two symmetrical figures is bisected perpendicularly by the axis of symmetry.

Hence MQ and NR are bisected perpendicularly at Y and Z by AB.

In the isosceles △ABC which has AB = AC, if D is the mid-point of the base, AD is obviously an axis of symmetry.

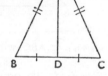

$$\therefore A\hat{D}B = A\hat{D}C = 1 \text{ rt. angle,}$$

since B and C are corresponding points,

$$\therefore B\hat{A}D = C\hat{A}D, \text{ since these are corresponding } \angle s.$$

It follows therefore from considerations of symmetry that the straight line, joining the vertex to the mid-point of the base of an isosceles triangle, bisects the vertical angle, and is perpendicular to the base.

Exterior Angle of Triangle

When one side of a triangle is produced the angle so formed is **an exterior angle.** Thus in the figure, BC is produced to D and the exterior angle is AĈD. The angle ACB is then referred to as the **interior adjacent** angle and Â and B̂ as the **interior opposite** angles.

We have already shown by measurement that the sum of the three angles of a triangle is two right angles. This is now proved in the following theorem.

Theorem 3

If one side of a triangle is produced, the exterior angle so formed is equal to the sum of the two interior opposite angles, and the sum of the three angles of the triangle is two right angles.

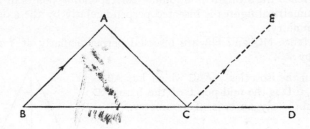

Given: △ABC with BC produced to D.

Required: To prove that (1) $\hat{ACD} = \hat{A} + \hat{B}$.

                   (2) $\hat{A} + \hat{B} + \hat{ACB} = 2$ rt. angles.

Construction: Through C draw CE parl. to BA.

Proof: 1. $\hat{ACE} = \hat{A}$ (alt. ∠s, CE, BA parl.).

             $\hat{ECD} = \hat{B}$ (corresp. ∠s, CE, BA parl.).

∴ By addition

$\hat{ACE} + \hat{ECD} = \hat{A} + \hat{B}$

    ∴ $\hat{ACD} = \hat{A} + \hat{B}$.

    2. $\hat{ACD} = \hat{A} + \hat{B}$ (proved).

To each side add $\hat{ACB}$

∴ $\hat{ACD} + \hat{ACB} = \hat{A} + \hat{B} + \hat{ACB}$.

But $\hat{ACD} + \hat{ACB} = 2$ rt. angles (adj. ∠s, BCD a str. line)

∴ $\hat{A} + \hat{B} + \hat{ACB} = 2$ rt. angles.

Cor.—The exterior angle of a triangle is greater than one interior opposite angle.

EXERCISES 14

1. In the figure name the six exterior angles of the triangle. Name the three angles which are **not** exterior angles although they are outside the triangle. How many different sizes of exterior angle are there here?

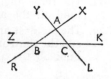

2. Find BÂC.

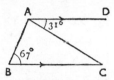

3. If AB̂C = 56° and AĈB = 42°, find BÔC.

4. If in the figure for Exercise 3, Â = 84°, AB̂C = 42°, find BÔC.

5. Find AD̂C.

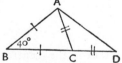

6. If in the figure for Exercise 5, AD̂B = 40°, find B̂.

7. If in the figure for Exercise 5, B̂ = x° and D̂ = y°, prove that x + 4y = 180.

8. If AB̂C = 64°, Â = 56°, find BD̂C.

9. If in the figure for Exercise 8, AB̂C = 52°, AX̂D = 86°, find AĈB and DĈE.

10. Prove that if one angle of a triangle is equal to the sum of the other two angles the triangle is right-angled.

11. The three angles of a triangle are proportional to 1, 2, 3. Find all the angles.

12. The greatest angle of a triangle is three times the smallest and the third angle exceeds twice the smallest angle by 12°. Find all the angles.

13. XD bisects YX̂Z. Find DX̂E.

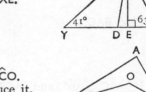

14. Prove that
BÔC − BÂC = AB̂O + AĈO.
[*Hint:* Join AO and produce it. to any point D.]

15. Prove that AB̂P = AĈQ.

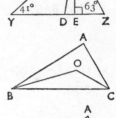

16. O is the centre of the circle. Calculate AÔB.

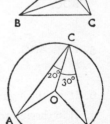

17. ABC is an acute-angled triangle and O is a point inside the triangle, equidistant from A, B, C. Prove that BÔC = 2Â.

18. Prove △s ABD, ACD, BAC equiangular.

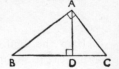

19. ABC is an isosceles triangle in which each base angle is double the vertical angle A. The bisector of $\widehat{B}$ meets AC at E. Find $\widehat{CEB}$ and prove that BE = BC.

20. ABC is a triangle with $\widehat{C} = 90°$. CD meets BA at D making $\widehat{DCB} = \widehat{DBC}$. Prove that DC = DA.

21. Prove that the sum of the interior angles of a quadrilateral is four right angles.

22. In quadrilateral ABCD the four angles are $x°$, $3x°$, $7x°$, $9x°$. What is the value of x ?
Prove that either (a) one pair of opposite sides are parallel or (b) opposite angles are supplementary.

23. Through a point X are drawn two straight lines PQX, RSX. PR and QS are joined. $\widehat{RPX} = 82°$, $\widehat{XQS} = 57°$ and $\widehat{XSQ} = 2\widehat{SXQ}$. Find $\widehat{PRX}$.

24. The quadrilateral PQRS has all its sides equal and all its angles right angles. PS is produced to T. The bisector of $\widehat{QST}$ meets PR produced at X. Calculate the size of $\widehat{RXS}$ and prove that RS = RX.

25. ABC is an isosceles triangle with AB = AC. D is any point within △ABC and ADE is another isosceles triangle with AD = AE, such that D, E are on opposite sides of AC. If $\widehat{AED} = \widehat{ACB}$ prove that DB = EC.

26. The bisectors BI and CI of the angles B and C of △ABC meet in I. Prove that $\widehat{BIC} = 90° + \dfrac{A}{2}$.

27. The sides AB, AC of the triangle ABC are produced to F and E respectively ; the bisectors of the angles ABC, ACB meet in X, and those of the angles CBF, BCE meet in Y. Show that $\widehat{BXC}$ is obtuse and that $\widehat{BYC}$ is acute.

28. From the vertex A of a right-angled triangle a perpendicular is drawn to the hypotenuse BC. The bisector of the angle B meets this perpendicular at R and meets AC at S. Prove that the triangle ARS is isosceles.

29. ABCD is a quadrilateral with all its sides equal and all its angles right angles. AC is a diagonal and AE bisects angle CAB, meeting CB in E. Prove that AC = AB + BE.
[*Hint*: Draw EX perpendicular to AC.]

CONSTRUCTIONS

The following constructions are carried out with ruler and compasses only. The graduated scale on the ruler is unnecessary since at no time will it be necessary to measure a length. The ruler is required only to join two points and to produce a given straight line. Compasses are required to draw circles or arcs of circles with a given point as centre and with a given radius, and also to cut off from a given line a length equal to the length of another given line.

The proofs of the correctness of the constructions illustrate the application of cases of congruence.

CONSTRUCTION I

To bisect a given angle

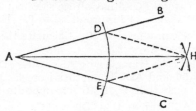

Given : B$\hat{A}$C.

Required : To bisect B$\hat{A}$C.

Construction : With centre A and any suitable radius draw an arc to cut AB at D and AC at E.

With centres D and E and any suitable radius, the same for each, draw arcs to cut at H. Join AH.

Then AH bisects B$\hat{A}$C.

Proof : Join DH, EH.

In △s ADH and AEH

1. AD = AE (radii of same ⊙).
2. DH = EH (radii of equal ⊙s).
3. AH is common.

∴ △ADH ≡ △AEH (three sides)

∴ D$\hat{A}$H = E$\hat{A}$H, i.e. B$\hat{A}$C is bisected by AH.

CONSTRUCTION 2

To bisect a straight line

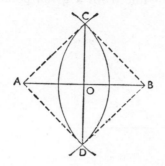

Given : Str. line **AB**.

Required : To bisect **AB**.

Construction : With centres **A** and **B** and any suitable radius, the same for each, draw arcs to cut at **C** and **D**. Join **CD** and let it cut **AB** at **O**. Then **AB** is bisected at **O**.

Proof : Join **AC, CB, BD, DA**.
In △s ACD and BCD
    1. **AC = BC** (radii of equal ⊙s).
    2. **AD = BD** (radii of equal ⊙s).
    3. **CD** is common.
∴ △ACD ≡ △BCD (three sides)
  ∴ **A$\hat{\text{C}}$D = B$\hat{\text{C}}$D**.

Comparing △s ACO and BCO
    1.   **AC = BC** (radii of equal ⊙s).
    2. **A$\hat{\text{C}}$O = B$\hat{\text{C}}$O** (proved).
    3. **CO** is common.
∴ △ACO ≡ △BCO (two sides and incl. ∠)
  ∴ **AO = OB**
  ∴ **AB** is bisected at **O**.

CONSTRUCTION 3

To draw a straight line perpendicular to a given straight line from a given point in it

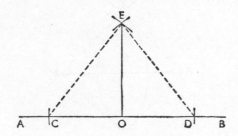

Given: Str. line **AB** with point **O** in it.

Required: To draw through **O** a straight line perpendicular to **AB**.

Construction: With centre **O** and any suitable radius draw an arc to cut **AB** at **C** and **D**.
With centres **C** and **D** and any suitable radius, the same for each, draw arcs to cut at **E**.
Join **OE**.
Then **OE** is perpendicular to **AB**.

Proof: Join **CE** and **ED**.
In △s **ECO** and **EDO**
1. **OC** = **OD** (radii of same ⊙).
2. **CE** = **DE** (radii of equal ⊙s).
3. **OE** is common.
∴ △**ECO** ≡ △**EDO** (three sides)
∴ **EÔC** = **EÔD**.
But these are adjacent angles standing on a straight line.
∴ Each is a right angle
∴ **OE** is perpendicular to **AB**.

CONSTRUCTION 4

To draw a straight line perpendicular to a given straight line from a given point outside it

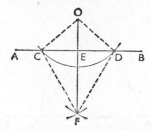

Given: Straight line AB with O a point outside it.

Required: To draw from O a straight line perpendicular to AB.

Construction: With centre O and any suitable radius draw an arc cutting AB at C and D,

With centres C and D and any suitable radius, the same for each, draw arcs to cut at F.

Join OF and let it cut AB at E.

Then OE is perpendicular to AB.

Join OC, CF, FD, DO.

Proof: In △s OCF and ODF
1. OC = OD (radii of same ⊙).
2. CF = DF (radii of equal ⊙s).
3. OF is common.

∴ △OCF ≡ △ODF (three sides)

∴ CÔF = DÔF.

In △s COE and DOE
1. OC = OD (radii of same ⊙).
2. CÔE = DÔE (proved).
3. OE is common.

∴ △COE ≡ △DOE (two sides and incl. ∠)

∴ OÊC = OÊD.

But these are adjacent angles standing on a straight line.

∴ Each is a right angle

∴ OE is perpendicular to AB.

CONSTRUCTION 5

To construct an angle of 60°

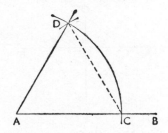

Required: To construct an angle of 60°.

Construction: Draw any str. line AB.
　　　　　With centre A and any suitable radius draw an arc
　　　　　to cut AB at C.
　　　　　With centre C and the same radius draw an arc to
　　　　　cut the former arc at D.
　　　　　Join AD.
　　　　　Then DÂB = 60°.

Proof: Join DC.
　　　　AC = AD (radii of same ⊙).
　　　　AC = CD (radii of equal ⊙s).
　　　　∴ In △ACD, AD = AC = CD
　　　　∴ △ACD is equilateral
　　　　∴ △ACD is equiangular
　　　　∴ DÂB = 60°.

CONSTRUCTION 6

To construct an angle of 30°

Construct an angle of 60° and bisect it.

CONSTRUCTION 7

To construct an angle of 90° at a given point in a given straight line

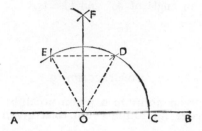

Given: Straight line **AB** and **O** a point in it.

Required: To construct at **O** an angle of 90°.

Construction: With centre **O** and any suitable radius draw an arc to cut **AB** at **C**. With centre **C** and the same radius draw an arc to cut the former arc at **D**. With centre **D** and the same radius draw an arc to cut the first arc at **E**. With centres **D** and **E** and any suitable radius, the same for each, draw arcs to cut at **F**. Join **OF**.

Then $F\hat{O}B = 90°$.

Proof: Join **OD**, **OE**, **DE**.

$D\hat{O}C = 60°$.

In $\triangle EDO$, **OE** = **OD** (radii of same ⊙).

$\qquad\qquad$ **OE** = **DE** (radii of equal ⊙s)

$\therefore$ **OE** = **OD** = **DE**

$\therefore \triangle EDO$ is equilateral

$\qquad \therefore E\hat{O}D = 60°$.

By construction **OF** bisects $E\hat{O}D$

$\qquad \therefore F\hat{O}D = 30°$

$\qquad \therefore F\hat{O}B = F\hat{O}D + D\hat{O}B$

$\qquad\qquad = 30° + 60°$

$\qquad\qquad = 90°$.

CONSTRUCTION 8

To construct an angle of 45°

Construct an angle of 90° and bisect it.

CONSTRUCTION 9

At a given point in a given straight line, to construct an angle equal to a given angle

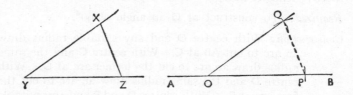

Given: Straight line AB with O a point in it, and XŶZ.

Required : To construct at O an angle equal to XŶZ.

Construction: In YX and YZ take any points X and Z and join XZ.
Construct △OPQ having OP = YZ, PQ = ZX, QO = XY.
Then QÔP is the required angle.

Proof: In △s QOP and XYZ
1. OP = YZ (constr.).
2. PQ = ZX (constr.).
3. QO = XY (constr.).
∴ △QOP ≡ △XYZ (three sides)
∴ QÔP = XŶZ.

CONSTRUCTION 10

Through a given point to draw a straight line parallel to a given straight line

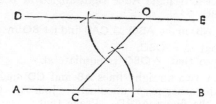

Given: Straight line AB and point O outside it.

Required: To draw through O a straight line parallel to AB.

Construction: Take any point C in AB and join OC.

At O in CO construct an angle CÔD equal to OĈB. Then DO is parallel to AB.

Proof: DÔC = OĈB (constr.).

But these are alternate angles to DO and AB

∴ DO and AB are parallel.

EXERCISES 15

Use only ruler and compasses for the following exercises.

1. Construct an angle of 15°.
2. Construct an angle equal to one quarter of a right angle.
3. Construct an angle of 120° and show how to divide it into four equal parts.
4. Draw any triangle ABC. Bisect the angles B and C and let the bisectors meet in I. Join IA and measure the angles BAI and CAI. What do you infer about the bisectors of the three angles of a triangle?
5. Draw any triangle ABC. Construct the perpendicular bisectors of AB and AC and let them meet in O. Construct the perpendicular bisector of BC. Does it pass through O? What do you infer about the perpendicular bisectors of the sides of a triangle?

6. In the previous exercise, prove that **OA** = **OB** and that **OA** = **OC**. Draw the circle with centre **O** and radius **OA**. Through which points in the figure must this circle pass ?

7. Construct a triangle **ABC**, right-angled at **B** and having **AC** = 2**BC**.

At **B**, in **AB**, make **ABO** = **CAB** and let **BO** meet **AC** in **O**.
Prove that $\hat{C}$ = **OBC**.
Prove also that $\triangle$**OBC** is equilateral.

8. Construct two straight lines **AB** and **CD** such that each bisects the other perpendicularly. Join **AC**, **CB**, **BD**, **DA** to form the figure **ACBD**. Prove that
   (1) **AC** = **BD**.
   (2) **AC** = **AD**.
What can be inferred about all four sides of the figure ?

9. Draw a straight line **AB**. With centres **A** and **B** and any suitable radius, the same for each, draw arcs to cut at **C**.

Join **AC** and **BC**. Bisect **ACD** letting the bisector **CD** meet **AB** at **D**.
Prove that **D** is the mid-point of **AB**.

10. Prove that the following construction gives a straight line perpendicular to a given straight line **AB** at a given point **O** in **AB**.
Take **C** any point not on **AB**.
With centre **C** and radius **CO** draw an arc of a circle to cut **AB** at **D**.
Join **DC** and produce it to meet the arc at **E**.
Join **EO**. Then **EO** is perpendicular to **AB**.

11. Draw a straight line **AB** and take **O** a point outside **AB**. With centre **O** and any suitable radius draw an arc cutting **AB** at **C** and **D**. Join **OC** and **OD**. Bisect **COD** and let the bisector meet **CD** at **E**. Prove that **OE** is perpendicular to **AB**.

12. Draw a straight line **AB** and take **O** a point outside **AB**. Draw **OD** any straight line from **O** to meet **AB** in **D**. Bisect **OD** at **C**.
With centre **C** and radius **CO** draw an arc of a circle to cut **AB** at **E**. Join **OE**.
Prove that **OE** is perpendicular to **AB**.

13. In any circle draw three chords **AB, CD, EF.** Construct the perpendicular bisectors of the chords. What do you notice ?

14. Draw any circle. Divide the angle at the centre into six equal parts by lines meeting the circumference in six points. Join up the points and so form a six-sided figure (a **hexagon**).

15. Draw any circle. Divide the angle at the centre into eight equal parts by lines meeting the circumference in eight points. Join up the points and so form an eight-sided figure (an **octagon**).

16. Prove that the figures formed in Exercises 14 and 15 have all their sides equal and all their angles equal. [Such figures are said to be **regular** figures.]

17. If your compasses could open only until the points were 2 inches apart, how would you bisect—by means of ruler and compasses—a line more than 4 inches long ?

18. In triangle ABC construct the three perpendiculars from A, B, C to the opposite sides. Verify that these perpendiculars are concurrent.

19. ABC is a triangle with **AB, AC** produced to **D** and **E** respectively. Bisect $\hat{A}$, $\hat{CBD}$, $\hat{BCE}$ and verify that these bisectors are concurrent.

20. Show how to trisect a right angle.

21. Using ruler and compasses only construct an angle of 75°. Describe each step of your method.

22. Using ruler and compasses only construct an angle of $52\frac{1}{2}$°. Describe each step of your method.

Inequalities concerning the sides and angles of a triangle

If we try to construct a triangle ABC given that $a = 6$ cm., $b = 3$ cm., $c = 2$ cm., we find it impossible, because with the usual construction the arcs, radii 3 cm. and 2 cm. respectively, will not meet. What would happen if $a = b + c$?

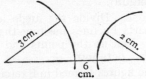

Hence, in a triangle any two sides are together greater than the third side.

THEOREM 4

If one side of a triangle is greater than another, the angle opposite the greater side is greater than the angle opposite the smaller side.

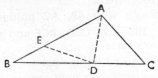

Given: △ABC in which AB > AC.

Required: To prove that $\hat{C} > \hat{B}$.

Construction: Bisect $\hat{A}$ by AD meeting BC in D.
From AB cut off AE = AC. Join DE.

Proof: In △s AED and ACD

    1.   AE = AC (constr.).

    2. AD is common.

    3. EÂD = CÂD (constr.).

∴ △AED ≡ △ACD (two sides and incl. ∠)

∴ AÊD = $\hat{C}$.

But AÊD > $\hat{B}$ (exterior ∠ of △BDE > one int. opp. ∠)

∴ $\hat{C} > \hat{B}$.

The converse of Theorem 4 is : **If one angle of a triangle is greater than another, the side opposite the greater angle is greater than the side opposite the smaller angle.**

We now proceed to prove that this converse is true and the method used is called **Proof by Exhaustion.** This method is used when only one of a number of alternatives can be true. The method involves proving that all of the alternatives but one are false. The remaining one must then be true.

THEOREM 5

If one angle of a triangle is greater than another, the side opposite the greater angle is greater than the side opposite the smaller angle.

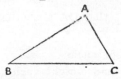

Given : △ABC with $\hat{C} > \hat{B}$.

Required : To prove that AB > AC.

Proof : The alternatives are either :

(1) AB = AC, or (2) AB < AC, or (3) AB > AC.

1. If AB = AC then △ABC would be isosceles and $\hat{B} = \hat{C}$.

 But $\hat{B}$ is not equal to $\hat{C}$

 ∴ AB and AC are not equal.

2. If AB < AC, then by Theorem 4 the angle opposite the greater side would be greater than the angle opposite the smaller side, i.e. $\hat{B} > \hat{C}$.

 But it is given that $\hat{B} < \hat{C}$

 ∴ AB is not less than AC.

Since AB is not equal to AC and AB is not less than AC

∴ AB > AC.

Worked Example

Prove that the perpendicular is the shortest straight line that can be drawn to a straight line from a point outside it.

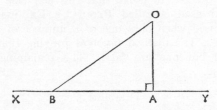

Given: Str. line XY, and point O outside it. OA is perpendicular to XY and OB is any other straight line from O to XY.

Required: To prove that OA is shorter than OB.

Proof: In △OBA

$\hat{A}$ is a right angle

∴ $\hat{B}$ is less than a right angle (sum of ∠s of △ is 2 rt. angles)

∴ $\hat{A}$ is greater than $\hat{B}$

∴ OB is greater than OA [in △OBA the greater side is opposite the greater angle].

Hence OA is less than any other straight line drawn from O to XY.

∴ OA is the shortest straight line that can be drawn from O to XY.

Exercises 16

1.

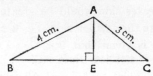

Prove $E\hat{A}B > E\hat{A}C$.

2. ABCD is a quadrilateral with AD the greatest side and BC the least side. Prove that $A\hat{B}C > A\hat{D}C$.

[*Hint:* Join BD.]

3.

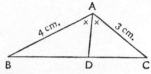

Prove that $A\hat{D}C$ is an acute $\angle$.

4.

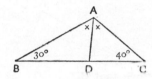

Prove that $AC > DC$ and $AB > BD$.

5.

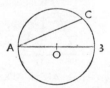

AB is a diameter. Prove that $AB > AC$.

[*Hint:* Join OC and BC.]

6.

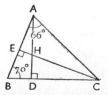

Prove that $AH < HC$ and $DC > DH$.

7.

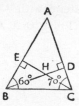

Prove that
(1) **AC > BC**, (2) **BH > HC**.

8. In a right-angled triangle prove that the hypotenuse is the greatest side.

9

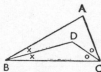

AB > AC   Prove that **BD > CD**.

10.

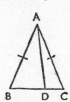

AB = AC.   Prove that **AB > AD**.

11. ABC is an isosceles triangle with **AB = AC**. D is any point in **BC** produced.   Prove that **AB < AD**.

12.

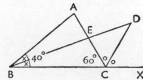

Prove that **ED < DC**.

13. ABC is an isosceles triangle with **AB = AC**.
   (1) If $\widehat{A} < 60°$ prove that **BC < AB**.
   (2) If $\widehat{A} > 60°$ prove that **BC > AB**.

14. **ABC** is a triangle in which **BA** is produced to **D** so that **AD = AC**. Prove that (1) **BD > BC**, (2) **BA + AC > BC**.

15. **ABC** is any triangle and **D** is any point within it. Prove that **AB + AC > DB + DC**.
[*Hint:* Produce **BD** to meet **AC** in **E** and consider (1) $\triangle$**DEC** to prove **BE + EC > BD + DC**, (2) $\triangle$**BAE**.]

16. **ABCD** is a quadrilateral. Prove that
AB + BC + CD + DA > AC + BD.

17. **ABC** is an isosceles triangle in which **AB = AC**. **BC** is produced to any point **D**. A straight line **DQP** is drawn cutting **AB, AC** in **P, Q** respectively. Prove that **AP < AQ**.

18. **AD** is a median of $\triangle$**ABC**. Prove that **AD < ½(AB + AC)**.
[*Hint:* Produce **AD** its own length to **E**. Join **CE**.]

19. **AD** is a median of $\triangle$**ABC**. If **AB < AC** prove that **BÂD > CÂD**.

20. Using the result of Exercise 18, prove that the sum of the medians of a triangle is less than the perimeter of the triangle.
[*Note:* The **perimeter** of a figure is the length of the bounding line or lines.]

21. **ABCD** is a quadrilateral. **X** is any point within it. Prove that **AB + BC + CD + DA < 2(XA + XB + XC + XD)**.

22. In $\triangle$**ABC**, **AB > AC**, **BD** is perpendicular to **AC**, and **CE** is perpendicular to **AB**. **BD** and **CE** intersect at **H**. Prove that **BH > HC**.

23. In $\triangle$**ABC**, **AB = AC**, **AD** is perpendicular to **BC** and is produced to any point **Y**. A straight line **YZX** cuts **AB** at **Z**, and **CA** produced, at **X**. Prove that
BY + YX > BA + AX.
[*Hint:* Join **CY**.]

24. A straight line **AB** is bisected at **O**, and **ON** is drawn perpendicular to **AB**. **C** is any point on the same side of **ON** as **A**, and **CB** cuts **ON** at **P**. Prove that **CQ + QB > CP + PA**, where **Q** is any other point on **ON**.

25. **ABC** is an equilateral triangle. **BC** is produced to **D** so that **CD = BC**. **E** is any point on **BA** produced. Prove that $\triangle$**DAB** is right-angled and that **ED + DC > EB**.

CONSTRUCTION OF QUADRILATERALS

A **quadrilateral** is a plane figure bounded by four straight lines.

The straight line joining two opposite vertices is called a **diagonal.**

ABCD is a quadrilateral.

AC and BD are diagonals.

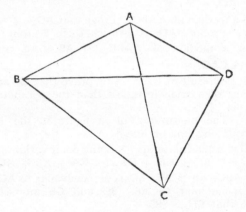

A quadrilateral has eight elements, four sides and four angles. To construct a definite quadrilateral it is necessary to know five independent elements. Since the sum of the angles of a quadrilateral is four right angles, if three of the angles are known, the fourth is also known. Hence the four angles cannot be regarded as independent elements. In general any five independent elements are sufficient but ambiguity may arise in certain cases. Before beginning the actual construction a rough sketch should be drawn, and the given elements marked on it. Then the figure should be completed by constructing the two triangles which will be clearly indicated by the sketch.

Example 1.—Given the four sides and one angle, construct the quadrilateral.

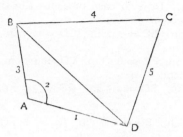

△ABD can be constructed since we know two sides and the included angle

∴ BD is fixed.

△BCD can be constructed since we know the three sides

∴ quadrilateral ABCD is constructed.

Example 2.—Given two sides and three angles, construct the quadrilateral.

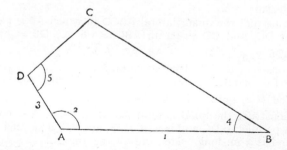

The order in which the various elements could be used are indicated by the numbers.

EXERCISES 17

In Exercises 1–10 construct quadrilateral ABCD from the following data. In each case measure the sides and angles that are not given.

1. AB = 1·8 in., BC = 1·2 in., CD = 2·3 in., DA = 2·6 in., AC = 2·1 in.

2. AB = 3·2 cm., BC = 6·5 cm., CD = 4·7 cm., AC = 5·8 cm., BD = 4·1 cm.

3. AB = 3·7 in., BC = 2·5 in., CD = 2·7 in., DA = 1·6 in., $\widehat{A} = 76°$.

4. AD = 4·6 cm., BD = 6·2 cm., DC = 2·3 cm., $A\widehat{D}B = 41°$, $B\widehat{D}C = 78°$.

5. AC = 2·9 in., BD = 4·1 in., BC = 2·7 in., $\widehat{B} = 71°$, $\widehat{C} = 103°$.

6. $\widehat{A} = 117°$, $\widehat{B} = 124°$, $\widehat{C} = 62°$, AB = 3·2 cm., BC = 2·8 cm.

7. AB = 1·8 in., $A\widehat{B}D = 66°$, BD = 2·9 in., AC = 2·7 in., $B\widehat{D}C = 32°$.

8. AB = 7·6 cm., BC = 2·8 cm., $\widehat{B} = 82°$, $\widehat{C} = 112°$, $\widehat{D} = 118°$.

9. $\widehat{B} = 70°$, $\widehat{C} = 95°$, $\widehat{D} = 105°$, AB = 4·8 in., AD = 4·1 in.

10. AB = 4·2 in., $C\widehat{A}B = 34°$, $A\widehat{B}D = 43°$, $A\widehat{C}B = 64°$, $A\widehat{D}B = 52°$.

11. Construct the quadrilateral ABCD in which AB = BC = 1·6 in., and AD = DC = 3·4 in., and BD = 4 in. Measure AC.

12. Construct the quadrilateral ABCD in which AB is parallel to DC, and CD = 4·2 in., BC = 1·8 in., DB = 3·8 in., $A\widehat{D}B = 30°$. Measure AB, AD, $A\widehat{D}C$.

13. Construct the quadrilateral ABCD in which AB is parallel to DC, and BC is parallel to AD. AB = 5 cm., AD = 8 cm. and $\widehat{B} = 132°$. Measure BC, CD, $\widehat{A}$.

14. Construct the quadrilateral ABCD in which $\widehat{A} = 90°$, AB is parallel to DC and is 2 in. long, and AD is parallel to BC and is 3 in. long. Measure all the angles.

15. Construct the quadrilateral ABCD in which AB is parallel to DC, BC is parallel to AD, and BC = CD = 3·2 in. Measure the remaining sides.

16. Construct the quadrilateral ABCD in which AB is parallel to DC, BC is parallel to AD, $\widehat{A} = 90°$, AB = BC = 6 cm. Measure the remaining sides and angles.

17. Construct a quadrilateral ABCD in which AB = 2·2 in., $\widehat{A} = 30°$, $\widehat{C} = 80°$, and the angle D is divided by the diagonal DB so that the angle ADB is 65° and the angle BDC is 15°. Measure AC.

18. Construct a quadrilateral ABCD with diagonals intersecting at O, such that AB = 2·2 in., BC = 2·7 in., BD = 3·3 in., AC = 4 in., $A\widehat{O}B = 106°$. Measure $A\widehat{D}C$.

19. The sides of a quadrilateral are of lengths 1 in., 2·5 in., 3 in., 4·5 in., and one diagonal is of length 4 in. How many different quadrilaterals can be drawn to satisfy these conditions? Give full reasons for your answer. Construct one such quadrilateral and measure the second diagonal.

20. Construct the quadrilateral ABCD given that AB = AD = 1·8 in., $\widehat{A} = 50°$, BC = CD = 1 in. How many different quadrilaterals can be drawn to satisfy these conditions?

Special Forms of Quadrilaterals and their Properties

Kite:—If a quadrilateral has two adjacent sides equal and the other two sides equal, it is called a **kite**.

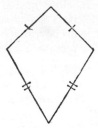

Exercise.—Draw a kite ABCD in which AB = AD and BC = CD. Draw the diagonals and let them cut at O. Measure AO, OC, BO, OD, $B\widehat{A}C$, $D\widehat{A}C$, $B\widehat{C}A$, $D\widehat{C}A$, $B\widehat{O}A$. What do you notice?

Trapezium :—If a quadrilateral has two sides parallel, it is called a **trapezium.**

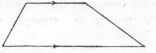

Parallelogram.—If a quadrilateral has its opposite sides parallel, it is called a **parallelogram.**

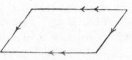

Exercise.—Construct a parallelogram ABCD. Measure the sides and the angles. What do you notice? Draw the diagonals, cutting at O. Measure OA, OB, OC, OD. What do you notice?

Rhombus.—If a parallelogram has two adjacent sides equal, it is called a **rhombus.** [Later it will be proved that **all** the sides of a rhombus are equal.]

Exercise.—Draw a rhombus ABCD and its diagonals, cutting at O. Measure OA, OB, OC, OD and AÔB. What do you notice?

Rectangle.—If a parallelogram has one angle a right angle, it is called a **rectangle.** [Later it will be proved that **all** the angles of a rectangle are right angles.]

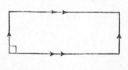

Exercise.—Construct a rectangle ABCD. Draw the diagonals, cutting at O. Measure AC, BD, OA, OB, OC, OD. What do you notice?

Square.—If a rectangle has two adjacent sides equal, it is called a **square.** [Later it will be proved that **all** the sides of a square are equal.]

Exercise.—Draw a square ABCD. Draw the diagonals, cutting at O. Measure AC, BD, OA, OB, OC, OD, AÔB. What do you notice?

These exercises have shown that :

(1) One diagonal of a kite is bisected by the other, and the diagonals cut at right angles.

(2) The opposite sides and angles of a parallelogram are equal, and the diagonals of a parallelogram bisect each other.

(3) The diagonals of a rhombus bisect each other, and cut each other at right angles.

(4) The diagonals of a rectangle are equal and bisect each other.

(5) The diagonals of a square are equal and bisect each other, and cut each other at right angles.

Some of these facts must be used in constructions in the following exercises.

Exercises 18

1. Construct a kite ABCD in which AB = AD = 1·75 in., AC = 3·75 in., and BD = 2·5 in. Measure AB̂C and AD̂C.

2. Construct the kite ABCD in which AB = 5 cm. The diagonal AC is 6 cm. long and is bisected by the other diagonal BD which is 10 cm. long. Measure CD and AD̂C.

3. Construct the trapezium ABCD in which AB is parallel to DC, D̂ = 82°, Ĉ = 42°, DC = 3·4 in., AD̂B = 45°. Measure AB.

4. Construct the parallelogram ABCD in which AB = 3·2 in., BC = 1·8 in., Ĉ = 118°. Verify that the diagonals bisect each other.

5. Construct the parallelogram ABCD in which AC = 4·3 in., BD = 3·2 in., AÔB = 64° where O is the point of intersection of the diagonals. Measure angles A and B.

6. Construct the parallelogram ABCD in which AB = 2 in., AC = 2·4 in., BD = 3·6 in. Measure BC.

7. Construct a rectangle with adjacent sides 3·5 in. and 2·5 in. Draw and measure the diagonals.

8. Construct a rectangle in which AB = 2 in., AC = 3·5 in. Measure BC.

9. Construct a rectangle ABCD in which AC = 3·8 in., and AÔB = 132° where O is the point of intersection of the diagonals.

10. Construct a rhombus ABCD in which AB = 2·5 in., and = 45°. Measure the angles between the diagonals.

11. Construct a rhombus whose diagonals are 2·2 in. and 3·8 in. Measure the side.

12. Construct a rhombus ABCD in which AC = 3·6 in. and AĈB = 32°. Measure BD.

13. Construct a square on a side 2·5 in. long. Measure the diagonal.

14. Construct a square whose diagonal is 3 in. long. Measure the sides.

15. With ruler and compasses only, construct a quadrilateral PQRS such that PQ = PS, RQ = RS, the angle at P is 90°, the diagonal QS is 3 in. and the diagonal PR is 4½ in. Measure QR.

16. Construct a trapezium ABCD in which AB and DC are parallel. AB = 3 in., BC = 1 in., CD = 1·5 in., DA = 1 in. State your construction and show that it is correct. (In preliminary sketch draw parm. BCDE.)

17. Draw any rectangle ABCD. Show, without measurement, how to construct a square which has the same perimeter as that of the rectangle.

18. Draw any straight line AB about 4½ in. long. Using ruler and compasses only and without measurement, construct a square with AB as its perimeter.

19. Construct a trapezium ABCD with AB = 2 in., CD = 1 in., AC = 1·5 in., BD = 2 in. DC is parallel to AB. [*Hint:* In preliminary sketch draw DE parallel to CA to meet BA produced in E.]

20. Construct a quadrilateral ABCD having AD = 1½ in., BD = 2½ in., BC = CA = 2 in., and with AC perpendicular to BD. How many solutions are there? [*Hint:* In preliminary sketch construct parm. DAXB: then start by constructing △AXC.]

Theorem 6

The opposite sides and angles of a parallelogram are equal, and each diagonal bisects the parallelogram.

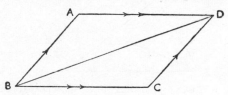

Given: Parallelogram ABCD and diagonal BD.

Required: To prove that
    1. AD = BC and AB = DC.
    2. $\hat{A} = \hat{C}$ and $A\hat{B}C = A\hat{D}C$.
    3. BD bisects parm. ABCD.

Proof: In △s ABD, CDB

    1. $A\hat{D}B = D\hat{B}C$ (alt. ∠s, AD, BC parl.).
    2. $A\hat{B}D = C\hat{D}B$ (alt. ∠s, AB, DC parl.).
    3. BD is common.

∴ △ABD ≡ △CDB (two ∠s and corresp. side)
∴ 1.   AD = BC and AB = DC.
    2. $\hat{A} = \hat{C}$ and $A\hat{B}D + D\hat{B}C = C\hat{D}B + A\hat{D}B$,
              i.e. $A\hat{B}C = A\hat{D}C$.
    3. △ABD = △CDB in area,
        i.e. BD bisects parm. ABCD.

Similarly it could be proved that AC bisects the parm.

Cor. 1. If one angle of a parallelogram is a right angle, all the angles are right angles; i.e. all the angles of a rectangle and of a square are right angles.

Cor. 2. If two adjacent sides of a parallelogram are equal, all its sides are equal; i.e. all the sides of a rhombus and of a square are equal.

Theorem 7

The diagonals of a parallelogram bisect one another.

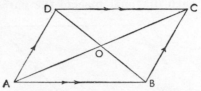

Given: Parm. ABCD with diagonals AC, BD intersecting at O.

Required: To prove that AO = OC, BO = OD.

Proof: In △s AOB, COD

    1.   AB = DC (opp. sides of parm.).

    2. A$\hat{O}$B = D$\hat{O}$C (vert. opp. ∠s).

    3. O$\hat{A}$B = O$\hat{C}$D (alt. ∠s, DC, AB parl.).

∴ △AOB ≡ △COD (two ∠s and corresp. side)

  ∴ AO = OC and BO = OD.

Theorem 8

If one pair of opposite sides of a quadrilateral are equal and parallel, the quadrilateral is a parallelogram.

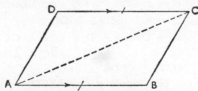

Given: Quad. ABCD with AB = DC and AB parl. to DC.

Required: To prove that ABCD is a parm.

Construction: Join AC.

Proof: In △s ABC, ADC

    1.   AB = DC (given).

    2. B$\hat{A}$C = D$\hat{C}$A (alt. ∠s DC, AB parl.).

    3. AC is common.

∴ △ABC ≡ △ADC (two sides and incl. ∠)
   ∴ BĈA = DÂC.

But these are alternate angles to AD and BC
∴ AD and BC are parallel.
But AB and DC are parallel (given)
∴ ABCD is a parallelogram.

EXERCISES 19

1. Prove that, if the opposite sides of a quadrilateral are equal, the quadrilateral is a parallelogram.

2. Prove that, if the diagonals of a quadrilateral bisect each other, the quadrilateral is a parallelogram.

3. Prove that, if the opposite angles of a quadrilateral are equal, the quadrilateral is a parallelogram.
   [*Hint:* Sum of angles of quadrilateral is 4 right angles.]

4. Prove that, if the diagonals of a parallelogram are equal, the parallelogram is a rectangle.
   In Exercises 5–13 ABCD is a parallelogram.

5. X is the mid-pt. of AD, Y is the mid-pt. of BC. Prove that AYCX is a parallelogram, and that XY and BD bisect each other.

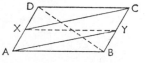

6. XY is any straight line through O. Prove that XO = OY.

7. If, in the figure for Exercise 6, PQ is any other straight line through O, prove that PYQX is a parallelogram.

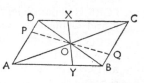

8. BM bisects AB̂C.
   DN bisects AD̂C. Prove that
   (1) BM = DN.
   (2) BNDM is a parallelogram.

9. Prove that
   (1) BE = CH.
   (2) BCHE is a rectangle.

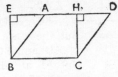

10. BM bisects $\widehat{B}$.
    AN bisects $\widehat{A}$. Prove that
    (1) MN = CD.
    (2) ABNM is a rhombus.

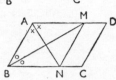

11. AX = CY. Prove that BXDY is a parallelogram.

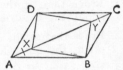

12. P, Q, R, S are the mid-pts. of the sides. Prove that PQRS is a parallelogram.

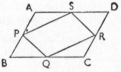

13. AO = OB. Prove that
    (1) DA = AE.
    (2) ACBE is a parallelogram.

14. PQRS is a parallelogram in which the bisectors of angles P and Q meet on RS. Prove that PQ = 2QR.

15. ABCD and ABEH are two parallelograms on a common base AB. Prove that DHEC is a parallelogram unless DC and EH are in one straight line.

16. P is the mid-point of the side AC of △ABC. BP is produced its own length to D. Prove that ABCD is a parallelogram. Q is the mid-point of AB and CQ is produced its own length to E. Prove that
    (1) EAD is a straight line.
    (2) ED = 2BC.

17. Through the vertices A, B, C of △ABC, straight lines XAY, XBZ, YCZ are drawn parallel to the opposite sides forming △XYZ. Prove that A, B, C are the mid-points of the sides of △XYZ.

18. D is the mid-point of the side AB of △ABC. DH is drawn parallel to BC and meets, in H, CH which is drawn parallel to BA. Prove that
    (1) AD = CH.
    (2) DH and AC bisect each other.

19. D and E are the mid-points of sides AB and AC, respectively, of △ABC. DE produced meets a line through C, parallel to BA, in H. Prove that
    (1) △ADE ≡ △CHE.
    (2) DBCH is a parallelogram.
    (3)   DE = ½BC.

20. ABCD is a parallelogram and PQ is any straight line through A which does not meet the parallelogram. Prove that the perpendicular from C to PQ is equal to the sum of the perpendiculars from B and D to PQ.

21. ABCD is a parallelogram. A straight line is drawn through C parallel to the bisector of $\hat{B}$ and meets AB, AD produced in X and Y respectively. Prove that △AXY is isosceles and that the perimeter of the parallelogram is equal to the sum of AX and AY.

22. O is any point inside △ABC. The parallelograms BOCD, COAE, AOBF are completed. Prove that △s ABC and DEF are congruent.

23. Two parallelograms ABCD and AECF have the same diagonal AC. Prove that BDEF is a parallelogram if B, E, D, F are not collinear.

24. ABCD is a parallelogram with $\hat{A}$ an obtuse angle. Through D a straight line DK is drawn to meet BA produced in K so that DK = CB. Prove that $\hat{K} = \hat{B}$.

25. In the parallelogram ABCD, AB = 2AD. The bisector of $\hat{ABC}$ meets CD at K. Prove that CK = KD, AK bisects $\hat{BAD}$, $\hat{AKB} = 90°$.

26. In △ABC, AB = AC. D is any point on AB. AC is produced to E so that CE = BD. DE cuts BC at K. Prove that DK = KE.
[*Hint :* Draw DX parl. to AC to meet BC in X.]

27. The figure represents a cuboid. Prove that
(1) ABGH and BFHD are parallelograms.
(2) AG = BH.

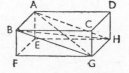

28. With the figure for Exercise 27, prove that AG, BH, FD, EC have a common point.

Proofs of Certain Properties of Special Types of Quadrilaterals

The Kite

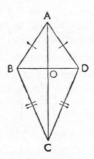

Compare △s ABC and ADC and prove that they are congruent.
Hence BÂO = DÂO.
Then compare △s ABO and ADO and prove that they are congruent.
Hence (1) BO = OD.
(2) AÔB = a rt. angle.

Therefore in a kite the diagonals cut at right angles, and one diagonal is bisected.

[Note that AC is an axis of symmetry, B and D being corresponding points. It follows from symmetry that BD is bisected at rt. angles by AC.]

The Rhombus

Compare △s **AOD** and **DOC** and prove that they are congruent. Hence AÔD = DÔC = 1 rt. angle. Also AD̂O = CD̂O.

Therefore the diagonals of a rhombus bisect each other at right angles and bisect the angles through which they pass.

[Note that **AC** and **BD** are both axes of symmetry, **B** and **D** being corresponding points for the axis **AC**, and **A** and **C** being corresponding points for the axis **BD**. It follows from symmetry that **AC** and **BD** bisect each other at rt. angles.]

The Rectangle

Compare △s **ABC** and **DBC** and prove that they are congruent, the case of congruence being two sides and the included angle.

∴ **AC = BD.**

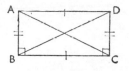

Hence the diagonals of a rectangle are equal.

[Note that neither of the diagonals is an axis of symmetry.]

The Square

Compare △s **AOD** and **DOC** and prove that they are congruent.

Hence prove AÔD = a rt. angle, and AD̂O = CD̂O.

Since by definition a square is a rectangle, **AC = BD.**

Therefore the diagonals of a square are equal and cut at right angles and bisect the angles through which they pass.

[Note that both **AC** and **BD** are axes of symmetry, from which it follows that **AB** and **CD** bisect each other at rt. angles.]

EXERCISES 20

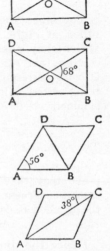

1. ABCD is a rectangle.
   Find OB̂C and DÔA.

2. ABCD is a rectangle.
   Find DĈA and AD̂B.

3. ABCD is a rhombus.
   Find AD̂C and AB̂D.

4. ABCD is a rhombus.
   Find AB̂C.

5. Prove that the diagonals of a rhombus bisect the angles through which they pass.

6. Prove that the diagonals of a square bisect the angles through which they pass.

7. A and B are the centres of the circles. Prove (in two ways, one of them by symmetry) that AB bisects XY at right angles.

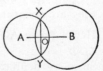

8. ABCD is a rectangle and AC = 2AB. Prove that
   (1) PX is perp. to CA.
   (2) XP = AD.

9. ABCD is a rectangle with $\widehat{COB} = 60°$. Prove that $AC = 2BC$.

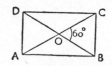

10. BD bisects $\widehat{B}$ of $\triangle ABC$. Prove that BGDH is a rhombus.

11. PQRS is a square. $PK = PT$. Prove that $\widehat{PKT} = 3T\widehat{K}Q$.

12. ABCD is a parm. ABEF and ADGH are squares. Prove that $\triangle CGE$ is isosceles.

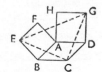

13. AB and CD are diameters. Prove that ACBD is a rectangle.

14. ABCD is a square. E, F, G, H are the mid-points of the four sides. Prove that the figure EFGH is also a square.

15. ABCD is a rectangle and E, F, G, H are the mid-points of the sides. Prove that the figure EFGH is a parallelogram. What special type of parallelogram is it?

16. ABCD is a rhombus, whose diagonals intersect in O. AR is drawn parallel to BD and DR is drawn perpendicular to AR meeting it in R. If OR cuts AD in K, prove that $AB = 2OK$.

17.

ABCD is a square. E is any point in BC. BF is perpendicular to AE. Prove that AE = BF.

18.

ABCD is a square. Prove that VXYZ is also a square.

19.

ABCD is a square. Prove that EF is parl. to BD.

20. PQRS is a rectangle. The bisectors of the angles intersect to form a quadrilateral ABCD. Prove that ABCD is a rectangle.

21. ABCD is a square with the diagonals AC and BD intersecting at O. Y is any point on DO. BZ is drawn perpendicular to AY to cut AO in X. Prove that AX = DY.

22. PQR is a triangle. PA bisects $\hat{P}$ and meets QR in A. QP is produced to E. PB is perpendicular to PA and meets QR produced in B. Through B, BE, BH are drawn parallel to RP, PQ respectively, meeting QP and PR produced in E and H respectively. Prove that PHBE is a rhombus.

23. PQRS is a square. From T, any point in PR, TA is drawn perpendicular to PS and TB perpendicular to PQ meeting PS, PQ respectively in A, B. RC and TD are drawn perpendicular to AQ. Prove that AD = CQ.

POLYGONS

A **polygon** is a plane figure bounded by more than four straight lines.

A polygon is said to be **equiangular** if all its angles are equal.

A polygon is said to be **equilateral** if all its sides are equal.

A polygon is said to be **regular** if all its angles are equal and all its sides are equal.

When the polygon has five sides it is called a **pentagon**; six sides, **hexagon**; eight sides, **octagon**; ten sides, **decagon**.

The interior angles of a polygon of n sides are together equal to $(2n - 4)$ right angles.

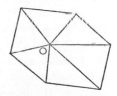

Suppose the polygon divided into triangles by joining the vertices to any point O inside the figure. Since each side of the polygon is the base of a triangle, vertex O, and there are n sides, the number of triangles formed must be n.

The sum of the angles of each $\triangle = 2$ rt. angles

$\therefore$ the sum of the angles of the n $\triangle$s $= 2n$ rt. angles.

But the sum of the angles of the n $\triangle$s $=$ all the interior angles of the figure $+$ angles at O

$\therefore$ all the interior angles of the polygon $+$ the angles at O $= 2n$ rt. angles.

But the angles at O $= 4$ rt. angles

$\therefore$ all the interior angles of the polygon $+ 4$ rt. angles $= 2n$ rt. angles

$\therefore$ all the interior angles of the polygon $= (2n - 4)$ rt. angles.

If the sides of a convex * polygon are produced in order, the sum of the exterior angles so formed is 4 right angles.

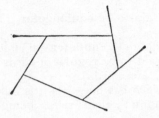

Suppose the polygon has n sides.   At each vertex

the exterior angle + the interior angle
$$= 2 \text{ rt. angles (adj. angles on a str. line)}$$

∴ the n exterior angles + the n interior angles
$$= 2n \text{ rt. angles}$$

∴ the n exterior angles + $(2n - 4)$ rt. angles
$$= 2n \text{ rt. angles}$$

∴ the n exterior angles + $2n$ rt. angles − 4 rt. angles
$$= 2n \text{ rt. angles}$$

∴ the n exterior angles
$$= 4 \text{ rt. angles.}$$

* A **convex** polygon is one in which each interior angle is less than 180°.   If at least one of the interior angles is greater than 180° the polygon is said to be **re-entrant**.

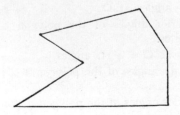

EXERCISES 21

1.

What is the sum of the three
exterior ∠s of the △ ?

2.

Find *x*.

3. What is the sum of the interior angles of the following
figures ?

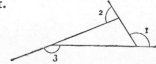

(a)   (b)   (c)

4. What is the size of each exterior angle of a regular
   (1) hexagon, (2) octagon ?
   Now write down the size of each interior angle of a regular
   (1) hexagon, (2) octagon.

5. What is the size of each interior angle of a regular polygon
   with (1) 12 sides, (2) 20 sides ?   (Find first the size of
   each exterior angle.)

6. How many sides has a regular polygon whose exterior
   angle is (1) 45°, (2) 36° ?

7. How many sides has a regular polygon whose interior
   angle is (1) 162°, (2) 156° ?

8. Find *x*.

9. Two angles of a hexagon are right angles.   A third angle
   is 150° and the remaining angles are equal.   Find the
   size of each.

10. The angles of an octagon are *x*°, 2*x*°, 3*x*°, 4*x*°, 5*x*°, 5*x*°,
    8*x*°, 8*x*°.   Find all the angles.

11. The sum of the interior angles of a convex polygon is double the sum of its exterior angles. How many sides has the polygon?

12. Two angles of a convex polygon are 100° and 140°. The others, which are equal, are angles of 120°. How many sides has the polygon?

13.

(a) B   (b) B   (c) B

What is the size of AÔB in each case?

14.

Prove that **ABDE** is a rectangle.

15.

Prove △**EBC** isosceles and that each of its base angles is double the vertical angle.

Note: The figures for exs. 14 and 15 are equiangular.

16. Two regular polygons are such that the number of sides in one is double that in the other, and an angle of the first is $1\frac{1}{4}$ times that of the second. Find the number of sides in each.

17. **ABCDE** is a regular pentagon. **AB** and **DC** are produced to meet in **T**. Find the size of BT̂C, and prove that BDT is an isosceles triangle.

18. Construct a regular hexagon **ABCDEF**. On the sides **AB**, **BC** construct squares **ABPQ**, **BCLM** lying outside the hexagon.
Prove that **PM = QP** and find the number of degrees in QP̂M and prove that **QP**, **PM**, **ML** are consecutive sides of a regular twelve-sided polygon.

19. **ABC** is an isosceles triangle in which $\hat{B} = \hat{C} = 2\hat{A}$.   **BX** bisects $\hat{B}$ and meets **AC** in **X**.
Prove that **BX** and **XA** are consecutive sides of a regular pentagon.

20. In a pentagon **ABCDE** the angle **D** is double the angle **B,** and the angles **A**, **C** and **E** are each half of the sum of the angles **B** and **D**.   Find all the angles of the pentagon.

THEOREM 9

The straight line drawn through the mid-point of one side of a triangle parallel to another side of the triangle bisects the third side.

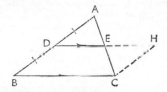

Given: △ABC with D the mid-point of **AB** and **DE** parallel to **BC** meeting **AC** in **E**.

Required: To prove that **AE = EC**.

Construction: Through **C** draw **CH** parallel to **BA** meeting **DE** produced in **H**.

Proof: Because **BD** is parallel to **CH** (constr.) and **DH** is parallel to **BC** (given)

∴ **BCHD** is a parallelogram
  ∴ **CH = BD** (opp. sides of parm.).
  But **BD = DA** (given)
  ∴ **CH = DA**.
In △s ADE, CEH
  1.   **AD = CH** (proved).
  2. $\hat{A} = E\hat{C}H$ (alt. ∠s DA, CH parl.).
  3. $A\hat{E}D = C\hat{E}H$ (vert. opp. ∠s).
∴ △ADE ≡ △ CEH (two ∠s and corresp. side)
  ∴ **AE = EC**.

Theorem 10

The straight line joining the mid-points of two sides of a triangle is parallel to the third side and equal to half of it.

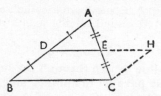

Given: △ABC with D, E mid-points of AB, AC respectively, and DE joined.

Required: To prove that
(1) DE is parallel to BC,
(2) DE = ½BC.

Construction: Through C draw CH parallel to BA, meeting DE produced in H.

Proof: In △s ADE, CHE

1. AE = EC (given).
2. $\hat{A}$ = EĈH (alt. ∠s DA, CH parl.).
3. AÊD = CÊH (vert. opp. ∠s).

∴ △ADE ≡ △CEH (two ∠s and corresp. side)
∴ AD = CH, and DE = EH.
But AD = DB (given)
∴ CH = BD.
But CH is parallel to BD (constr.)
∴ BD and CH are equal and parallel
∴ BCHD is a parm. (quad. with pair of opposite sides equal and parl.)
∴ BC = DH (opp. sides of parm.) and BC is parallel to DH.
But DE = ½DH (proved)
∴ DE is parallel to BC and DE = ½BC.

Theorem 11

If three or more parallel straight lines make equal intercepts on one transversal, they make equal intercepts on any other transversal.

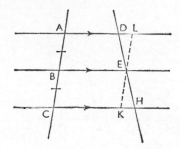

Given: AD, BE, CH three parallel straight lines, cutting off equal intercepts AB, BC on transversal ABC.

Required: To prove that the intercepts DE, EH made on any other transversal DH are equal.

Construction: Through E draw KEL parallel to CA, meeting CH in K and AD in L.

Proof: ABEL is a parm. (quad. with opp. sides parl.)

∴ AB = LE.
Similarly BC = EK.
But AB = BC (given)

∴ LE = EK.
In △s LED, KEH

1. LE = EK (proved).

2. DÊL = KÊH (vert. opp. ∠s).

3. L̂ = K̂ (alt. ∠s AL, CH parl.).

∴ △LED ≡ △KEH (two ∠s and corresp. side)
∴ DE = EH.

CONSTRUCTION II

To divide a straight line into any number of equal parts.

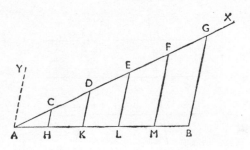

Given: Str. line **AB**.

Required: To divide **AB** into any number of equal parts, say 5.

Construction: Draw any straight line **AX** making an angle with **AB**.

From **AX** cut off 5 equal parts **AC, CD, DE, EF, FG**. Join **GB**.

Through **C, D, E, F** draw str. lines parallel to **GB**, meeting **AB** in **H, K, L, M** respectively.

Then **AB** is divided into 5 equal parts.

Proof: Draw **AY** parallel to **BG**.

Since the intercepts made on the transversal **AX** by a system of parallel straight lines are equal, therefore the intercepts made by the same parallel straight lines on the transversal **AB** are equal.

∴ **AH = HK = KL = LM = MB**,

i.e. **AB** is divided into 5 equal parts.

THEOREM 12

The medians of a triangle are concurrent, and the point of concurrence is a point of trisection of each median.

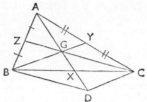

Given: △ABC.

Required: To prove (i) that the medians are concurrent;
(ii) that the medians are trisected at the point of concurrence.

Construction: Draw the medians BY and CZ and let them cut at G.
Join AG and produce AG to D, so that AG = GD.
Let GD cut BC at X.
Join BD and CD.

Proof: In △ABD, Z is the mid-point of AB, G is the mid-point of AD
∴ ZG is parallel to BD and ZG = ½BD (str. line joining mid-points of two sides of △ is parl. to the third side and equal to half of it).
Similarly YG is parallel to CD
∴ BGCD is a parm. (quad. with opp. sides parl.)
∴ BX = XC (diags. of parm. bisect each other)
∴ AX is a median
∴ the medians are concurrent.
ZG = ½BD (proved).
But BD = GC (opp. sides of parm.)
∴ ZG = ½GC
∴ G is a point of trisection of CZ.
Similarly G is a point of trisection of BY and AX.

[*Note:* The point of concurrence of the medians is called the **centroid** of the triangle.]

EXERCISES 22

1. Draw a straight line 7·3 cm. long and divide it into seven equal parts. Measure the length of one part.

2.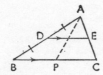

In △ABC, P is any point in BC. Prove that DE bisects AP.

3.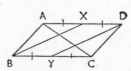

ABCD is a parm. Prove that BX and DY trisect AC.

4.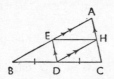

Prove that EH = ½BC.

5.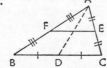

Prove that AD bisects EF.

6. Show how to construct a triangle given the mid-points of the sides.

7.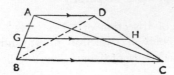

Prove that
(1) DH = HC.
(2) GH bisects both AC and BD.
(3) GH = ½(BC + AD).

8.

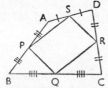

Prove that PQRS is
a parallelogram.

9.

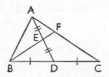

Prove that AF = ⅓AC.

10.

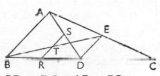

BD = DG, AE = EC,
BR = RD, AS = SD.
Prove that BT = TE.

11.

PQRS is a square
Prove that OA = ½RB.

12.

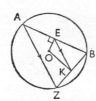

In circle ABZ centre O, OE is perp.
to AB.
EK is parallel to AZ.
Prove OK perp. to ZB.

13. AD is a median of △ABC. BX and CY are drawn parallel
to AD. GH is any straight line perpendicular to AD and
meeting BX and CY in G and H respectively. Prove
that AG = AH.

14. In the parallelogram ABCD, AB is produced its own length
to E. DE cuts AC in H and BC in G. Prove that

(1) G is the mid-point of BC.
(2) CH = ½HA.

15. **PQRS** is a parallelogram with **T** the mid-point of **RS**. **PT** produced cuts **QR** produced in **K**. **PR** and **QT** intersect in **O**. Prove that

    (1) **QR** = **RK**.
    (2) **KO** produced bisects **PQ**.

16. **ABCD** is a parallelogram and **E** is a point on **AC** such that **AE** = ½**EC**. Prove that **BE** produced bisects **AD** in **H** and that **EH** = ½**BE**.

17. **PQRS** is a parallelogram with **T** the mid-point of **PQ**. If $S\widehat{T}R = 90°$ prove that **PQ** = 2**QR**.

18. **ABC** is a triangle with **CE** perpendicular to **AB**. Any line from **B** to **AC** cuts **EC** in **H**. If **P**, **Q**, **R** are mid-points of **BH**, **BC**, **CA** respectively, prove $P\widehat{Q}R = 90°$.

19. **BE** and **CF** are perpendiculars from the vertices **B** and **C** to the opposite sides **AC**, **AB** respectively of △**ABC**. **BE** and **CF** cut in **H**. If **X**, **Y**, **Z** are the mid-points of **AH**, **AB**, **BC** respectively, prove that $X\widehat{Y}Z = 90°$.

20. **ABCD** is a parallelogram with **AD** produced its own length to **E**. **BE** and **CD** intersect in **K**. **AK** produced meets **CE** in **H**. Prove that **KH** = ⅓**AK**.

21. **PQR** is a triangle with **X** the mid-point of **PQ**, and **Y** a point in **PR**, so that **RY** = ⅓**PY**. **XY** produced meets **QR** produced in **Z**. Prove that **QR** = 2**RZ**.

22. **P**, **Q**, **R**, **S** are the mid-points of **BA**, **AC**, **CD**, **DB** of the quadrilateral **ABCD**. If **BC** = **AD** prove that **PR** and **QS** bisect each other at right angles.

23. **ABCD** is a parallelogram and **XY** is any line outside the parallelogram. **AP**, **BQ**, **CR**, **DS** are perpendiculars from **A**, **B**, **C**, **D** to **XY**. Prove that **AP** + **CR** = **BQ** + **DS**.

    [*Hint:* If **O** is the point of intersection of the diagonals draw the perpendicular from **O** to **XY**. Then see Exercise No. 7 above.]

24. The figure represents a triangular pyramid. **E**, **F**, **G**, **H** are the mid-points of **AB**, **BC**, **CD**, **DA** respectively. Prove that **EG** and **FH** bisect each other at **O**. What other straight line joining the mid-points of two edges will also pass through **O** ?

For Exercises 25–30 **AX**, **BY**, **CZ** are the medians of △**ABC** and they meet at **G**. The figure is the same as that in Theorem 12. **BGCD** was proved to be a parallelogram.

$GX = \frac{1}{3}AX$, $GY = \frac{1}{3}BY$, $GZ = \frac{1}{3}CZ$, $GD = AG$.

State the construction in each case.

25. Construct △**ABC** if **AX** = 6 cm., **BY** = 9 cm., **CZ** = 7·5 cm. Measure **AB**, **BC**, **CA**.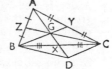

    [Calculate the sides of △**GDC** and construct this △ as the first step.]

26. Construct △**ABC** if **BC** = 9 cm., **BY** = 8·4 cm., **CZ** = 6·9 cm. Measure **AB** and **AC**.

    [Calculate **BG** and **GC** and construct △**GBC** first.]

27. Construct △**ABC** if **AB** = 10 cm., **BY** = 9 cm., **CZ** = 7·8 cm. Measure **BC** and **CA**.

    [Calculate the sides of △**GZB** and construct this △ first.]

28. Construct △**ABC** if **AB** = 3 in., **BC** = 4·5 in., **AX** = 3·9 in. Measure **CA**.

    [Construct first △**ABX**.]

29. Construct △**ABC** if **AB** = 2·5 in., **AC** = 3·5 in., **AX** = 1·8 in. Measure **BC**.

    [Draw a sketch of △**ABC** with **AX** a median. Produce **AX** its own length to **E**. Join **BE** and **CE**. **BACE** is a parm. Construct first △**ABE**.]

LOCI

If a point moves so as to satisfy certain conditions, it traces out a path called a **locus**.

For example, if a point moves in a plane so that it is at a constant distance from a fixed point **O**, it will trace out the circumference of a circle. If a point moves in space, satisfying the same condition, the locus will be the surface of a sphere, of which the point **O** is the centre.

To prove that a locus is correct we must prove

(1) that any point satisfying the conditions lies on the locus,

(2) that any point on the locus satisfies the given conditions.

This involves proving a theorem and its converse.

Exercises 23

1. What is the locus of the tip of the minute hand of a watch?

2. What is the locus of a point on the rim of a rotating fly-wheel of a stationary engine?

3. A dog is tied to a rope which is fastened to a peg in the ground. If the rope is kept taut what is the locus of any point on the rope?

4. A dog is tied to a rope which is fastened to a ring, and the ring slides freely along a fixed wooden bar. If the rope is kept taut what is the locus of any point on the rope?

5. What is the locus of a point on the handle of a door which opens through one right angle?

6. What is the locus of a point on the handle of a garage door which moves vertically?

7. What is the locus of a point on one of the weights in an eight-day clock?

8. What is the locus of a point on the pendulum of an eight-day clock?

9. A rectangular box is fitted with a hinged lid. What is the locus of any point on the lid as the box is opened?

10. A penny held vertically is rolled along a straight line on a table. What is the locus of the centre?

11. A penny is laid on a table and kept fixed. A sixpence is laid on the table and rolled round the rim of the penny, always touching it. What is the locus of the centre of the sixpence?

12. The cuboid rests with EFGH on a horizontal plane. If it

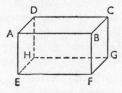

is tilted about the edge EH until the face AEHD rests on the table what is the locus of B, F, D?

THEOREM 13

The locus of a point which is equidistant from two fixed points is the perpendicular bisector of the straight line joining the points.

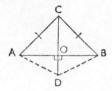

1st Part.

Given: Two fixed points A and B, and C any point equidistant from A and B.

Required: To prove that C lies on the perp. bisector of AB.

Construction: Join AB and bisect AB at O.
Join CO, CA, CB.

Proof: In △s AOC, BOC

    1. AO = OB (constr.).

    2. CA = CB (given).

    3. CO is common.

∴ △AOC ≡ △BOC (three sides)

∴ CÔA = CÔB

∴ CO is perp. to AB (adj. ∠s, AOB a str. line)

∴ C lies on the perp. bisector of AB.

2nd Part.

Given: D, any point on the perp. bisector of AB.

Required: To prove that D is equidistant from A and B.

Construction: Join DA and DB.

Proof: In △s AOD, DOB

    1.   AO = OB (given).

    2. OD is common.

    3. AÔD = BÔD (each a rt. angle, given).

∴ △AOD ≡ △BOD (two sides and incl. ∠)

∴ DA = DB

∴ D is equidistant from A and B.

Theorem 14

The locus of a point equidistant from two straight lines meeting at a point is the bisector of the angle between them.

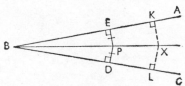

1st Part

Given: Two str. lines AB and CB meeting at B and P any point equidistant from BA and BC.

Required: To prove that P lies on the bisector of AB̂C.

Construction: Join PB. Draw PE, PD perp. to BA and BC resp.

Proof: In △s PBE and PBD

     1.   PE = PD (given).

     2.   PB is common.

     3.   PÊB = PD̂B (rt. angles, given).

   ∴   △PBE ≡ △ PBD (rt. angle, hyp. and one side)

     ∴   EB̂P = DB̂P

     ∴   P is on the bisector of AB̂C.

2nd Part

Given: Two str. lines AB and CB meeting at B and X any point on the bisector XB of AB̂C.

Required: To prove that X is equidistant from AB and BC.

Construction: Draw XK, XL perp. to BA, BC resp.

Proof: In △s KBX and LBX

     1.   KB̂X = LB̂X (given).

     2.   XK̂B = XL̂B (rt. angle, constr.).

     3.   BX is common.

   ∴   △KBX ≡ △LBX (two ∠s and corresp. side)

     ∴   XK = XL

     ∴   X is equidistant from BA and BC.

Intersection of Loci

The method of Loci is used to find the position of a point which is subject to two conditions. Corresponding to each of the given conditions there will be one locus on which the point must lie. Hence, when two conditions are involved, the possible positions of the point will be those points which are common to both loci, i.e. the required point is located at the intersection or intersections of the two loci.

Example 1.—Find the point or points which are 2 cm. from a fixed line AB and 3 cm. from a fixed point C. All points

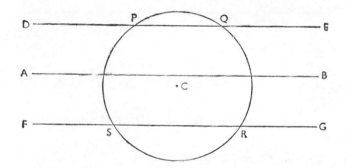

distant 2 cm. from AB lie on one or other of the lines DE and FG. All points distant 3 cm. from C lie on the circumference of the circle with centre C and radius 3 cm.

These loci intersect at 4 points, P, Q, R, S. Hence these 4 points satisfy the given conditions.

[*Note:* In this problem depending on the relative positions of the given fixed line AB and the given fixed point C, and the two measurements involved, there will be 1, 2, 3 or 4 points satisfying the given two conditions, and in the exceptional case the problem will not admit of any solution.]

Example 2.—Construct the triangle ABC, given that the base BC is fixed, that the vertex A lies on a given straight line and that the distance of A from BC is fixed.

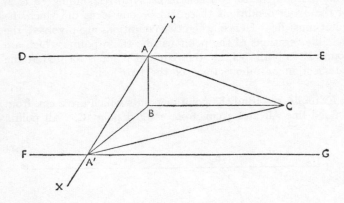

Let BC be the fixed base, and XY the straight line on which A must lie.

Draw the straight lines DE and FG at the fixed distance from BC.

Let DE and XY cut at A, and FG and XY at A'.

Then either △ABC or △A'BC is the required triangle.

[*Note:* (1) If the given line XY were parallel to BC and coincided with DE or FG then an infinite number of solutions would be found.

(2) If XY were parallel to BC and at a greater or smaller distance from BC than the fixed distance no solution could be found.]

THEOREM 15

The perpendicular bisectors of the three sides of a triangle are concurrent.

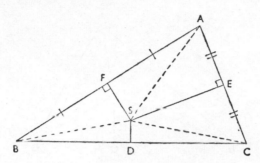

Given: △ABC.

Required: To prove that the perp. bisectors of the three sides are concurrent.

Construction: Draw FS and ES the perp. bisectors of AB and AC respectively. Let FS and ES meet at S.
Let D be the mid-point of BC.
Join SA, SB, SC, SD.

Proof: FS is the perp. bisector of AB.
∴ It is the locus of points equidistant from A and B
∴ SA = SB.
Similarly SA = SC
∴ SB = SC
∴ S is on the locus of points equidistant from B and C
and D is equidistant from B and C
∴ SD is perp. to BC
∴ the perp. bisectors of the three sides are concurrent.

[*Note:* Since SA = SB = SC a circle can be drawn with centre S and radius SA and it will pass through B and C. This circle is called the **circumcircle** of the triangle.]

Theorem 16

The bisectors of the three angles of a triangle are concurrent.

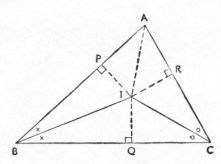

Given : △ABC.

Required : To prove that the bisectors of the three angles are concurrent.

Construction : Draw IB and IC the bisectors of $\hat{B}$ and $\hat{C}$ resp. Let them meet at I.
Join IA.
Draw IP, IQ, IR perp. to AB, BC, CA resp.

Proof : IB is the bisector of $\hat{B}$.

∴ It is the locus of points equidistant from AB and BC
∴ IP = IQ.
Similarly IQ = IR
∴ IP = IR
∴ I is on the locus of points equidistant from AB and AC
∴ IA is the bisector of $\hat{A}$
∴ the bisectors of the three angles are concurrent.

[*Note :* Since IP = IQ = IR a circle can be described with centre I and radius IP and it will pass through Q and R. This circle is called the **incircle** of the triangle.]

EXERCISES 24

1. Mark a point **A** on your paper. Find the locus of the centres of circles of radius 3 cm. which pass through **A**. Draw the locus.

2. Draw a straight line **BC**, $2\frac{1}{2}$ in. long. Draw any triangle **ABC** with the median **AD** 2 in. long. Find the locus of **A** if the median **AD** is always 2 in. long.

3. Draw a circle, radius $1\frac{1}{2}$ in. Mark any two points **A** and **B** within the circle 1 in. apart. Find points on the circumference of the circle equidistant from **A** and **B**. How many such points are there ?

4. **A** and **B** are two points 6 cm. apart. Find two points each of which is 4 cm. from **A** and 5 cm. from **B**.

5. **A** and **B** are two points 5 cm. apart. A point **P** moves so that it is always 4 cm. from **A**. Draw the locus. What is its maximum distance from **B** ? What is its minimum distance from **B** ?

6. Draw any two straight lines **AB** and **CD**. Find all the points which are 2 cm. from **AB** and 3 cm. from **CD**. How many such points are there ?

7. Draw a straight line **BC** 4 cm. long. Find the locus of a point **A** if the triangle **ABC** is always an isosceles triangle, with **AB** = **AC**.

8. Draw a straight line **AB** 3 in. long. Find the locus of a point **C** if the triangle **CAB** has angle **C** always 90°.

9. **AB** and **BC** represent two straight rulers placed at right angles to each other. **XY** represents one position of a rod

of length 4 cm. which slides between the rulers. Find the locus of **Z**, the mid-point of **XY**.

[*Hint:* Join **ZB**.]

10. Draw a triangle ABC with AB = 5·5 cm., BC = 6 cm., CA = 7 cm. Find a point equidistant from A, B and C.

11. Repeat Exercise 10 if AB = 3·6 cm., BC = 4·8 cm., CA = 6 cm.

12. Repeat Exercise 10 if AB = 5 cm., BC = 4 cm., CA = 8 cm.

13. Draw a triangle ABC with AB = 6 cm., BC = 7 cm., CA = 8 cm. Find a point equidistant from the three sides.

14. Draw a straight line BC and mark a point A, 1 in. from BC. Draw any straight line from A to BC meeting it in X. P is the mid-point of AX. Find the locus of P for different positions of AX.

15. Construct △ABC if base BC = 2½ in., altitude = 1½ in., median AD = 2 in.

16. Draw a straight line BC and mark a point A, 1 in. from BC. Find several points which are equidistant from BC and from point A. Draw a freehand sketch of the locus.

17. A and B are two fixed points 2 in. apart. Find a point P such that AP + PB = 3 in. Find several positions of the point P. Draw a sketch of the locus of P.

18. Draw two parallel straight lines AB and CD 1 in. apart. Mark any point P between AB and CD. Find a point ¾ in. from P and equidistant from AB and CD. How many such points are there? Mark a point X ½ in. from AB and **not** between the parallels. Find a point 1¼ in. from X and equidistant from AB and CD. How many such points are there?
How many points are there ¾ in. from X and equidistant from AB and CD?
How many points are there 1 in. from X and equidistant from AB and CD?

19. The base BC of △ABC is fixed and is 2 in. long. The centroid of the triangle is ½ in. from BC, and AB is 2 in. long. Construct the △ABC. How many solutions are there?

20.

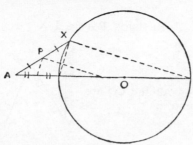

Draw a circle, centre O, radius 3 cm. Mark a point A
outside the circle, 5 cm. from O. Draw any line from A
to the circumference meeting it in X. Find P, the mid-
point of AX. As X moves round the circumference find
the locus of P.

[*Hint:* See figure.]

21. △ABC has a fixed base BC 3 in. long, and is of a fixed
altitude 2 in. BD bisects the angle ABC and D is the foot
of the perpendicular from A to BD. Find the locus of D.

22. What is the locus of a point—not confined to one plane —
in the following cases :

(1) a point at a constant distance from a fixed point,
(2) a point equidistant from two fixed points,
(3) a point at a constant distance from a fixed straight
line,
(4) a point equidistant from two parallel straight lines,
(5) a point equidistant from two intersecting straight
lines ?

REVISION PAPERS I–X

I

1. In the figure, AB and CD are parallel. Find x.

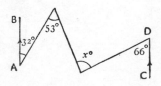

2. In △ABC, AB = AC and BR bisects $A\hat{B}C$. Prove that BR = BC.

3. PQRS is a parallelogram. X and Y are points on QS such that SX = QY. Prove that PX = YR and that PXRY is a parallelogram.

4. In △ABC, X is the mid-point of AC, and AD bisects $B\hat{A}C$, meeting BC in D. XE is drawn parallel to AB and meets AD in E. Prove that $A\hat{E}C = 90°$.

5. ABCD is a parallelogram with AB = 5 cm. and BC = 6 cm. O is a point in AD such that OD = 2 cm. and BO produced meets CD produced in E. Prove that △s ABO, EOD, EBC are similar and calculate ED.

II

1. In the figure, SI = SC. Prove that

    (1) $B\hat{C}S = B\hat{A}I$.

    (2) $\hat{S} = A\hat{B}C$.

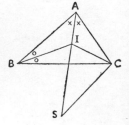

2. In the figure, AXB and AYC are equilateral △s and AB = AC. Prove that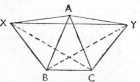
   (1) BY = CX.
   (2) XY is parl. to BC.

3. ABCD is a square with Y any point in DC. BK is drawn perpendicular to AY and produced to meet AD in X. Prove that AX = DY.

4. C is the mid-point of a straight line AB. CD is perpendicular to AB. A straight line drawn from A cuts CD at E, and the parallel to CD drawn through B, at Y. Prove that EB = EY.

5. PQRS is a quadrilateral in which PQ = RS but they are not parallel. X and Y are the mid-points of PS and QR respectively. XO, the perpendicular to PS at X, meets the perpendicular to QR at Y, in the point O. Prove that PQ and RS subtend equal angles at O.

III

1. In the figure, $P\hat{Q}R = 45°$. Prove △s PQS and PRT congruent.

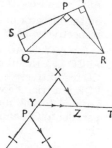

2. In the figure (not drawn accurately), PR and XZ are parallel and YZ and QR are parallel. PQ = PR. Prove △XYZ isosceles and find $X\hat{Z}T$.

3. ABC is an isosceles triangle with AB = AC. D is any point in BC. Through E and H, the mid-points of BD and DC respectively, are drawn perpendiculars ES and HT, cutting BA and CA at S and T respectively. Prove that
   (1) SDTA is a parallelogram.   (2) TC = AS.

4. Two angles of a nine-sided polygon are each 70°. The other angles are equal, each being $x°$. Find x.

5. ABC is a triangle with $\hat{A}$ a right angle. D is a point in BC such that BD = AC. DE is drawn outside the triangle perpendicular to BC, and a circle with centre B, and radius BC, cuts DE at E. Prove that ABEC is a trapezium.

IV

1. In the figure, ABCD and DBCH are parallelograms. Prove that AH is parallel to XY and that AH = 4XY.

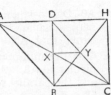

2. In the figure, ABE and DBC are equilateral triangles. $X\hat{C}E = X\hat{E}C = 60°$. Prove that

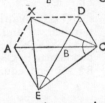

    (1) $\triangle XAE \equiv \triangle BEC$.
    (2)   AX = DB.
    (3) ABDX is a parallelogram.

3. ABC is an isosceles triangle with AB = AC. G is any point on the bisector of $\hat{A}$. BG, CG are produced to meet AC, AB respectively at Y, X. Prove that

    (1) $A\hat{B}Y = A\hat{C}X$.   (2) BG = CG.   (3) GX = GY.

4. ABCD is a rhombus with X, Y, Z the mid-points of AB, BC, CD respectively. Prove that ZX subtends a right angle at Y.

5. PQR is a triangle with X the mid-point of PQ. XY is drawn parallel to QR, meeting PR in Y. Through P, PS is drawn parallel to QR and equal to $\frac{1}{2}$QR. XS cuts PR in T. Prove that

$$\frac{PT}{TR} = \frac{1}{3}.$$

V

1. In the figure, AB = AC, AD = AE. Prove that

    (1)   BE = DC.
    (2) $D\hat{B}E = D\hat{C}E$.
    (3)   OD = OE.

2. In the figure, AB = AC. Prove that
   (1)   △BED ≡ △BXD.
   (2) ED + DG = BH.

3. ABC is a triangle in which AB > AC. BA is produced to D
   so that AD = AC. CE is drawn perpendicular to CD to
   meet BA in E. Prove that

   (1) AE = AC.   (2) $A\widehat{E}C = \frac{1}{2}(A\widehat{B}C + A\widehat{C}B)$.

4. PQR is an isosceles triangle on the base QR with each base
   angle double the vertical angle. The bisector of angle Q
   meets PR in T, and the straight line through P parallel to QR
   in S. Prove △PST isosceles.

5. PQR is a triangle with PS, the bisector of $\widehat{P}$, meeting QR in S.
   RW is drawn perpendicular to PS, meeting it in T, and PQ
   in W. TX is drawn parallel to QP, meeting PR in X. Prove
   that TX = $\frac{1}{4}$WP.

VI

1. In the figure, PQRS is a parallelo-
   gram. AR = PC and RT = PB.
   Prove that AT = BC and that
   AC bisects BT.

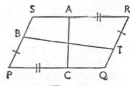

2. In the figure, CE = radius of circle.
   Find the size of $O\widehat{A}D$.

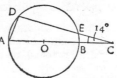

3. Draw a straight line XY. Take A and B any two points on
   the same side of XY. From A draw AC perpendicular to
   XY meeting it at C, and produce AC to D, making AC = CD.
   Join DB cutting XY at E. Prove that AE and BE are equally
   inclined to XY.
   Take H any other point on XY, and prove that
   $$AH + HB > AE + EB.$$

4. PQRS is a square with its diagonals intersecting at O.   RX is drawn perpendicular to PR and meets the bisector of $R\hat{P}Q$ in X.   PX cuts OQ in T and RQ in W.   Prove that

(1) RW = RX.   (2) OT = $\frac{1}{2}$RW.

5. ABC is an isosceles triangle with AB = AC.   BD is drawn perpendicular to AC and BX is drawn perpendicular to AB, meeting AC produced in X.   Prove that $D\hat{B}C = X\hat{B}C$.

VII

1. In the figure, AD = BC.   Prove that $\hat{D} = \hat{C}$.   If $\hat{D} = 70°$ and DA and CB are produced to meet at O calculate the size of $\hat{O}$.

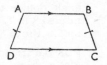

2. In the figure, OX is parallel to CB, OY is parallel to CD.   Name two pairs of similar triangles, giving reasons for your answers.
Calculate x, y, z, w.
Prove that $Y\hat{O}A = Y\hat{A}O$.

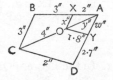

3. ABCDEF is a regular hexagon with O the centre point. OA, OC, OE are produced their own lengths to X, Y, Z respectively.   Prove that XY passes through B and that $\triangle$XYZ is equilateral.

4. ABCD is a parallelogram.   The bisector of $\hat{B}$ meets AD or AD produced in E.   Through C a straight line YCX is drawn parallel to EB to meet AD and AB produced in Y and X respectively.   Prove that

(1) BC = BX.
(2) AY = AX.
(3) Perimeter of parallelogram = AY + AX.

5. Draw any triangle ABC.   State how you would construct a rhombus with one vertex at B, the other three vertices being one on each of the three sides of the triangle.   Prove that your construction is correct.

VIII

1. In the figure, prove that $a - b = 9$.

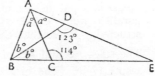

2. In the figure, prove that the two triangles are similar and calculate the lengths of AB and BD.

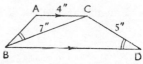

3. Draw any angle BAC. Let P and M be two points in AB and Q and N two points on AC such that AM = AN and AP = AQ. Let PN and QM cut at S. Prove that

   (1) $\widehat{APN} = \widehat{AQM}$.   (2) SP = SQ.   (3) AS bisects $\widehat{BAC}$.

4. ABCD is a parallelogram. AX and CY are drawn perpendicular to the diagonal BD. Prove that

   (1) AX = CY.   (2) AY is parallel to XC.

5. PQR is a triangle with B and C the mid-points of PQ and QR respectively. Through P any straight line is drawn outside the triangle. QTZ is a straight line meeting this line in Z and cutting PR in T. A is the mid-point of PZ. BA cuts PR in S. BC cuts QT in X. Prove that BS = XT.

IX

1. In the figure, CA and DE are parallel. AB = AC. Prove that CDE is an isosceles triangle.

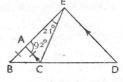

2. In the figure, AB = AC and △ACX is equilateral. Calculate $\widehat{ABX}$ and $\widehat{BRC}$.

3. **ABCDEH** is a regular hexagon. **AE** and **CH** intersect in **X**. Prove that $AX = \frac{1}{2}CE$.

4. **ABCD** is a parallelogram. Any point **O** is taken and the parallelograms **OAEB**, **OBFC**, **OCGD** and **ODHA** constructed. Prove that the figure **EFGH** is a parallelogram.

5. The sides **AB** and **AC** of $\triangle ABC$ are produced to **D** and **E** respectively. The bisectors of $D\hat{B}C$ and $E\hat{C}B$ meet at **K**. Prove that $B\hat{K}C = 90° - \dfrac{A}{2}$.

X

1. In the figure, **OAB** and **OCD** are isosceles triangles.
Calculate $A\hat{O}E$.

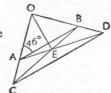

2. In the figure, **ABCD** is a parm. $AB = BE$; **BE** bisects $X\hat{B}C$. $AD = DF$; **DF** bisects $Y\hat{D}C$. Prove that $A\hat{E}B = D\hat{F}A$.

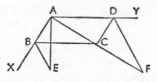

3. **PQRS** is a parallelogram. **SX, RY, QZ** are drawn perpendicular to any straight line drawn through **P**, this line being outside the parallelogram. Prove that

(1) $XY = PZ$. (2) $RY = SX + QZ$.

4. Four angles of a hexagon are 126°, 110°, 85°, 61°. The remaining two angles are equal. How many degrees are there in each?

5. On the same base **AB** and on opposite sides of it, parallelograms **ABCD** and **ABFG** are described so that the side **AD** of the first is equal to the diagonal **AF** of the second and the diagonal **AC** of the first is equal to the side **AG** of the second. Prove that

(1) **C, A, G** are collinear. (2) **D, A, F** are collinear.

BOOK II

AREA

Definitions

(1) The **altitude** of a parallelogram is the perpendicular

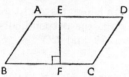

distance of the base from the opposite side. In the figure, the altitude of the parallelogram ABCD is the length of EF.

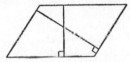

Any side of a parallelogram can be taken as the base so that a parallelogram has two altitudes.

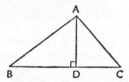

(2) The **altitude** of a triangle is the perpendicular distance of the vertex from the base. In the figure, the length of **AD** is the altitude of △ABC.

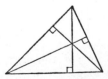

Any side of a triangle can be regarded as the base so that a triangle has three altitudes.

149

(3) Parallelograms and triangles are said to be **between the same parallels** if they are situated as shown below.

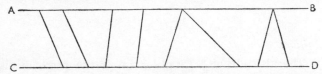

In such cases the parallelograms and the triangles have **the same altitude,** which is the perpendicular distance between the two parallel lines **AB** and **CD**.

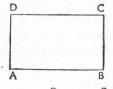

(4) The rectangle **ABCD** is denoted by rect. **AB, AD** or by **AB** × **AD** or by **AB.AD**.

(5) The square **ABCD** is denoted by sq. on **AB** or **AB²**.

(6) The **area** of a plane figure is the amount of surface enclosed by its bounding lines.

To measure any area a unit is required; e.g. a square foot, a square inch, a square centimetre. Two of these units are shown below.

A **square inch** (sq. in.) is the area of a square, each of whose sides is 1 inch long.

A **square centimetre** (sq. cm.) is the area of a square, each of whose sides is 1 centimetre long.

Area of a Rectangle

If a rectangle is a units long and b units broad its area is ab square units.

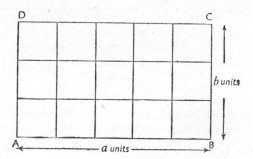

Consider a rectangle ABCD with $AB = a$ units, and $BC = b$ units. Divide AB into a equal parts, each 1 unit long. Divide BC into b equal parts, each 1 unit long. Through the points of division draw parallel lines as shown, thus dividing the rectangle into squares, whose sides are all 1 unit long.

The area of each square is 1 sq. unit.

There are b rows of squares, and in each row there are a squares.

∴ Total number of squares $= a \times b$.

∴ Area of the rectangle (in sq. units)

= (number of units of length in the length)

× (number of units of length in the breadth).

This result is often stated thus

area of rectangle = length × breadth.

Theorem 17

A rectangle and a parallelogram on the same base and between the same parallels are equal in area.

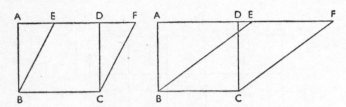

Given: Rect. ABCD and parm. EBCF on the same base BC and between the parallels BC and AF.

Required: To prove that rect. ABCD = parm. EBCF in area.

Proof: In △s ABE, DCF

    1. BE = CF (opp. sides of parm.).

    2. $\hat{A}$ = C$\hat{D}$F (corresp. ∠s, AB, DC, parl.).

    3. A$\hat{E}$B = D$\hat{F}$C (corresp. ∠s, BE, CF, parl.).

∴ △ABE ≡ △DCF (two ∠s, and corresp. side)

∴ △ABE = △DCF in area.

Quad. ABCF − △DCF = quad. ABCF − △ABE

∴ rect. ABCD = parm. EBCF.

Area of a Parallelogram

Since area of parallelogram EBCF = area of rect. ABCD and area of rect. ABCD = BC × CD,

    ∴ area of parm. EBCF = BC × CD.

If BC is regarded as the base of the parallelogram then CD is the altitude, the altitude of the parallelogram being the perpendicular distance between any side taken as base and the opposite side.

    ∴ area of a parallelogram = base × altitude.

From this it follows that :

(*a*) Parallelograms on the same base and between the same parallels are equal in area, *or* parallelograms on the same base and of the same altitude are equal in area.

(*b*) Parallelograms on equal bases and between the same parallels are equal in area, *or* parallelograms on equal bases and of the same altitude are equal in area.

Parallelograms I, II, III are equal in area because their bases are equal and their altitudes are equal and the area of each = base × altitude.

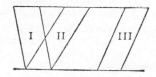

EXERCISES 25

1. ABCD is a parallelogram with AB = 7 cm., BC = 5 cm.,

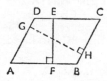

$\widehat{A} = 50°$. Construct the figure accurately and find its area

(1) by taking **AB** as the base,
(2) by taking **BC** as the base.

2. The area of parallelogram ABCD is 49·6 sq. cm. The base **AB** = 6·2 cm. Find the altitude. If $\widehat{A} = 62°$ construct the parallelogram.

3. The area of a parallelogram ABCD is 23·4 sq. cm. The altitude for the base **BC** is 3·6 cm. If **AB** = 7 cm., construct the parallelogram.

4. In the figure for Exercise 1 above, if **AB** = 4·8 in., **BC** = 3·6 in., **EF** = 2·1 in., find **GH**.

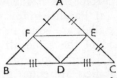

5. D, E, F are the mid-points of the sides. Name three equal parallelograms.

6. Draw any parallelogram ABCD. Construct a rectangle equal in area to ABCD and with BC as one of its sides.

7. Draw any parallelogram ABCD. Construct a rhombus equal in area to ABCD.

8. Draw a parallelogram ABCD. Divide it into two equal parallelograms. In how many ways can this be done?

9. Draw a parallelogram ABCD. Divide it into four equal parallelograms. In how many ways can this be done?

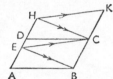

10. ABCD is a parallelogram. X and Y are the mid-points of AB and DC. Prove that XBYD is a parallelogram and that it is half the area of ABCD.

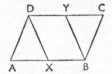

11. E is any point on the side AD of parallelogram ABCD. CH is parallel to BE meeting AD produced. HK is parallel to EC meeting BC produced. Prove that

fig. ECKH = parm. ABCD.

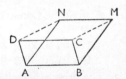

12. ABCD and ABMN are parallelograms. Prove that DCMN is a parallelogram and that

parm. ABMN — parm. ABCD
= parm. DCMN.

13. If ABMN and ABCD are drawn on opposite sides of AB prove that parm. ABMN + parm. ABCD = parm. DCMN.

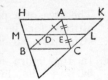

14. Straight lines through A, B, C are parallel to the opposite sides of △ABC. D, E are the mid-points of AB, AC resp. DE produced cuts HB at M and CK at L. Prove that fig. HMEA = fig. DBCL.

15.

ABCD and ABPQ are both parallelograms. AB produced bisects CP. Prove that parm. ABCD = parm. ABPQ.

16. Construct parallelogram ABCD if AB = 3 in., BC = 2·6 in., area = 6 sq. in. State your construction.

17. Parallelograms ABPQ and BCRS are described outwards on the sides AB, BC of △ABC. QP and RS, produced if necessary, meet in T. Prove that the parallelogram described on AC, with the side adjacent to AC equal and parallel to TB, is equal in area to the sum of the two parallelograms ABPQ and BCRS.

18. ABCD is a parallelogram with E any point on AD. Through C is drawn CG parallel to BE meeting AD produced in G. Through G is drawn FGH parallel to CE meeting BC produced in F, and BE produced in H. Prove that parallelogram ECGH = parallelogram ABCD.

19. In the figure, ABC is a △ with Â a rt. angle. BF is perp. to BC. ABDE is a square. ED produced meets BF at F.

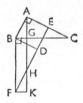

FK is parl. to BC and AK parl. to BF.   Prove that square BDEA = rect. BFKG.

20. ABC is a triangle. D is any point in BC. DG and DH are drawn parallel to CA and BA to meet AB and AC in G and H respectively. Produce DH to K making DK = BA. Prove that fig. AGDH is equal in area to the parallelogram which has HK and HC as its adjacent sides.

The two statements in (*a*) and (*b*) on page 153 can be combined into one statement :

Parallelograms on the same base, or on equal bases, and between the same parallels are equal in area, *or* parallelograms on the same base, or on equal bases, and of the same altitude are equal in area.

The statement has two converses and taking the latter form of the statement the two converses are :

(1) Parallelograms that are equal in area, and that are on the same base, or on equal bases, have the same altitude.

(2) Parallelograms that are equal in area, and that have the same altitude, have the same base or are on equal bases.

The truth of the converses can be proved as follows : Consider two parallelograms, bases b_1 and b_2, altitudes h_1 and h_2, areas A_1 and A_2.

Then since area of parm. = base × alt.

$$\therefore A_1 = b_1 h_1,$$
$$A_2 = b_2 h_2.$$

If $b_1 = b_2$ and $h_1 = h_2$ then $A_1 = A_2$ [see p. 153 (*b*)]. But if $A_1 = A_2$ and $b_1 = b_2$ then it follows that $h_1 = h_2$.

This is converse 1 above.

Also if $A_1 = A_2$ and $h_1 = h_2$ then it follows that $b_1 = b_2$. This is converse 2 above.

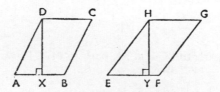

For example, if parm. ABCD = parm. EFGH

and   the base AB = base EF

then   the altitude DX = the altitude HY.

The area of a triangle = ½(base × altitude).

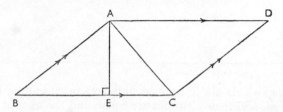

Consider the triangle ABC. Through A draw a straight line parl. to BC to meet in D a straight line drawn through C parallel to BA.

BCDA is a parm. by construction.

∴ △ABC = ½parm. BCDA (diag. bisects parm.).

But area of parm. = base (BC) × altitude (AE)

∴ area of △ABC = ½BC × AE

= ½(base × altitude).

Hence

(1) The area of a triangle is half the area of any parallelogram on the same base and between the same parallels.

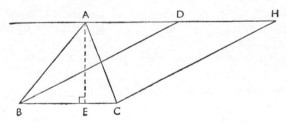

Area of parm. BCHD = base × altitude = BC × AE,

area of △ABC = ½base × altitude = ½BC × AE.

(2) Triangles on the same base and between the same parallels are equal in area.

(3) Triangles on equal bases and between the same parallels are equal in area.

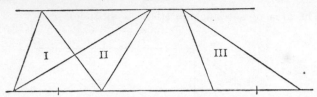

Triangles I, II and III are equal in area because their bases are equal, and their altitudes are equal, and the area of each $= \frac{1}{2}(\text{base} \times \text{altitude})$.

The two statements in (2) and (3) can be combined into one statement :

Triangles on the same base, or on equal bases, and between the same parallels are equal in area, *or* triangles on the same base, or on equal bases, and of the same altitude are equal in area.

The statement has two converses, and, taking the latter form of the statement, the two converses are :

(1) Triangles that are equal in area, and that are on the same base, or on equal bases, have the same altitude.

(2) Triangles that are equal in area, and that have the same altitude, have the same base or are on equal bases.

The truth of these converses can be proved as follows : Consider two triangles, bases b_1 and b_2, altitudes h_1 and h_2, areas A_1 and A_2.

Then since area of triangle $= \frac{1}{2}(\text{base} \times \text{altitude})$

$$\therefore \ A_1 = \tfrac{1}{2}b_1 h_1,$$
$$A_2 = \tfrac{1}{2}b_2 h_2.$$

If $b_1 = b_2$ and $h_1 = h_2$ $\therefore$ $A_1 = A_2$. This is the combined statement above.

If $A_1 = A_2$ and $b_1 = b_2$ then it follows that $h_1 = h_2$.

This is converse 1 above.

Also if $A_1 = A_2$ and $h_1 = h_2$ then it follows that $b_1 = b_2$.

This is converse 2 above.

EXERCISES 26

1. Construct △ABC with sides 7 cm., 8 cm., and 9 cm. Calculate the area, taking as base each of the three sides in turn.

2. The area of △ABC is 9·8 sq. in.   BC = 3·5 in.   Find the perpendicular distance of A from BC.

3. If in the figure for Exercise 1 above, BC = 2 in., AD = 1·8 in., BE = 1·5 in., find AC.

4. Show how to divide any △ABC into six equal parts.

5. AD is a median. E is any point on AD. Prove that

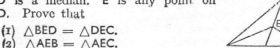

    (1) △BED = △DEC.
    (2) △AEB = △AEC.

6. DE is parallel to BC. Prove that

    (1) △BDC = △BEC.
    (2) △BDE = △CED.
    (3) △BAE = △CAD.
    (4) △BXD = △CXE.

7. ABCD is a parm. Prove that △s 1, 2, 3, 4 are equal in area.

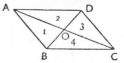

8. Prove that, if the diagonals of a quadrilateral divide it into 4 equal triangles, the quadrilateral is a parallelogram.

9. ABCD is a parm. E is any point in AC. Prove that
    △ABE = △ADE.

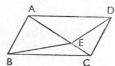

10. ABCD is a parm. E is any point in CD. Prove that

$$\triangle 1 + \triangle 3 = \triangle 2.$$

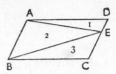

11. O is any point within parm. ABCD. Prove that △OAB + △OCD = ½parm. ABCD.

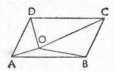

12. Prove that parm. ABCD = parm. APQR.
[*Hint:* Join DP.]

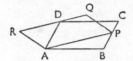

13. ABCD is a parm. P is any point in DC. Prove that
    (1) △AQD = △APB.
    (2) △DPQ = △BPC.

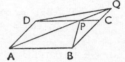

14. ABCD is a quadrilateral. X is the mid-pt. of AC. Prove that quad. ABXD = ½quad. ABCD.

15. R and Q are mid-points of AB, AC. Prove that △BXC = quad. AQXR.

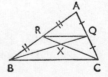

16. AB is the base of a given parallelogram ABCD. Show how to construct a rhombus equal in area to the parallelogram and having AB as the diagonal.

17. Draw a rectangle ABCD. Show how to construct an equivalent rectangle, having AC as one side.

18. Draw any equilateral triangle ABC. From O any point within it draw perpendiculars to the sides. Prove that the sum of these three perpendiculars is the same no matter where the point O is situated.

19. PQRS is a trapezium with PQ parallel to SR. The diagonals intersect at X. Prove that △PXS = △QXR.

20. Draw any quadrilateral ABCD. Through A and C draw straight lines parallel to BD to meet any other straight line drawn through B in S and P respectively and meeting any other straight line drawn through D in R and Q respectively. Prove that △QBR = quad. ABCD = △SDP.

21. Draw any quadrilateral ABCD. Through D draw a straight line parallel to AC to meet BC produced in E. Prove that △ABE = quad. ABCD.

22. If the mid-points of the sides of a quadrilateral are joined in order, prove that the resulting figure is a parallelogram whose area is half that of the quadrilateral.

23. ABCD is a parallelogram, and a straight line drawn parallel to AB meets AD in P, AC in Q, BC in R. Prove that △APR = △AQD.

24. Prove that the straight line joining the mid-points of the oblique sides of a trapezium is parallel to the parallel sides.

25. ABCD and APQR are two parallelograms with a common angle at A, P lying on AB. If the parallelograms are equal in area prove that DP is parallel to QC.

26. ABC is a triangle with AB = AC. BD and CE are drawn perpendicular to the opposite sides. Prove that ED is parallel to BC.

CONSTRUCTION 12

To construct a triangle equal in area to a given quadrilateral

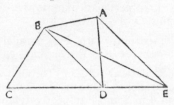

Given: Quad. ABCD.

Required: To construct a triangle equal in area to ABCD.

Construction: Join BD.

Through A draw AE parl. to BD to meet CD produced in E.

Join BE.

Then area of △BCE = area of quad. ABCD.

Proof: △EBD = △ABD (△s on same base BD, and bet. same parls. BD, AE).

Add △BCD to each.

∴ △BCD + △ABD = △BCD + △EBD

∴ quad. ABCD = △BCE.

Note: A triangle can be constructed equal in area to any given polygon by the successive application of the above construction. Each application reduces the number of sides by one.

The figure shows the construction in the case of a pentagon:

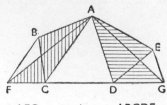

△AFG = pentagon ABCDE.

EXERCISES 27

1. Draw a parallelogram ABCD with AB = 7 cm., BC = 4 cm., $\widehat{A} = 55°$. Construct an equivalent parallelogram ABPQ, having AQ = 4·5 cm. How many such parallelograms can you construct?

2. Draw a parallelogram ABCD with AB = 2 in., BC = 1·5 in., $\widehat{A} = 60°$. Construct an equivalent parallelogram on a base of 1·2 in. having one angle equal to angle A.
   [From AB cut off AX = 1·2 in. Through X draw XY parallel to AD meeting DC in Y, and produce AY to meet BC produced in E. Complete parallelogram ABEK. Produce XY to meet KE in Z. Then AXZK is the required parallelogram.]

3. Draw △ABC with $a = 2$ in., $b = 1$ in., $c = 1·4$ in. Draw an equivalent △XBC with XB = 1·2 in. How many such triangles can you construct?

4. Draw △ABC with $a = 7$ cm., $b = 6$ cm., $c = 5$ cm. Construct an equivalent rectangle with BC as one of its sides. Measure the other side.

5. Repeat Exercise 4, the rectangle to have BD as one of its sides, D being the mid-point of BC. Measure the sides.

6. Construct the quadrilateral ABCD if AB, BC, CD are equal to 1·2, 1·6 and 2 in. respectively, and with angles ABC, BCD equal to 90° and 108° respectively. Construct an equivalent triangle and find its area.

7. Construct a regular hexagon ABCDEF, the length of the side being 1 in. Find its area (1) by constructing an equivalent triangle, (2) by finding the area of △OAB, where O is the central point of the figure.

8. Construct a quadrilateral ABCD with AB = 2 in., BC = 3 in., and the angles at A, B, and D equal respectively to 125°, 70°, 95°. Construct an equivalent parallelogram with one side along AB and with $\widehat{A} = 50°$.

9. ABC is a triangle with BC produced to any point D. Show how to construct on BD a triangle equal in area to △ABC, with one side lying along BA.
   [*Hint:* Join AD. Draw CX parl. to DA to meet BA in X. Join DX.]

10. D is any point in the side BC of △ABC. Show how to construct on BD a triangle equal in area to △ABC, with one side lying along BA.

11. ABC is any triangle. Show how to construct on BC as base a triangle equal in area to
    (a) one-fifth of △ABC,
    (b) one-half of △ABC.

12. Draw any triangle ABC, and take X any point in BC. Show how to draw through X a straight line which will divide △ABC into two equal parts.
    [Bisect BC at D. Join AX. Draw DE parl. to XA, meeting AC in E. Join XE.]

13. P is any point in any side of △ABC. Show how to draw two straight lines through P to divide the triangle into three equal parts.

14. ABC is a triangle and P is any given point. Show how to construct a triangle equal in area to △ABC, having its vertex at P and its base in the same straight line as BC.
    [*Hint:* Draw through P a straight line parallel to BC to meet BA or BA produced in Q. Now draw △ with vertex Q and with its base lying along BC and having an area = △ABC.]

15. Construct a quadrilateral ABCD. Construct an equivalent triangle having its vertex at a point P in DC and its base in the same straight line as AB.

16. Draw any quadrilateral ABCD. Show how to bisect it by a straight line drawn through the vertex D.
    [*Hint:* Join AC and bisect it at E. Through E draw str. line EX parallel to DB, cutting AB at X. Join DX.]

17. Draw any quadrilateral ABCD. Show how to cut off from ABCD, a third part, by a straight line drawn through vertex D.

18. Construct two triangles each having two sides 2 in. long and having an area of 1 sq. in. Measure the angles of the triangles.

19. Construct △ABC with $a = 2\frac{1}{2}$ in., $b = 2$ in., $c = 1\frac{1}{2}$ in. On BC construct a rhombus whose area is twice that of the triangle.

20. Draw any △ABC. Show how to construct an isosceles triangle which shall be equal in area to △ABC.

Area of a Quadrilateral

The area of a quadrilateral can be found either (1) by reducing it to an equivalent triangle and finding the area of this triangle, *or* (2) by drawing a diagonal and finding the areas of the two triangles so formed.

1st Method:

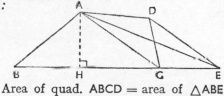

Area of quad. ABCD = area of $\triangle$ABE
$$= \tfrac{1}{2}BE \times AH.$$

2nd Method:

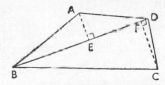

[AE and CF are called **offsets.**]

Area of quad. ABCD = area of $\triangle$ABD + area of $\triangle$BCD
$$= \tfrac{1}{2}BD \times AE + \tfrac{1}{2}BD \times CF$$
$$= \tfrac{1}{2}BD(AE + CF)$$
$$= \tfrac{1}{2} \text{ diag.} \times \text{sum of offsets.}$$

Area of trapezium

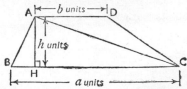

Area of trapezium ABCD = area of $\triangle$ABC + area of $\triangle$ACD
$$= \tfrac{1}{2}ah + \tfrac{1}{2}bh$$
$$= \tfrac{1}{2}h(a + b)$$
$$= \tfrac{1}{2} \text{ altitude} \times \text{sum of parl. sides.}$$

Area of Rectilineal Figure

This can be found either (1) by reducing the figure to an equivalent triangle and finding the area of this triangle, or (2) by taking a base line and offsets, as shown below, and thus dividing the figure into triangles and trapeziums. This second method is called the Field Book Method and is used by surveyors.

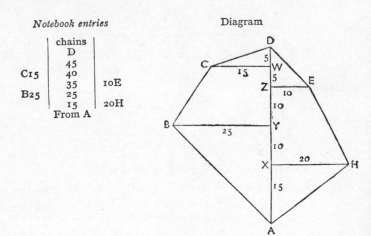

Notebook entries

	chains	
	D	
	45	
C15	40	
	35	10E
B25	25	
	15	20H
	From A	

Diagram

sq. chains

Area of rt.-angled $\triangle$AXH $= \frac{1}{2} \times 15 \times 20$ $= 150$

,, ,, trap. EZXH $= \frac{1}{2} \times 20(10 + 20) = 300$

,, ,, rt.-angled $\triangle$DZE $= \frac{1}{2} \times 10 \times 10$ $= 50$

,, ,, rt.-angled $\triangle$DWC $= \frac{1}{2} \times 5 \times 15$ $= 37\frac{1}{2}$

,, ,, trap. CWYB $= \frac{1}{2} \times 15(15 + 25) = 300$

,, ,, rt.-angled $\triangle$AYB $= \frac{1}{2} \times 25 \times 25$ $= 312\frac{1}{2}$

Area of fig. ABCDEH $= 1150$

Area of Circle

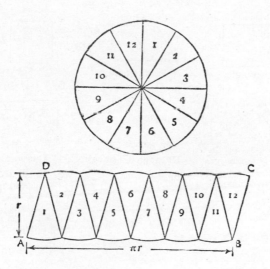

The figure shows a circle divided into 12 equal parts and the parts placed together. Area of circle = area of figure ABCD, and this is true no matter how many parts there are. As the number of parts is increased the figure becomes more nearly a parallelogram.

$\therefore$ Area of circle = area of parm.

                = base × alt.

                = $\frac{1}{2}$(circumference) × radius

                = $\frac{1}{2}(2\pi r)$ × r units of area

                = πr^2 units of area.

EXERCISES 28

(Mensuration)

Find the areas of the following figures (not drawn accurately).

1.

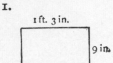

1 ft. 3 in.

9 in.

Rectangle.

2.

1 ft. 6 in.

6 in. 8 in.

Parallelogram.

3.

2·5 in.

Square.

4.

5 cm. 6 cm.

3 cm.

Triangle.

5.

4 ft. 3 ft.

Rt.-angled Triangle.

6.

1 ft. 2 ft. ft. 6 in.

2 ft. 3 ft.

Quadrilateral.

7.

4 cm.

6 cm.

10 cm.

Trapezium.

8.

2″ 3″

3″ 2″

Rhombus.

9. Find area of shaded part.

$3\frac{1}{2}$

10. Find area of shaded part.

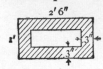

11.

$\frac{1}{2}″$

1″ $1\frac{1}{2}″$

1″

12.

6′ 6′

5′

⊢— 3′ —⊣

13. Find area of shaded part.

2′ 6″

1′ 3″

3″

14. Find total surface area.

3″

5″ 4″

Cuboid

15. Find total surface area.

4″ 3″ 6″

5″

Right Prism on Rt.-angled △r Base.

16. Find the areas of the following figures:
    (1) Rectangle — length = 12 ft. 8 in.,
        breadth = 3 ft. 9 in.
    (2) Square — side = 3 yd. 2 ft.
    (3) Parallelogram — base = 30 ft., altitude = 18 ft.
    (4) Triangle — base = 3 ft. 6 in., altitude = 2 ft. 3 in.
    (5) Quadrilateral — diagonal 32 yd. 9 in., offsets,
        22 yd. and 10 yd. 2 ft.
    (6) Trapezium — parallel sides 28 ft. 4 in. and 32 ft.
        8 in., height 10 ft. 9 in.
    (7) Circle — radius = 3·5 in.
    (8) Circle — diameter = 4·9 cm.
    (9) Rhombus — diagonals 8 cm. and 6 cm.

17. The area of a rectangular field is 142,500 sq. ft. On a map
    where 1 in. represents 100 ft. the length of the field is
    4·5 in. Find the actual breadth of the field.

18. The area of a square is 6·76 sq. cm. Find the length of
    each side.

19. On a map, where 6 in. represent 1 mile, a rectangular
    reservoir measures $1\frac{1}{2}$ in. by $\frac{1}{2}$ in. Find its area in acres.

20. Construct a parallelogram with an area of 14 sq. cm., its
    two adjacent sides being 5 cm. and 6 cm.

21. Construct a rhombus with an area of 4 sq. in., the length
    of a side being 2·5 in.

22. Construct a triangle ABC with base BC = 3 in.,
    area = 3·75 sq. in., $\widehat{B} = 56°$. Measure AB.

23. Construct △ABC with AB = 2 in., BC = 3 in.,
    area = 2·4 sq. in. Produce BC to D so that the area of
    △ABD may be 4 sq. in. Explain your method.

24. Area of △ABC = 28 sq. cm., $b = 8$ cm., $a = 10$ cm.
    Calculate the lengths of the perpendiculars drawn from
    X the mid-point of AB, to AC and BC respectively.

25. Draw a regular pentagon on a side of 1 in. Reduce it to
    an equivalent triangle and hence find its area.

26. Draw a quadrilateral ABCD with AB = 3 in., $\widehat{A} = 70°$,
    $\widehat{B} = 60°$, BC = 2·5 in., AD = 1 in. Reduce the quadri-
    lateral to an equivalent triangle and hence find its area.

27. Draw a plan of a field **ABCD** in which **AB** = 250 yd., **BC** = 170 yd., **CD** = 140 yd., **DA** = 220 yd., **AC** = 210 yd. On your plan let 1 in. represent 100 yd. Reduce the plan to an equivalent triangle and calculate the area of the field in acres.

28. Draw a plan of a field which is in the form of a trapezium, the lengths of the parallel sides being 300 yd. and 230 yd., and the lengths of the oblique sides 150 yd. and 120 yd. Find the area of the field in acres.

29. Find the radius of a circle whose area is 25·3 sq. cm. (answer correct to nearest mm.).

30. Find the side of a square equal in area to a circle, radius 14 in. (answer correct to one decimal place).

31. Three circles are drawn with the same centre, the radii of the two larger circles being 2·5 in. and 2 in. Find the radius of the smallest circle if the two outer rings are equal in area.

32. The following are entries in a field book. Draw a plan in each case and find the area of the field.

(1) *Metres*			(2) *Yards*			(3) *Chains*	
	D			C			E	
	180			210			9·35	
	115	90C	D65	130			8·20	1·34D
E60	85			90	80B		7·00	0·55C
	60	75B	E45	70		H1·26	5·84	
			F65	40			4·31	1·84B
	A			A		K0·45	2·64	
						L1·20	0·82	
							A	

Geometrical Illustration of Algebraic Identities

$$x(a + b + c) \equiv xa + xb + xc.$$

Let ABCD be a rectangle with length $(a + b + c)$ units, breadth x units.

$$\text{Area of ABCD} = \text{AB} \times \text{AD}$$
$$= x(a + b + c) \text{ sq. units.}$$

If AD is divided at E and G so that AE = a units, EG = b units, GD = c units, and the lines EF and GH drawn parallel to AB, then ABCD is divided into 3 rectangles, ABFE, EFHG, GHCD.

$$\text{Area of ABCD} = \text{area of ABFE} + \text{area of FHGE} + \text{area of GHCD}$$
$$= \text{AB} \times \text{AE} + \text{EF} \times \text{EG} + \text{GH} \times \text{GD}$$
$$= (xa + xb + xc) \text{ sq. units.}$$

$\therefore x(a + b + c) \equiv xa + xb + xc.$

The following figures can be used to illustrate certain other identities :

I. $(x + a)(x + b) \equiv x^2 + ax + bx + ab.$

II. $(a + b)^2 \equiv a(a + b) + b(a + b).$

a   b

a $a\,(a + b)$

b $b\,(a + b)$

III. $(a + b)^2 \equiv a^2 + 2ab + b^2.$

a   b

a a^2 ab

b ab b^2

IV. $(a - b)^2 \equiv a^2 - 2ab + b^2.$

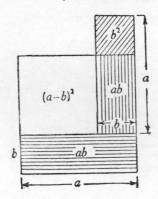

V. $a^2 - b^2 \equiv (a + b)(a - b).$

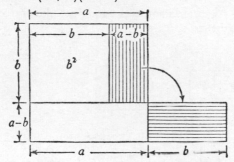

VI. $(a + b)^2 - (a - b)^2 \equiv 4ab.$

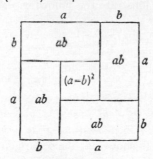

Exercises 29

State the algebraic identities which are illustrated by the following figures :

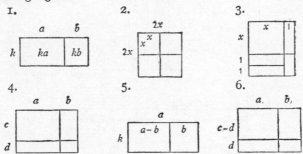

Draw figures to illustrate the following algebraic identities.

7. $(3x)^2 \equiv 9x^2$.

8. $(x + 2)(x + 3) \equiv x^2 + 5x + 6$.

9. $(x + 1)^2 \equiv x^2 + 2x + 1$.

10. $(x + 3)(x - 2) \equiv x^2 + x - 6$.

11. $(x + y)(2x + y) \equiv 2x^2 + 3xy + y^2$.

12. $(a - b)(2a - b) \equiv 2a^2 - 3ab + b^2$.

13. $(a + b + c)^2 \equiv a^2 + b^2 + c^2 + 2ab + 2bc + 2ca$.

14. $(a + b)(x + y + z) \equiv ax + ay + az + bx + by + bz$.

15. Draw a figure to show that the square on any straight line is equal to sixteen times the square on one quarter of the line. State the corresponding algebraic identity.

16. AB is a straight line bisected at C and produced to D. If $AD = 2AB$, prove that $AD.DB = 8AC^2$. (Let $AC = x$ units of length.) State the corresponding algebraic identity.

17. A, B, C, D are four points in order on a straight line. Draw a diagram to show that $AC.BD = AB.CD + AD.BC$. Let x, y, z be the number of units of length in AB, BC, CD respectively. State the corresponding algebraic identity.

18. The straight line AB is bisected at C and produced to any point D. Draw a diagram to show that

$$AC.AD = CB.BD + 2AC^2.$$

State the corresponding algebraic identity.

The Theorem of Pythagoras

Construct in thin cardboard the following figure which shows a right-angled triangle **ABC**, right-angled at **A**, with squares described on its sides. **O** is the centre of the square on **AC**, the point of intersection of the diagonals. The lines drawn through **O** are parallel to and perpendicular to the hypotenuse **BC**. The square **AC** can then be cut into four pieces, numbered 1, 2, 3, 4. If these, together with the square on **AB**, numbered 5, be placed as shown on the square on **BC**, they will be found to fit this square exactly. Hence

the sq. on **AB** + the sq. on **AC** = the sq. on **BC**. This is usually written

$$AB^2 + AC^2 = BC^2.$$

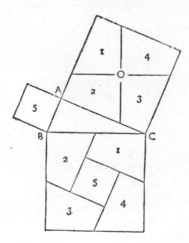

This theorem, which states that in a right-angled triangle the square on the hypotenuse is equal to the sum of the squares on the other two sides, is usually attributed to the Greek philosopher Pythagoras. Pythagoras lived in the sixth century B.C., but the truth of the theorem in certain simple cases at least was known much earlier.

Theorem 18

In a right-angled triangle the square on the hypotenuse is equal to the sum of the squares on the other two sides.

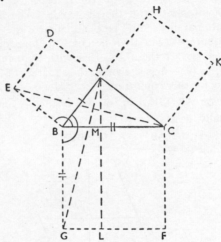

Given: △ABC with BÂC a rt. angle.

Required: To prove that BC² = AB² + AC².

Construction: On AB, BC, CA draw squares BADE, BCFG, CAHK. Through A draw AL parl. to BG, meeting GF in L and BC in M.
Join EC and AG.

Proof: Because BÂD is a rt. angle (∠ in a sq.) and BÂC is a rt. angle (given)
∴ DA and AC are in one str. line (adj. angles supp.).
In △s EBC and ABG
   1.   EB = AB (sides of a sq.).
   2.   BC = BG (same reason).
   3.   EB̂C = AB̂G (each a rt. angle + AB̂C).
∴ △EBC ≡ △ABG (2 sides and incl. ∠).

The square BADE and △EBC are on the same base EB
and between the same parls. EB and DC
∴ sq. BADE = 2△EBC.
Also the rect. BGLM and △ABG are on the same base
BG and between the same parls. BG and AL
∴ rect. BGLM = 2△ABG.
But △EBC = △ABG (proved)
∴ sq. BADE = rect. BGLM.
Similarly by joining BK and AF it can be proved that
sq. ACKH = rect. FCML
∴ sq. BADE + sq. ACKH = rect. BGLM + rect. FCML
— sq. BGFC
∴ AB² + AC² = BC².

EXERCISES ON THE THEOREM OF PYTHAGORAS

1. ABC is a rt.-angled triangle with Â a rt. angle.
If BA = 3 cm., CA = 4 cm., find
BC.
BC² = AB² + AC² (Pythagoras'
Theorem)
= 3² sq. cm. + 4² sq. cm.
= 25 sq. cm.
∴ BC = 5 cm.

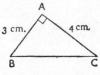

2. PQR is a triangle with P̂ a rt. angle.
If PQ = 9 cm., QR = 17 cm., find PR.

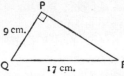

PR² + PQ² = QR² (Pythagoras' Theorem)
∴ PR² + 9² = 17²
∴ PR² = 289 sq. cm. — 81 sq. cm.
= 208 sq. cm.
∴ PR = √208 cm.
= 14·4 cm. (correct to 1 dec. pl.).

3. To find the value of $\sqrt{2}$, $\sqrt{3}$, $\sqrt{5}$, etc.

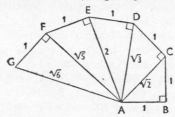

Draw **AB** = 1 unit, **BC** = 1 unit and perp. to **AB**.
Then by Pythagoras' Theorem $AC^2 = AB^2 + BC^2$
$$= (1 + 1) \text{ sq. units}$$
$$= 2 \text{ sq. units}$$
$$\therefore AC = \sqrt{2} \text{ units.}$$
Now draw **CD** perp. to **AC** and make **DC** = 1 unit.
Then by Pythagoras' Theorem $AD^2 = AC^2 + CD^2$
$$= (2 + 1) \text{ sq. units}$$
$$= 3 \text{ sq. units}$$
$$\therefore AD = \sqrt{3} \text{ units.}$$

Similarly as shown in the figure we can find the value of $\sqrt{5}$, $\sqrt{6}$, etc.

EXERCISES 30

In Examples 1–11, the figure referred to is shown below. $\hat{A}$ is a right angle.

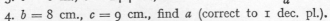

1. $b = 9$ in., $c = 12$ in., find a.
2. $b = 4 \cdot 8$ cm., $c = 6 \cdot 4$ cm., find a.
3. $b = 6$ in., $c = 14 \cdot 4$ in., find a.
4. $b = 8$ cm., $c = 9$ cm., find a (correct to 1 dec. pl.).
5. $a = 13$ in., $b = 5$ in., find c.
6. $a = 25$ cm., $c = 24$ cm., find b.
7. $a = 3 \cdot 4$ in., $c = 3$ in., find b.
8. $a = 15$ in., $b = 7$ in., find c (correct to 1 dec. pl.).
9. $b = 2n$, $c = n^2 - 1$, find a.
10. $b = 2n^2 + 2n$, $c = 2n + 1$, find a.
11. $a = x^2 + y^2$, $b = x^2 - y^2$, find c.

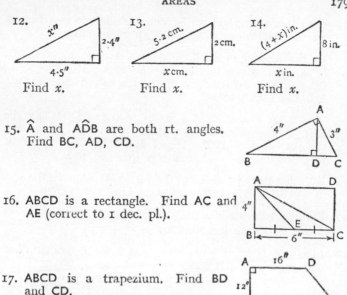

12. Find x.

13. Find x.

14. Find x.

15. $\widehat{A}$ and $\widehat{ADB}$ are both rt. angles. Find BC, AD, CD.

16. ABCD is a rectangle. Find AC and AE (correct to 1 dec. pl.).

17. ABCD is a trapezium. Find BD and CD.

18. The difference in level of the banks of a stream 15 ft. wide is 8 ft. Find the length of the shortest plank which can bridge the stream.

19. Find the length of the side of a rhombus whose diagonals are 9 cm. and 12 cm. long.

20. One side of a rhombus is 17 in. and one diagonal is 30 in. long. Find the length of the other diagonal.

21. A ladder 30 ft. long has one end on the ground and leans against the wall of a house with 5 ft. of the ladder projecting over the roof. If the wall of the house is 24 ft. high, how far is the foot of the ladder from the wall?

22. Two walls are 25 ft. apart. A 20 ft. ladder when placed against one wall reaches to a height of 12 ft. The lower end being kept fixed, it is swung over to touch the other wall. To what height will it reach? (Answer to the nearest foot.)

23. Find the altitude of an isosceles triangle whose base is 7·2 in. and whose equal sides are 6 in. long.

24. In the trapezium ABCD one of the oblique sides, AD, is at right angles to the parallel sides. If AB = 6 in., CD = 9 in., and the area of the trapezium is 30 sq. in., find the length of BC.

25. △ABC has $a = 28$ in., $b = 25$ in., $c = 17$ in. If D is the foot of the perpendicular from A on BC, prove that $c^2 - BD^2 = b^2 - DC^2$. Hence find BD. Use this result to calculate AD. What is the area of △ABC?

26. By using the altitude from the vertex A, calculate the area of △ABC if $a = 14$ cm., $b = 15$ cm., $c = 13$ cm.

27. Find, as accurately as possible from a figure, the value of $\sqrt{61}$. (Use the fact that $61 = 36 + 25$.)

28. Find the values of $\sqrt{17}$, $\sqrt{13}$, $\sqrt{41}$ from the construction of right-angled triangles.

29. The figure represents a cube, each edge being 2 in. Find EG and AG (correct to 1 dec. pl.).

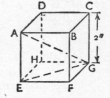

30. The figure represents a cuboid. X is the mid-point of HG. Find EG, AG, AX (correct to 2 dec. pl.).

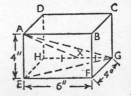

31. In the figure for Exercise 30, if the cuboid is a in. long, b in. broad, c in. high, prove that $AG^2 = a^2 + b^2 + c^2$.

32. A rectangular box has inside measurements, length 6 ft., breadth 3 ft., height 2 ft. What is the length of the longest straight stick which may be placed in the box?

Exercises 31

1. Prove that $AB^2 - AC^2 = BD^2 - DC^2$.

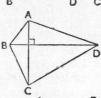

2. Prove that $AB^2 + CD^2 = BC^2 + AD^2$.

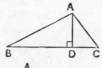

3. ABCD is a rhombus.
   Prove that $AC^2 + BD^2 = 4AB^2$.

4. Prove that $5AC^2 = 4(CD^2 + AE^2)$.

5. $\triangle$ is equilateral.
   Prove that $3BC^2 = 4AD^2$.

6. Prove that $AC^2 + BD^2 = BC^2 + AD^2$.

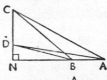

7. Prove that $BP^2 + CQ^2 + AR^2$
   $\qquad = PC^2 + QA^2 + RB^2$

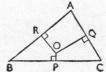

8. ABCD is a rectangle and P is any point. Prove that $PA^2 + PC^2 = PB^2 + PD^2$.

9. ABC is an equilateral triangle. D, E are the mid-points of BC and DC respectively. Prove that $AE^2 = 13EC^2$.

10. $\triangle$ABC is right-angled at A and squares ABGH, ACKL, BCDE are drawn outwards on its sides. Prove that

   (1) GAK is a straight line.
   (2) BH is parallel to CL, and each is perpendicular to GK.
   (3) AE cuts GC at right angles.

11. In the figure for Exercise 10 prove that the four triangles HAL, GBE, DCK, ABC are all equal in area.

12. Construct a square equal in area to the sum of (1) two given squares, (2) three given squares.

13. Construct a square equal to the difference between two given squares.

14. ABCD is a square. Prove that the square on AC is double the given square ABCD.

15. Construct a square equal in area to half of a given square ABCD.

16. Prove that the square on the hypotenuse of a right-angled isosceles triangle is four times the area of the triangle.

17. In an obtuse-angled triangle, prove that the square on the side opposite the obtuse angle is greater than the sum of the squares on the sides containing the obtuse angle.

18. In any triangle, prove that the square on a side opposite an acute angle is less than the sum of the squares on the sides containing the acute angle.

19. PQRS is a square. Points T, W, Y, Z are taken in RS, SP, PQ, QR respectively such that $RT = SW = PY = QZ$. Prove that $TY^2 = 2(QZ^2 + ZR^2)$.
   [*Hint:* Join TZ, ZY.]

20. PQR is a triangle with $\widehat{Q}$ a right angle. PS is a median. ST is perpendicular to PR. Prove that

$$PT^2 + QS^2 = TR^2 + PS^2.$$

21. ABC is a triangle with $\widehat{B} = 45°$ and CD perpendicular to AB, meeting AB in D. Prove that $AC^2 = AD^2 + DB^2$.

22. Draw a straight line AB, 3 in. long. Show how to divide it at a point D so that $AD^2 + DB^2 =$ square on a line 2·5 in. long.

23. ABC is a right-angled isosceles triangle with $\widehat{C} =$ a rt. angle. AB is produced to E so that $B\widehat{C}E = 22\frac{1}{2}°$. Prove that $AB^2 = 2BE^2$.

  [Draw CD perp. to AB.]

24. Draw a straight line AB, 3 in. long. Show how to divide it at a point C so that $AC^2 = 2CB^2$. Measure AC and CB.

25. ABCD is a rectangle in which BC > AB but 2AB > BC. Points X and Y are taken in BC and CD respectively so that CX = AB and CY = BX. XZ is drawn perpendicular to AY. Prove that $ZY^2 - CY^2 = AB^2 - ZY^2$.

26. ABC is a triangle with $\widehat{A}$ a right angle. AD is drawn perpendicular to BC. Prove that $\dfrac{1}{AD^2} - \dfrac{1}{AC^2} \quad \dfrac{1}{AB^2}$.

27. PQRS is a square. Through S, outside the square, a straight line WST is drawn and PW and RT are perpendiculars drawn from P and R to this line. Prove that
$$ST^2 + SW^2 + SP^2 = SQ^2.$$

28. ABC is a triangle with $\widehat{C}$ a right angle. Show that if E and H are the points of trisection of BC, E being between B and H, $3AB^2 + 5AH^2 = 8AE^2$.

29. ABCD is a square and the bisector of angle BAC meet BC at E, and DC produced at F. Prove that $EF^2 = DE + CD^2$.

30. ABC is a triangle with AD, BE two altitudes meeting at H. Prove that
$$BC^2 + AH^2 = AB^2 + CH^2 = AC^2 + BH^2.$$

THEOREM 19

If the square on one side of a triangle is equal to the sum of the squares on the other two sides, the angle contained by these two sides is a right angle.

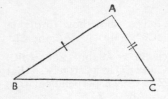 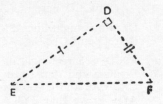

Given : △ABC with $BC^2 = AB^2 + AC^2$.

Required : To prove that $\widehat{A}$ is a rt. angle.

Construction : Draw DE = AB.
Draw DF perp. to DE and equal to AC.
Join EF.

Proof : By construction AB = DE and AC = DF
∴ $AB^2 + AC^2 = DE^2 + DF^2$.
But $AB^2 + AC^2 = BC^2$ (given)
and $DE^2 + DF^2 = EF^2$ (Pythagoras' Th.)
∴ $BC^2 = EF^2$
∴ BC = EF.
In △s ABC, DEF

    1. AB = DE (constr.).

    2. AC = DF (constr.).

    3. BC = EF (proved).

∴ △ABC ≡ △DEF (three sides)
∴ $\widehat{D} = \widehat{A}$.
But $\widehat{D}$ = a rt. angle (constr.)
∴ $\widehat{A}$ = a rt. angle.

Exercises 32

In Exercises 1–7 prove that △ABC is right-angled.

1. $a = 5$ in., $b = 3$ in., $c = 4$ in.

2. $a = 3\cdot6$ cm., $b = 4\cdot8$ cm., $c = 6$ cm.

3. $a = 5$ in., $b = 12$ in., $c = 13$ in.

4. $a = 8$ cm., $b = 17$ cm., $c = 15$ cm.

5. $a = 1$ in., $b = 2\cdot4$ in., $c = 2\cdot6$ in.

6. $a = m^2 + n^2$, $b = m^2 - n^2$, $c = 2mn$.

7. $a = 4m$, $b = 4m^2 - 1$, $c = 4m^2 + 1$.

In Exercises 8, 9, 10 prove that $B\widehat{A}C$ is a right angle.

8.   9.

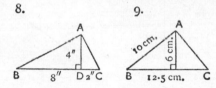

10. O is the mid-pt. of BC.   OB = 5 in.

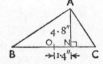

11. A right-angled triangle has squares drawn on its sides. Prove that the triangle whose sides are respectively the diagonals of these three squares is also a right-angled triangle.

12. In △ABC, AD is the altitude drawn from A to BC. If $BC^2 - 2AD^2 = BD^2 + DC^2$, prove that $B\widehat{A}C = $ a rt. angle.

13. In △ABC, AD is the altitude drawn from A to BC. If $AD^2 = $ rectangle contained by BD and DC, prove that $B\widehat{A}C$ is a right angle. [Let lengths of AD, BD, DC be k, x, y units respectively].

TRIGONOMETRICAL RATIOS OF AN ANGLE

Ratio.—If two articles cost respectively 10s. and 15s there is a relation between their costs. The cost of the first is $\frac{10}{15}$ or $\frac{2}{3}$ of the cost of the second. We say that the **ratio** of the first cost to the second cost is " 2 to 3 ", written $\frac{2}{3}$ or 2 : 3. Similarly, the ratio of the length of a line which measures 1 foot to that of a line which measures 9 inches is $\frac{12}{9}$ or $\frac{4}{3}$. A ratio can exist only between quantities of the same kind.

Consider the following two △s **ABC** and **DEF.**

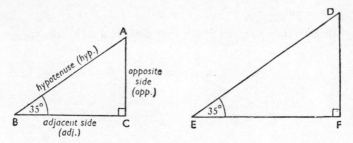

$\hat{B}$ and $\hat{E}$ are each 35°.

$\hat{C}$ and $\hat{F}$ are each 90° and therefore $\hat{A}$ and $\hat{D}$ are each 55°

∴ △s **ABC** and **DEF** are equiangular and are therefore similar

∴ the ratio $\frac{AC}{BC}$ is equal to the ratio $\frac{DF}{EF}$ and its value does not depend on the size of the right-angled triangle we construct.

If we give the sides of the triangle the names shown above :

AC, the side opposite $\hat{B}$, is named the opposite side (opp.) ;

BC, the side adjacent to $\hat{B}$, is named the adjacent side (adj.) ;

AB is named the hypotenuse (hyp.) ;

the ratio $\frac{AC}{BC}$ is $\frac{\text{opp.}}{\text{adj.}}$ and is a constant so long as the angle B remains constant. This ratio is given a special name. It is called the **tangent** of the angle B, usually written **tan B.** If therefore we construct a right-angled triangle with an angle of $x°$ as one of its angles and name the sides as explained with reference to this angle, then $\tan x° = \dfrac{\text{opp.}}{\text{adj.}}$

An approximate value for $\tan 35°$ can be obtained from the figure above by measuring BC and AC.

$$AC = 2·60 \text{ cm.}, \quad BC = 3·70 \text{ cm.},$$

$$\therefore \tan 35° = \frac{2·60 \text{ cm.}}{3·70 \text{ cm.}} = 0·7.$$

The value of $\tan 35°$ could be obtained by proceeding similarly with the sides DF and EF of the $\triangle$DEF above.

More accurate values for the tangents of angles than can be obtained by drawing and measuring are given in tables which have been compiled. These tables may give the values of the tangents of angles to 4 or more places of decimals, e.g. $\tan 35° = 0·7002$ to 4 places of decimals. The following table gives the values of the tangents of angles from 65° to 73°, the tangents being given correct to 3 decimal places. Use is made of this table in the worked example below :

angle	65°	66°	67°	68°	69°	70°	71°	72°	73°
tan	2·145	2·246	2·356	2·475	2·605	2·748	2·904	3·078	3·271

Example 1.—A ladder placed against a wall makes an angle of 70° with the ground. If the foot of the ladder is 6 feet from the wall, to what height on the wall does the top of the ladder reach ?

Let x ft. = reqd. height.

$$\frac{x \text{ ft.}}{6 \text{ ft.}} = \tan 70°$$

$$\therefore \frac{x}{6} = 2·748$$

$$\therefore x = 16·488$$

$\therefore$ height = 16·5 ft. (to 1 dec. place).

[In such problems a scale drawing may be made and the result checked approximately.]

Example 2.—The given figure represents a cuboid. If AB = 8 in., BC = 6 in. and the diagonal AG makes an angle of 30° with AC, find the height of the cuboid GC.

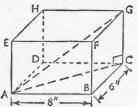

AB̂C is a rt. angle

∴ by Pythagoras' Theorem

   AC² = AB² + BC²

      = (8² + 6²) sq. in.

      = 100 sq. in.

∴ AC = 10 in.

Since GC is perp. to both CD and CB it is perpendicular to every line which meets it in the plane ABCD

∴ GĈA is a rt. angle

∴ from the rt.-angled △GCA

   $$\tan \hat{GAC} = \frac{GC}{AC}$$

∴ $$\tan 30° = \frac{GC}{10 \text{ in.}}$$

∴ $$\cdot577 = \frac{GC}{10 \text{ in.}}$$

∴ GC = 5·77 in.

EXERCISES 33

1. Find, by measurement and calculation, tan 20°, tan 30°, tan 45°, tan 70°.

   [Make the adjacent side in each case 10 units long.]

2. Find, from a figure, the angle whose tangent is (1) 1·2, (2) 0·6, (3) 2·0.

3. Read off from the tables : tan 15°, tan 31°, tan 42°, tan 57°, tan 84°.

In Exercises 4–9 find x in each case.

4.   5.   6.

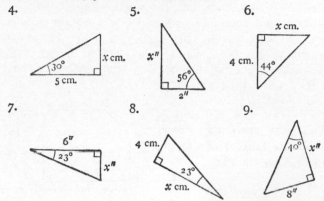

7.   8.   9.

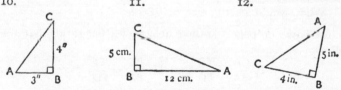

In Exercises 10–12 find from the tables, $\hat{A}$, in each case

10.   11.   12.

13. D is the foot of the perpendicular from A to BC in △ABC. If BC = 5 in., BD = 3 in., AD = 2 in., find the angles at B and C.

14. The diagonals of a rhombus are 8 cm. and 12 cm. long. Find the angles of the rhombus.

15. A ladder resting on level ground reaches to a point in a vertical wall, 20 ft. from the ground. If the ladder makes an angle of 72° with the ground, how far is the foot of the ladder from the wall?

16. The foot of a ladder is 7 ft. from a vertical wall. If the ladder is 25 ft. long and the upper end rests against the wall, what is the inclination of the ladder to the wall?

17. A guy rope on an aerial mast is fixed to a point 80 ft. high on the mast and is inclined at 60° to the ground which is level. At what distance from the base of the mast is the rope fixed to the ground?

18. The vertical angle of an isosceles triangle is 64°. If the altitude is 6 in. long, find the length of the base.

19. ABCD is a trapezium in which DC and AB are parallel. $\hat{A}$ = 90°, AB = 10 cm., DC = 4 cm., $\hat{B}$ = 34°. Find AD.

20. ABCD is a kite in which AB = AD, BC = CD. The diagonals meet at O. BD = 5 cm., AC = 12 cm., $A\hat{B}D$ = 40°. Find AO, OC, $B\hat{C}D$.

21. The figure represents a cuboid. Find the tangent of $G\hat{E}F$ and the tangent of $C\hat{E}G$.

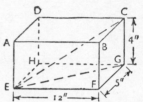

22. If there was a cube, each edge 2 in., instead of a cuboid in ex. 21 above, what then would be the value of tan $C\hat{E}G$? What would be the size of $C\hat{E}G$?

In the figure on page 186 there are two further ratios that are equal.

$$\text{I. } \frac{CA}{BA} = \frac{FD}{ED} \text{ and II. } \frac{BC}{BA} = \frac{EF}{ED}.$$

The first of these is the ratio $\dfrac{\text{opp.}}{\text{hyp.}}$ and is called the **sine** of the angle (written **sin** 35°).

The second of these is the ratio $\dfrac{\text{adj.}}{\text{hyp.}}$ and is called the **cosine** of the angle (written **cos** 35°).

As in the case of the tangent, approximate values for the sines and cosines of angles can be found by the construction of right-angled triangles, the measurement of the sides and the calculation of the ratios. More accurate values are obtainable from tables.

Experience will show that in the calculation of lengths of straight lines from diagrams, it is sometimes advisable to use the sine or cosine of an angle rather than the tangent, as in the following worked examples :

Example 1.—ABCD is a parallelogram with AB = 5 cm.,
BC = 6 cm., $\widehat{B}$ = 42°.

Calculate the area of the parallelogram.

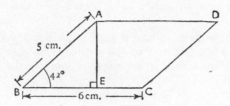

Draw AE the altitude of the parm.

$$\frac{AE}{BA} = \sin 42°$$

$$\therefore \frac{AE}{5 \text{ cm.}} = ·6691 \text{ (value obtained from tables)}$$

$$\therefore AE = 5 \times ·6691 \text{ cm.}$$

$$= 3·3455 \text{ cm.}$$

$$\therefore \text{ area of ABCD} = \text{base} \times \text{alt.}$$

$$= 6 \times 3·3455 \text{ sq. cm.}$$

$$= 20·07 \text{ sq. cm. (correct to 2 dec. pl.)}$$

Example 2.—A ladder 25 ft. long leans against a vertical
wall, the ladder making an angle of 74° with the ground.
How far from the wall is the foot of the ladder ?

Let distance be x ft.

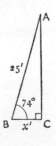

$$\frac{BC}{BA} = \cos 74°$$

$$\therefore \frac{x \text{ ft.}}{25 \text{ ft.}} = \cos 74°$$

$$\therefore \frac{x}{25} = ·2756 \text{ (obtained from tables)}$$

$$\therefore x = 25 \times ·2756$$

$$= 6·89$$

$$\therefore \text{ distance} = 6·9 \text{ ft. (correct to 1 dec. pl.).}$$

[*Note:* The same ratio $\dfrac{BC}{BA} = \sin \widehat{A}$

$$= \sin 16°$$

so that the problem could have been solved using the **table** of sines.

In the above figure $\widehat{A}$ and $\widehat{B}$ are complementary so that the sine of an angle is equal to the cosine of its complement.

Similarly, the cosine of an angle is equal to the sine of its complement.]

EXERCISES 34

1. Find, by measurement and calculation, sin 25°, sin 47°, sin 63°. [Make the hypotenuse 10 units long.]
2. Find from a figure the angle whose sine is (1) $\frac{1}{2}$, (2) ·7, (3) ·89.
3. Read off from the tables : sin 14°, sin 35°, sin 54°, sin 63°, sin 78°.

In Exercises 4–8 find x in each case.

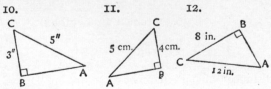

In Exercises 10–12 find $\widehat{A}$ in each case from the tables.

13. ABC is an isosceles triangle with AB = AC = 8 in. If $\hat{A} = 56°$, find BC.

14. ABC is an isosceles triangle with AB = AC = 10 cm. If BC = 12 cm., find $\hat{A}$.

15. PQR is a triangle with $\hat{Q} = 90°$. $\hat{RPQ} = 34°$, X is the mid-point of RQ and PR = 100 yds. Find RX, QP, and $\hat{QPX}$.

16. ABC is a triangle with AD drawn perpendicular to BC. If AB = 30 cm., $\hat{B} = 45°$, $\hat{C} = 55°$, find AD, BD, DC.

17. ABC is a triangle in which AB = 24 in, BC = 25 in., CA = 7 in. Prove that it is right-angled. If AD is the perpendicular drawn from A to BC, find $\hat{B}$ and AD.

18. A path makes an angle of 10° with the horizontal. If a man walks $\frac{1}{4}$ mile along this path, how many feet does he rise vertically?

19. A ladder 25 ft. long leans against a wall and is inclined to the ground at an angle of 70°. How far up the wall will it reach?

20. ABCD is a rhombus each side being 5 in. long. If $\hat{ACD} = 20°$, find the lengths of AC and BD.

EXERCISES 35

1. Find by measurement and calculation cos 34°, cos 52°, cos 70°. [Make the hypotenuse 10 units long.]

2. Find, from a figure, the angle whose cosine is (1) $\frac{1}{4}$, (2) ·32, (3) ·65.

3. Read off from the tables : cos 20°, cos 37°, cos 62°, cos 78°.

In Exercises 4–8 find x in each case.

4.   5.   6.

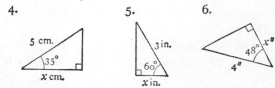

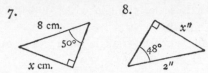

7.

8.

8 cm.   50°   x cm.

x″   48°   2″

In Exercises 9–11 find $\hat{A}$ in each case from the tables.

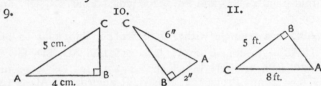

9.

10.

11.

5 cm.   C   A   4 cm.   B

C   6″   A   B   2″

5 ft.   B   C   8 ft.   A

12. **ABC** is an isosceles triangle with **AB = AC = 12** cm. Calculate the length of **BC**, if $\hat{B} = 35°$.

13. **ABC** is an isosceles triangle with **AB = AC = 8** in. If **BC = 10** in., find the size of the base angles.

14. In △**ABC**, **AB = 12** cm., **BC = 16** cm., $\hat{B} = 52°$ and **AD** is perpendicular to **BC**. Find **DC**, **AD**, **CÂD**.

15. A ladder 20 ft. long is placed against a wall and makes an angle of 72° with the ground. How far is the foot of the ladder from the wall?

16. **ABCD** is a rectangle with **AB = 12** in. and **AD = 5** in. **AN** is drawn perpendicular to **DB**. Find **AD̂B** and **DN**.

17. Draw **ABC** an acute-angled triangle. Draw **AD** perpendicular to **BC** and prove with the usual notation that
$$a = b \cos C + c \cos B.$$

18. A ladder 30 ft. long leaning against a wall makes an angle of 70° with the ground. Its foot is pulled out until the ladder makes an angle of 65° with the ground. How much farther is the foot of the ladder from the wall?

19. **ABC** is a triangle with $\hat{C} = 90°$. **BC = 5** ft., **AB = 10** ft. **BD** bisects **AB̂C** and meets **AC** in **D**. Find **AB̂C** and **DC**, **BD**, **DA**.

20. **ABCD** is a quadrilateral with **AĈB = CÂD = 90°**. If $\hat{B} = 50°$, **BA = 5** cm., **CD = 8** cm., calculate **BC**, **CA** and $\hat{D}$.

SCALE DRAWING

In scale-drawing exercises the following should be noted:

(1) A freehand sketch of the figure should be drawn and in this figure the given facts should be marked.

(2) The scale in use should be clearly stated; e.g. 1 inch represents 1 mile, generally expressed as 1 inch to 1 mile.

(3) Where necessary, direction should be indicated. This is often done by inserting a north-south line on the diagram thus

↑N

Angles of Elevation and Depression

The terms "Angle of Elevation" and "Angle of Depression" are explained in the following diagram.

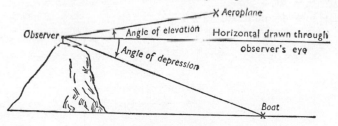

Bearing:

If A and B are two places and the north-south line is drawn through B as shown, then the bearing of A from B can be expressed in any one of the following 3 ways that are in current use:

(1) 50° E. of N.

(2) N. 50° E.

(3) 050° (the three figures are used to avoid mistakes).

Similarly the bearing of B from A can be expressed as (1) 50° W. of S., or (2) S. 50° W., or (3) 230°.

The 3rd method is the one most commonly used. In this method, the bearing of a place A from a place B is the angle, measured clockwise, between the north line through B and the line BA.

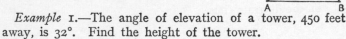

Bearings of A, C, and D from B are 040°, 140°, 235°, respectively.

Subtend.—The straight line AB is said to subtend the angle AOB at the point O.

Example 1.—The angle of elevation of a tower, 450 feet away, is 32°. Find the height of the tower.

(*a*) *By scale drawing:*

Draw BC = 4·5 cm.

Draw BA making angle $\widehat{B}$ = 32°.

At C draw CA perp. to BC meeting BA in A.

Measure AC.

By measurement AC = 2·8 cm.

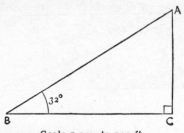

Scale 1 cm. to 100 ft.

∴ Height of tower = 280 ft.

(*b*) *By calculation:*

$$\frac{AC}{BC} = \tan B = \tan 32°$$

$$\therefore \frac{AC}{450 \text{ ft.}} = ·6249$$

$$\therefore AC = ·6249 \times 450 \text{ ft.}$$
$$= 281 \text{ ft. (to nearest foot).}$$

∴ Height of tower = 281 ft.

Example 2.—Two roads bear 52° E. of N. and 70° E. of S. from the same point O. A man walks 430 yards along the first road from O and then observes another man on the second road 20° W. of S. of himself. Find the distance between the two men.

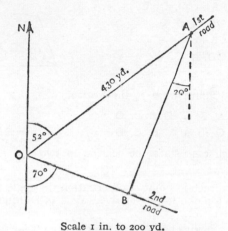

Scale 1 in. to 200 yd.

By measurement AB = 1·83 in.

∴ Distance between the two men = 366 yd.

In this case we can readily check the result by calculation

$A\widehat{B}O = 90°$ (proof of this is left as an exercise).
$A\widehat{O}B = 58°$

∴ From the rt.-angled △AOB, $\dfrac{AB}{OA} = \sin 58°$

$$\therefore \frac{AB}{430 \text{ yd.}} = ·8480$$

$$\therefore AB = ·8480 \times 430 \text{ yd.}$$
$$= 365 \text{ yd. (to nearest yard).}$$

EXERCISES 36

[Where possible check answers by calculation.]

1. In the figure what are the sizes of the angles subtended by

    (1) AB at O, D, C

    (2) OA at D, B

    (3) CB at O, A, D

    (4) OD at C, A ?

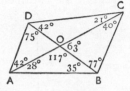

2. In the figure what is the bearing of

    (1) A, B, C, D from O,

    (2) O from A, B, C, D ?

In each case state the bearing in two ways.

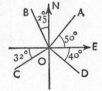

3. From a certain point of observation the angle of elevation of the top of a tower 500 ft. away is 35°. Find the height of the tower.

4. From a point at the edge of a cliff, 150 ft. above sea-level, the angle of depression of a ship at sea is 30°. Find the distance of the ship from the cliff.

5. A ship A is observed from two points B and C, 1000 yards apart. AB̂C is observed to be 40° and AĈB is observed to be 60°. Find the distance of the ship from the line joining B and C.

6. When the sun is 60° above the horizon, what is the length of the shadow cast by a vertical pole 25 feet long ?

7. A man observes the angle of elevation of the top of a flagstaff to be 25°. He walks 25 yards in a straight line towards it and now finds the angle of elevation to be 40°. Assuming the ground to be level, find the height of the flagstaff.

8. From the top of a tower the angle of depression of the top of another tower is 20°. How much higher is the first tower than the second tower, if the towers are 50 yards apart ?

9. From the bottom of a tower 200 ft. high the angle of elevation of a hill is found to be 30° and from the top of the tower the angle of elevation is found to be 20°. Find the height of the hill.

10. To find the position of a point C, a base line AB, 100 yd. long, is laid down and the following bearings taken :

   From A. {Bearing of B is N. 65° E.
           ,,   ,, C ,, N. 28° E.
   From B. Bearing of C is N. 55° W.
   Find AC and CB.

11. Three places P, Q, R are on a road running due north. A place S is due east of P. The bearing of S from Q is S. 40° E. and of S from R is S. 30° E. If S is 5 miles from P find PQ and RS.

12. From a point 350 ft. above sea-level the angles of depression of two boats in line with the observer are 25° and 37° respectively. Find the distance between the boats.

13. From A a road runs north-east to B, which is 3 miles from A. From A and B the bearings of C are E. 20° N. and E. 20° S. respectively. D is due north of C and north-east of B. Find BC and CD.

14. A man walks 2 miles due north, then 2 miles due east, then 3 miles due north. Find the distance and his bearing from his starting point.

15. A ship is sailing due north and at 1 p.m. the bearing of a lighthouse is N. 50° E. At 1.20 p.m. the bearing is N. 70° E. If the ship is travelling at 18 knots, find at what distance it will pass the lighthouse.

16. An observer 600 feet above sea-level noticed that the angle of depression of a boat approaching him directly was 20°. Two minutes later, the angle of depression was 35°, the course of the boat having remained unchanged. What was the speed of the boat in feet per second ?

17. A road runs due east and west. B and C are points on the road 100 yards apart. The bearings from B and C of a point A are 40° and 25° south of west respectively. Find the distance AB and the position of the point of the road which is due north of A.

18. A line OCD runs due east from O ; A is due north from C, B due north from D, and AB runs due east. OA is 235 yards and its direction is 63° N. of E : the direction of OB is 38° N. of E. Find the distances AC, OB, CD.

19. A ship sails from a port A to a port B which is 35 miles W. of A. From B it sails to a port C which is 38 miles in a direction N. 18° E. from B. In what direction and how far must it now sail in a straight line to reach a port D, which is 17 miles N.W. of A?

20. A field is in the shape of a quadrilateral ABCD, in which AB = 3 chains, BC = 10 chains, CD = 5 chains, $\hat{B}$ = 110°, $\hat{C}$ = 80°. Draw the figure on the scale of 2 chains to the inch. Measure AC and the perpendiculars to AC from B and D, giving their lengths in chains.

21. From two stations A and B, 350 yd. apart, two towers C and D on the same plane with A and B can be seen : to find the distance between the towers the following angles are measured :

     $B\hat{A}C$ = 108°, $B\hat{A}D$ = 56°, $A\hat{B}C$ = 37°, $A\hat{B}D$ = 78°.

Draw to scale a figure showing the positions of A, B, C and D, and from your drawing find the distance between the towers.

22. Draw a horizontal line AB 2·5 in. long to represent one side of a field ABCD, and complete the plan of the field from the following data :

     AB = 75 chains ; bearing of B from A is 90°.
     BC = 63 chains ; bearing of C from B is 45°.
     CD = 84 chains and D is on the northern side of line AB.
     DA = 90 chains.

Measure AC and the distance of D from AC. (Give answers to the nearest chain.)

23. From a point A, 3 posts B, C, and D can be seen. B is 75 chains east of A, C is 90 chains north-east of A, and D is north of A, but its distance from A is not known. If D lies north-west of C, find the distances AD, BD and BC.

24. AB is 15 miles. The bearing of B from A is 090°. The bearing of C from B is 015°, of D from A is 025°, and of D from C is 252°. If BC = 11 miles, find the distance and bearing of D from B.

25. From a point A the bearing of a lighthouse is 055°. A ship sailing at 12 miles per hour starts from A, and after sailing east for two hours finds that the bearing of the lighthouse is now 318°. Find (1) how near the ship passes the lighthouse ; (2) the time when she was nearest to the lighthouse.

REVISION PAPERS XI–XX

XI

1. In the figure, prove that parm. PQRS = parm. TQPX. Prove also that QP produced bisects XS.

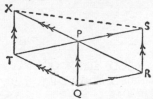

2. In the figure, ABCD and ABEF are parallelograms. Prove

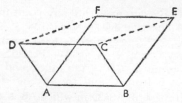

that DCEF is a parallelogram, and that parm. ABCD + parm. DCEF = parm. ABEF.

3. ABCD is a square with X the mid-point of AD. XY, drawn parallel to AB, meets AC in P and CB in Y. Prove that $XP^2 + DC^2 = XC^2$.

4. The area between the circumferences of two concentric circles is $192\frac{1}{2}$ sq. ft. The circumference of the outer circle is 66 ft. Find the radius of the inner circle.

5. Draw a rough plan and find the area of the field from the following entries in a field-book. Answer in acres.

	Links	
	E	
	750	
	600	250D
F200	500	300C
	250	200B
G250	100	
	A	

XII

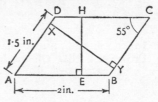

1. ABCD is a parallelogram. Calculate HE, XY and the area of ABCD.

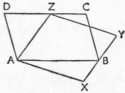

2. In the figure, ABCD and AXYZ are parallelograms. Prove that they are equal in area.

3. ABCD is a parallelogram with P any point in CD, and PX, parallel to CA, meeting AD in X. Prove △APC = △XAB.

4. From a town A, the bearings of three towns B, C and D are respectively E. 10° N., S. 35° W., E. 15° S. If AB = 40 miles, AC = 35 miles, CD = 130 miles, find by a diagram the bearing of B from C and the distance AD.

5. Construct a trapezium ABCD in which AB is parallel to DC. AB = 1·8 in., BC = 1·7 in., CD = 3·4 in., AD = 1·2 in. Find its area.

XIII

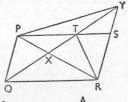

1. In the figure, PQRS is a parallelogram. Prove that

   (1) △QTR = △QPY.
   (2) △PXQ = △TXR.
   (3) △PTY = △TRS.

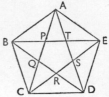

2. PQRST is a regular pentagon. Calculate CÂD. Prove that ABCDE is a regular pentagon, and find its area by calculation of the areas of △s ACD and ABC, using trigonometrical tables, given that CD = 1 in.

3. **ABCD** is a parallelogram with diagonals **AC** and **BD** intersecting in **O**. **P, Q, R, S** are the mid-points of **AD, AO, BO, OD** respectively. Express the area of the pentagon **PQRCS** as a fraction of the area of **ABCD**.

4. By drawing a figure on the scale one inch to 100 yards, calculate in acres the area of the field **ABCD** which has the shape of a quadrilateral. **AB** = 210 yd., **BC** = 290 yd. The bearings of **B** from **A**, **C** from **B**, **D** from **C** and **D** from **A** are respectively 065°, 145°, 250°, 148°.

5. **PQR** is a right-angled isosceles triangle with $\widehat{P}$ a right angle. **QS** bisects $\widehat{Q}$, meeting **PR** in **S**.   **ST** is drawn perpendicular to **QR**. Name 2 similar triangles, giving reasons for your answer. Prove that $PS^2 = \frac{1}{2}SR^2$.

XIV

1. In the figure, **D, E, H** are the mid-points of the sides. Express the area of the quadrilateral **AHOE** as a fraction of the area of $\triangle ABC$.

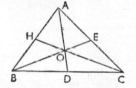

2. In the figure, calculate **RQ, SQ, TQ** and area of quadrilateral **TQRS**.

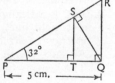

3. **ABC** is a triangle. What is the position of point **P** in **BC**, if $\triangle ABP = \triangle ACP$? Where inside the $\triangle$ must the point **Q** lie if $\triangle ABQ = \triangle AQC$? Hence find point **R** inside the $\triangle$ such that $\triangle ABR = \triangle BCR = \triangle CAR$.

4. The bearings of a ship at noon from two stations **A** and **B** are S. 27° E. and W. 46° S. respectively. At 12.45 p.m. its bearings from **A** and **B** are E. 13° N. and N. 39° W. respectively. Assuming that the ship is steaming on a straight course, find its speed in miles per hour, and the direction in which it is sailing. The station **B** is 15 miles east of **A**.

5. PQR is a triangle right-angled at P. PSTQ and PRXY are the squares described externally on PQ and PR. Prove that TY = TR and that △ TPY = △PQR.

XV

1. In the figure, calculate AD, BD, DC and DĈA. Find the area of △ADC.

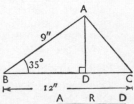

2. In the figure, ABCD is a square. P, Q, R are the mid-points of the sides. What fraction of the area of the square is the area of the figure APQR ?

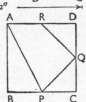

3. ABC is a right-angled isosceles triangle with Ĉ a right angle. Through C a straight line CD is drawn parallel to the bisector of BÂC and meeting BA produced in D. DE, parallel to AC, meets BC produced in E. Prove that $BD^2 = 2BE^2$ and that $BA^2 = 2AD^2$.

4. ABC is a triangle. Through D, any point in AB, is drawn a straight line parallel to BC meeting AC in E. Through E is drawn a straight line EF, parallel to AB, meeting BC in F. AF cuts DE in G. Prove that parm. BFED = 2△AGC.

5. The bearing of a place Q from a place P is E. 20° N. R is 2,000 yards from Q, its bearing from Q being N. 35° W. The bearing of R from P is N. 30° E. If S is due north of P and north-west of Q, find PQ, SR and the bearing of S from R.

XVI

1. Prove that BÂC = 90°.
   Calculate BÂD.

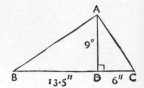

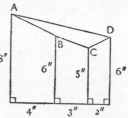

2. Calculate the area of the quadrilateral ABCD.

3. ABCD is a trapezium (AD parallel to BC). AC and BD intersect at O. Through O a straight line XOY is drawn parallel to AD, meeting AB and CD in X, Y respectively. Prove that △BXD = △AYC.

4. Draw a straight line BC = 2·5 in. long. What is the locus of point A if the area of △ABC = 2·5 sq. in. ? Draw the locus and construct an isosceles triangle on BC as base, having an area of 1·25 sq. in. State your construction.

5. A ship sails 12 miles E. 28° N., then 16 miles N. 24° E., and then 6 miles N. 20° W. Find the distance and bearing of the ship from its starting point.

XVII

1. In the figure, ABCD and BXYZ are equal parallelograms. Prove that AS = SX.
   [*Hint:* Join AR, RX.]

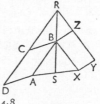

2. In the figure, ABCD is a rectangle (not drawn to scale). Calculate the area of quadrilateral PQRS.

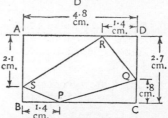

3. PQRS is a parallelogram with T any point in QR. ST and PQ are produced to meet at W. Prove that
   △RTW = △PQT.

4. ABC is a triangle with AD and CF medians, intersecting at H. BC is produced to G so that CG = DC. Prove that

 (1) △BCF = △FCA = △ACG.
 (2) △AHF = ⅓△ACG.

5. From the top of a cliff 500 ft. high, the angles of depression of two boats due south of the cliff are 40° and 54° respectively. Find, by a drawing to scale, the distance between the boats, and check the result by calculation.

XVIII

1. In the figure, AEGH and ABCD are parallelograms and GC is parallel to DE. Prove that

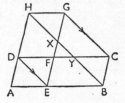

 (1) parm. AEGH = parm. ABCD.
 (2) parm. DFGH = parm. EBCF.
 (3) HB parallel to DE.
 (4) GX = CB and HX = YB.

2. In the figure, which is not drawn to scale, calculate the length of PS and the size of SR̂Q.

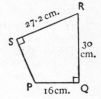

3. ABCD is a parallelogram with X any point in diagonal AC. Prove that △BXC = △DXC. If AX = ¼AC, express the area of quadrilateral DXBC as a fraction of parallelogram ABCD.

4. P, Q, R are 3 fixed points. S is a variable point. What is the locus of S when

 (1) △SQR = △PQR,
 (2) △SQR = 3△PQR,
 (3) △SQR = △SPQ,
 (4) quad. PQRS is a constant area?

5. **PQRS** is a parallelogram with a straight line **PX** cutting **QR** in **X**. **XY** is parallel to **QS** and cuts **RS** in **Y**. Prove that △**PQX** = △**PYS**.

XIX

1. The figure shows a rectangular prism in which **FG** = 5 in., **GH** = 4 in., **GC** = 3 in. Find the lengths of **EG** and **EC**. Name any other lines equal in length to (1) **EG**, (2) **EC**.
Calculate the size of **CÊG** and the area of △**CEG**.

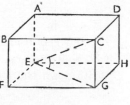

2. The figure represents an 8-in. square **ABCD**. **A'** is the mid-point of **BC** and the figure is folded about a straight line so that **A** falls on **A'**. What point on **AA'** must be on this straight line? Draw this straight line and let it cut **AB** in **X**, and **DC** in **L**. Calculate

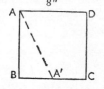

(1) **BÂA'**,
(2) length of **XL**.

3. The angle of elevation of the sun is 50°. Find the length of the shadow cast by an upright post 15 ft. long. If the length of the shadow increases by 1·5 feet, by how much has the angle of elevation of the sun decreased?

4. Construct a triangle **ABC** with a = 2·5 in., b = 3·4 in., c = 4 in. Construct an equivalent isosceles triangle on a base of 4·5 in. State your construction and prove that it is correct.

5. **ABCD** is a rhombus with **AB** = 8·5 cm., **BD** = 15 cm. Calculate **AC** and the angles **BAD** and **ADC**.

XX

1. The figure shows a rectangular prism in which AD = $4\frac{1}{5}$ in.,

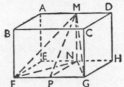

AE = $3\frac{1}{5}$ in., AB = 3 in.   M and N are the mid-points of AD and EH.   Calculate FN and FM.   Calculate FÑG and FM̂G and the area of △FMG.

2. Write down the formula for the area of a triangle whose

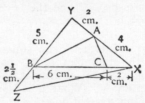

base is b units of length and whose altitude is a units of length.   Find the ratio of the areas of the following triangles.

$$(1) \ \frac{\triangle XYZ}{\triangle XBY}, \quad (2) \ \frac{\triangle XBY}{\triangle ABX}, \quad (3) \ \frac{\triangle ABX}{\triangle ABC}.$$

Hence find the ratio of △XYZ to △ABC.

[The figure is *not* drawn to scale.]

3. ABCD is a parallelogram with AB = 5·1 cm.   If AC = 9 cm. and BD = 4·8 cm. prove that ABCD is a rhombus.

4. ABCD is a trapezium with AD parallel to BC.   X is the mid-point of AB, and the straight line drawn through X, parallel to AD, meets CD in Y.   Prove that

$$\triangle AYD + \triangle BYC = \triangle ABY.$$

5. At noon a destroyer steaming due east at 36 miles per hour sees a ship, 10 miles distant, bearing 030°.   At 12.30 p.m. the ship is 7 miles distant, bearing 340°.   Find the speed and course of the ship.   If the destroyer now steams N.E. when will she cross the ship's course?

BOOK III

THE CIRCLE

Definitions (additional to those on page 47).

(1) **Equal circles** are circles whose radii are equal.

(2) **Concentric** circles are circles which have the same centre.

(3) A **chord** of a circle is a straight line joining any two points on the circumference.

(4) A **diameter** of a circle is a chord which passes through the centre of the circle.

(5) An **arc** of a circle is any part of the circumference.

(6) A **segment** of a circle is a plane figure bounded by a chord and one of the arcs into which the chord divides the circumference.

Thus a chord divides a circle into two segments. If these segments are equal, each is called a **semicircle**. The segments are equal when the chord passes through the centre of the circle, i.e. is a diameter. Hence, a semicircle is a plane figure bounded by a diameter and one of the arcs into which the diameter divides the circumference.

If the segments are unequal, the greater is called the **major segment**, and the less, the **minor segment**.

The arc of a major segment is a **major arc**: the arc of a minor segment is a **minor arc**.

(7) An **angle in a segment** is the angle subtended by the chord of the segment at any point on the arc of the segment.

AĈB is an angle in the segment ACB.

(8) **An angle** is said to be **at the centre** or **at the circum-ference** of a circle when its vertex is at the centre or at the circumference of the circle.   Such an angle is said to stand on the arc intercepted between its arms.

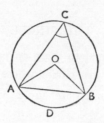

E.g. in the above figure, AĈB is an angle at the circumference, standing on the arc ADB.

Also, AÔB is the angle at the centre of the circle, standing on the arc ADB.

(9) Four or more points through which a circle may be drawn are said to be **concyclic.**

(10) A **cyclic quadrilateral** is a quadrilateral through whose vertices a circle may be drawn.

(11) A circle is said to be **circumscribed** about a recti-lineal figure when the vertices of the figure are on the circum-ference of the circle.

The circle is called the **circumcircle** and its centre is called the **circumcentre.**

Note : The rectilineal figure may then be said to be **inscribed** in the circle.

THEOREM 20

The straight line from the centre of a circle to the mid-point of a chord which does not pass through the centre, is perpendicular to the chord.

Conversely: The straight line from the centre of a circle perpendicular to a chord which does not pass through the centre, bisects the chord.

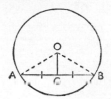

Given: Circle with centre **O** and chord **AB**, with **OC** the straight line joining **O**, the centre of the circle, to **C**, the mid-point of the chord.

Required: To prove that **OC** is perp. to **AB.**

Construction: Join **OA, OB.**

Proof: In △s **OAC** and **OBC**

     1. **OA** = **OB** (radii).

     2. **OC** is common.

     3. **AC** = **BC** (given).

  ∴ △**OAC** ≡ △**OBC** (three sides)

    ∴ **OĈA** = **OĈB**

    ∴ **OC** is perp. to **AB** (adj. ∠s equal, **ACB** a str. line).

Converse :

Given: Circle with centre **O** and chord **AB**, with **OC** the straight line from **O**, the centre of the circle, perp. to chord **AB**.

Required: To prove that **AC** = **CB**.

Construction: Join **OA, OB.**

Proof:

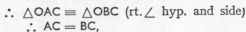

In △s OAC and OBC

   1. OA = OB (radii).

   2. OC is common.

   3. O$\hat{C}$A = O$\hat{C}$B (rt. angles).

∴ △OAC ≡ △OBC (rt. ∠ hyp. and side)

  ∴ AC = BC,

i.e. OC bisects AB.

Cor.—The perpendicular bisector of a chord passes through the centre of the circle.

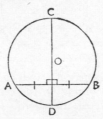

CD is the ⊥ bisector of a chord AB of a circle with centre O. Since CD bisects AB perpendicularly

  ∴ CD is the locus of points equidistant from A and B. But O, the centre of the circle, is equidistant from A and B

  ∴ O lies on CD,

i.e. CD passes through O.

Cor.—A straight line cannot have more than two points in common with the circumference of a circle.

Suppose the straight line AB, which has points A and B in common with the circumference, has a third point C in common with the circumference.

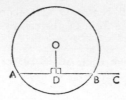

From **O**, the centre of the circle, draw **OD** perp. to **AB**.
Then, since **AB** and **AC** are chords of the circle

∴ AD = DB
and AD = DC
∴ DB = DC which is impossible.

∴ Str. line **AB** cannot cut the circumference in a third point **C**.

∴ A str. line cannot have more than two points in common with a circle.

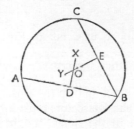

CONSTRUCTION 13

To find the centre of a given circle

Given: Circle **ABC**.

Required: To find the centre.

Construction: Take any two chords **AB** and **BC**.
Draw **DX** and **EY**, the perpendicular bisectors of **AB** and **BC** resp. These bisectors must intersect, since **BA** and **BC** are not in the same straight line.
Let them intersect at **O**.
Then **O** is the centre of the circle **ABC**.

Proof: **DX** is the perp. bisector of **AB**
∴ **DX** passes through the centre of the circle.
Similarly **EY** passes through the centre of the circle.
But **DX** and **EY** intersect in **O**.
∴ **O** is the centre of the circle.

CONSTRUCTION 14

To construct a circle to pass through any three points not in the same straight line

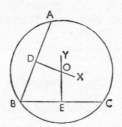

Given: Three points A, B, C not in the same straight line.

Required: To construct the circle passing through A, B, C.

Construction: Draw DX and EY the perp. bisectors of AB and BC resp. These bisectors must intersect since AB and BC are not in the same straight line.
Let them intersect in O.
With centre O and radius OA draw a circle.
This circle passes through A, B, C.

Proof: DX is the perp. bisector of AB
∴ DX is the locus of points equidistant from A and B.
But O is a point on DX
∴ OA = OB.
Similarly OB = OC
∴ O is equidistant from A, B, C.
∴ The circle with centre O and radius OA passes through A, B, C,
i.e. it is the required circle.

Cor.—There is only one such circle, since there is only one point in which the perp. bisectors DX and EY can meet.

CONSTRUCTION 15

To circumscribe a circle about a given triangle

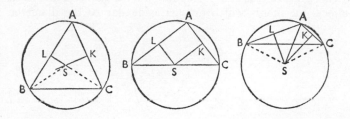

Given: △ABC.

Required: To draw the circumscribing circle of △ABC.

Construction: Bisect **AB** and **AC** perpendicularly by **LS** and **KS** and let the perp. bisectors meet at **S**. Join **SA**. With centre **S** and radius **SA** draw a circle. Then this circle is the circumscribing circle of △ABC

Proof: **LS** is the perp. bisector of **AB** (constr.)

∴ **LS** is the locus of pts. equidistant from **A** and **B**

∴ SA = SB.

Similarly SA = SC

∴ SA = SB = SC.

∴ Circle with centre **S** and radius **SA** passes through **B** and **C**.

∴ Circle ABC is the circumscribing circle of △ABC.

[*Note:* The figures illustrate the three cases in which △ABC is acute-angled, right-angled, obtuse-angled.]

Symmetry

Symmetry about an axis

Since the perpendicular drawn from the centre of a circle to a chord bisects the chord, it follows that a diameter of a circle bisects all chords which are perpendicular to the diameter.

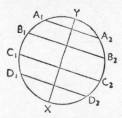

The diameter XY is perp. to each of the chords A_1A_2, etc.

∴ The diameter XY bisects each of the chords.

∴ A_1, A_2 are corresponding points; so also are B_1, B_2; C_1, C_2; D_1, D_2.

Hence the circle is symmetrical about the diameter XY.

Any diameter is therefore an axis of symmetry of a circle.

When two circles with centres P and Q intersect in two points A and B, the straight line AB is a chord of both circles and is called the common chord of the circles.

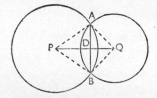

Since any circle is symmetrical about any diameter, the figure must be symmetrical about PQ, the line of centres of the two circles.

∴ A and B are corresponding points

$$\therefore AD = DB.$$

Also $A\hat{D}P = B\hat{D}P$

∴ AB is perp. to PQ.

Relation between the length of a chord and its distance from the centre of a circle.

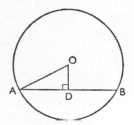

AB is any chord in a circle with centre O, and OD is the perpendicular from the centre to the chord,

∴ AD = DB.

△OAD is right-angled at D

∴ $AD^2 + OD^2 = OA^2$ (Pythagoras' Theorem)

$= r^2$ where r is the radius of the circle.

∴ The value of $AD^2 + OD^2$ is fixed for all positions of AB.

If AD^2 increases in value, OD^2 must decrease in value.

If AD^2 decreases in value, OD^2 must increase in value.

Hence if AD and therefore AB increases, OD decreases, and if AD and therefore AB decreases, OD increases.

∴ In any circle, the greater a chord is, the nearer it must be to the centre of the circle.

The converse is also true : The nearer a chord is to the centre of the circle, the greater it is.

It therefore follows that the diameter is the greatest chord in a circle.

These facts may be stated as follows :

The diameter is the greatest chord in a circle ; and of all other chords, that which is nearer the centre is greater than that which is more remote, and conversely, the greater chord is nearer to the centre than the smaller.

Equal Chords

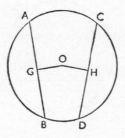

AB and CD are two equal chords in a circle with centre O and OG and OH are their distances from the centre O,

$$\therefore AG = \tfrac{1}{2}AB$$

$$\text{and } CH = \tfrac{1}{2}CD$$

$$\therefore AG = CH \ (AB = CD).$$

But $AG^2 + GO^2 = CH^2 + HO^2$ (each is equal to r^2)

$$\therefore GO^2 = HO^2$$

$$\therefore GO = HO.$$

$\therefore$ The chords are equidistant from the centre.

It is obvious that if the two chords AB and CD are equidistant from O, i.e. if OG = OH, then

$$AG = CH$$

and hence AB = CD.

$\therefore$ **Equal chords in a circle are equidistant from the centre of the circle, and conversely, chords which are equidistant from the centre of a circle are equal.**

EXERCISES 37

1.

Find **OC**.

2.

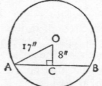

Find **AB**.

3.

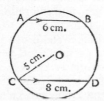

Find the distance between the parallel chords **AB** and **CD**.

4.

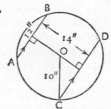

The parallel chords **AB** and **CD** are 14 in. apart. Find **CD**.

5.

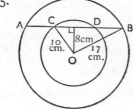

Circles are concentric, with centre **O**. Find **AC**.

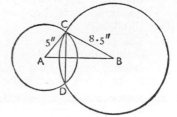

Chord **CD** is 8 in. long Find **AB**.

7. A chord 6 cm. long is drawn in a circle of diameter 10 cm. Calculate its distance from the centre.

8. A chord is drawn in a circle of radius 5·2 in. at a distance of 2 in. from the centre. Find the length of the chord.

9. A chord 3 in. long is at a distance of $\frac{4}{5}$ in. from the centre of a circle. Calculate the diameter of the circle.

10. Two parallel chords of a circle of radius 10 cm. are 12 cm. and 16 cm. long. How far are they apart?

11. In a circle of radius 2·5 in. two parallel chords are placed 3·1 in. apart. If the length of one chord is 4·8 in. find the length of the other.

12. Two parallel chords of lengths 4 in. and 8 in. are placed 2 in. apart in a circle. Find the radius of the circle, correct to 2 dec. pl.

13. AB is a chord of a circle with centre O. The perp. from O to the chord cuts the chord at C and meets the circle at D. If AB = 8 in. and CD = 2 in. find the radius of the circle.

14. If two parallel chords are drawn in a circle, prove that the perp. bisector of either chord, produced if necessary, bisects the other chord perpendicularly.

15. If two parallel chords are drawn in a circle, prove that their mid-points and the centre of the circle are collinear.

16. If a series of parallel chords is drawn in a circle, prove that their mid-points all lie on a diameter.

17. P is a point in a circle of radius 6 cm. whose distance from the centre is 3·6 cm. Find the lengths of (1) the longest, (2) the shortest chord, of the circle which can be drawn through P.

18. The greatest chord that can be drawn through a given point within a circle is 10 cm. long and the shortest chord is 6 cm. long. What is the radius of the circle and how far is the given point from the centre?

19. Two equal and parallel chords in a circle of radius 6·5 cm. are 7·8 cm. apart. Find the length of each chord.

20. Two perpendicular chords AB and AC of a circle with centre O are 6 cm. and 8 cm. long respectively. Calculate OA.

21. Two chords AB and CD of a circle intersect at O and make equal angles with the diameter drawn through O. Prove that AB = CD.

22. Prove that the parts of a straight line intercepted between the circumferences of two concentric circles are equal.

23. Two circles, with centres A and B, intersect at P and Q. AB and PQ cut in O. Prove that

    (1) O is the mid-point of PQ.
    (2) AB is perp. to PQ.

24. Two circles, with centres A and B, intersect at C. Through C a line DCE is drawn parallel to AB, meeting the circles in D and E. Prove that $AB = \frac{1}{2}DE$.

25. Two circles intersect at A and B. Through A, any straight line CAD is drawn, meeting the circles in C and D, and through B a straight line GBH is drawn parallel to CAD, meeting the circles in G and H. Prove that

    (1) CD = GH.
    (2) CG = DH.

26. Two circles, with centres P and Q, intersect in C and D. QP produced cuts the circle with centre P, at A. AC and AD produced cut the second circle in F and G resp. Prove that CF = DG.

27. PQ and XY are equal chords in a circle. They meet when produced outside the circle, at O. Prove that

    (1) QO = YO.
    (2) OP = OX.

28. AB and CD are two equal chords in a circle with centre O, intersecting at a point X within the circle. Prove that OX, or OX produced, bisects $A\hat{X}D$ and $C\hat{X}B$.

29. Two circles, with centres A and B, intersect at C. X is the mid-point of AB, and a straight line through C, perp. to CX, meets the circles in Y and Z. Prove that YC = CZ.

30. Two circles intersect in X and Y. AXB is any line through X, meeting the circles in A and B. Prove that AB has its maximum length when it is parallel to the line of centres of the circles.

THEOREM 21

An angle at the centre of a circle is twice any angle at the circumference standing on the same arc.

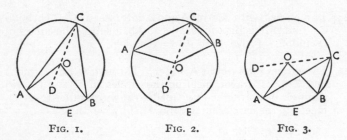

FIG. 1.   FIG. 2.   FIG. 3.

Given: Circle with centre O and AÔB an angle at the centre and AĈB any angle at the circumference standing on the same arc AEB.

Required: To prove that AÔB = 2AĈB.

Construction: Join CO and produce it to any point D.

Proof: OA = OC (radii of same circle)
∴ OĈA = OÂC (base ∠s of isos. △).
But AÔD = OĈA + OÂC (ext. ∠ of
                △ = sum of int. opp. ∠s)
∴ AÔD = 2OĈA.
Similarly BÔD = 2OĈB.

Figs. 1 and 2:

By addition AÔD + BÔD = 2OĈA + 2OĈB
∴ AÔB = 2AĈB.

Fig. 3:

By subtraction DÔB − DÔA = 2OĈB − 2OĈA
∴ AÔB = 2AĈB.

THEOREM 22

Angles at the circumference of a circle standing on the same arc are equal.

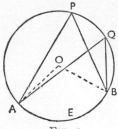

FIG. 1.

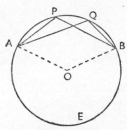

FIG. 2.

Given: Circle with centre O, and A$\hat{P}$B and A$\hat{Q}$B angles at the circumference, standing on the arc AEB.

Required: To prove that $\hat{P} = \hat{Q}$.

Construction: Join AO and OB.

Proof:

Fig 1:

> A$\hat{O}$B = 2$\hat{P}$ (∠ at centre is twice ∠ at circumference standing on same arc).

> A$\hat{O}$B = 2$\hat{Q}$ (same reason).

> ∴ $\hat{P} = \hat{Q}$.

Fig 2:

Reflex A$\hat{O}$B = 2$\hat{P}$ (∠ at centre is twice ∠ at circumference standing on same arc).

Reflex A$\hat{O}$B = 2$\hat{Q}$ (same reason).

> ∴ $\hat{P} = \hat{Q}$.

[*Note:* The theorem is often stated thus: **Angles in the same segment of a circle are equal.**]

THEOREM 23

The angle in a semicircle is a right angle

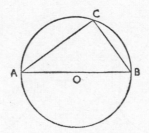

Given: Circle with centre O, and AĈB an angle in the semicircle ACB.

Required: To prove that AĈB = 1 rt. angle.

Proof: ACB is a semicircle

∴ AB passes through O.

AÔB = 2AĈB (∠s at centre and circumference
standing on same arc).

But AÔB = 2 rt. angles (AOB is a str. line)

∴ AĈB = 1 rt. angle.

From the two previous theorems it follows that

(1) the angle in a major segment of a circle is an acute angle,
or, an angle at the circumference of a circle, standing on a
minor arc, is an acute angle.

(2) the angle in a semicircle is a right angle.

(3) the angle in a minor segment of a circle is an obtuse
angle, *or*, an angle at the circumference of a circle, standing
on a major arc, is an obtuse angle.

EXERCISES 38

I.

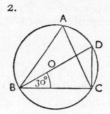

Find BÂC.

2.

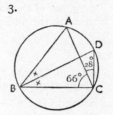

Find BÂC.

3.

B̂ is bisected by
BD. Find Â.

4.

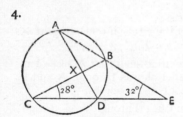

Find AD̂C and AX̂B.

5.

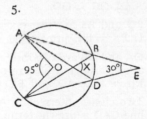

Find X̂.

6.

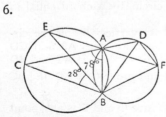

Find DB̂F and BF̂D.

7.

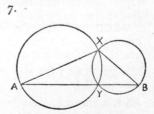

XA and XB are diameters.
Prove A, Y, B collinear.

N.C.G.—8

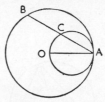

8. OA is a radius of the larger, and a diameter of the smaller, circle. Prove that C is the mid-point of the chord AB.

9. AB and CD are two chords of a circle, intersecting at O. Prove that triangles AOC and BOD are equiangular.

10. AB and CD are two chords of a circle which, when produced, meet outside the circle at a point O. Prove that triangles AOD and BOC are equiangular.

11. AB and CD are two parallel chords of a circle. AD and BC intersect at O. Prove that

    (1) OA = OB.
    (2) OC = OD.

12. PQ and RS are two chords of a circle intersecting at X. If PX = PR, prove that SX = SQ.

13. OA and OB are two radii of a circle such that $A\hat{O}B = 1$ rt. angle. AC and BD are parallel chords through A and B. Prove that AD and BC cut at right angles.

14. Two circles intersect in A and B. Through A, a straight line CAD is drawn, terminated by the circumferences at C and D. Prove that if any other such line is drawn through A, it subtends an angle at B equal to $C\hat{B}D$.

15. What is the size of the angle subtended (1) at the centre, (2) at the circumference of a circle, by a chord equal in length to the radius?

    ABCD is a quadrilateral whose vertices lie on the circumference of a circle. The opposite sides AB and CD are each equal to the radius of the circle. If AC and BD meet in E, find the size of $A\hat{E}B$ and prove that AD and BC are parallel.

16. AB is a chord of a circle with centre O and C is any point on the major arc. CA and CB meet the diameter perp. to AB, or this diameter produced, in D and E respectively. Prove that triangles ECD and AOD are equiangular.

17. Angle A of triangle ABC is bisected by AD which meets the circumcircle of △ABC in D.

 With centre D and radius DC a circle is drawn cutting AD in E. Prove that BE bisects $A\widehat{B}C$.

18. In △ABC, the perpendicular from A to BC meets BC in D, and the circumcircle of △ABC in F. The perpendicular from C to AB meets AD in G. Prove that △GCF is an isosceles triangle.

19. A and B are two points on the circumference of a circle with centre O. The circle through A, O, B is drawn. A straight line AXY cuts this circle in X and the first circle in Y. Prove that BX = XY.

20. ABC is an acute-angled triangle. The diameters of the circumcircle of △ABC, drawn through B and C, meet the circle again in X and Y respectively. AX and AY are joined. Prove $Y\widehat{A}B = X\widehat{A}C$.

21. AXB and CXD are two perpendicular chords of a circle with centre O. Prove that the angles AOD and BOC are supplementary.

22. A is a point outside a circle with centre B. On AB as diameter a second circle is drawn. A line from A cuts the first circle in C and D, and the second in E. Prove that CE = ED.

23. AD is the perpendicular from the vertex A of △ABC to the opposite side BC. AX is the diameter through A of the circumcircle of △ABC. Prove that △s ABD and AXC are equiangular.

24. Prove that the circles described on two sides of any triangle as diameters, intersect at a point in the third side, or in that side produced.

25. Circles described on two sides of a triangle as diameters, meet at the mid-point of the third side. Prove that the triangle is isosceles.

Theorem 24

If the straight line joining two points subtends equal angles at two points on the same side of it, the four points are concyclic.

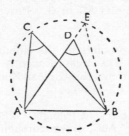

Given: Straight line AB subtending equal angles ACB and ADB at two points C and D on the same side of the line AB.

Required: To prove that A, C, D, B are concyclic.

Construction: Draw the circle through the three points A, C, B. If D does not lie on this circle, let the circle cut AD or AD produced at E. Join BE.

Proof: $A\hat{C}B = A\hat{E}B$ ($\angle$s in same seg.).

But $A\hat{C}B = A\hat{D}B$ (given)

$\therefore A\hat{D}B = A\hat{E}B$,

i.e. ext. $\angle$ of $\triangle$ = int. opp. $\angle$, which is impossible,

$\therefore$ D lies on the circle through A, C, B

$\therefore$ A, C, D, B are concyclic.

THEOREM 25

The circle described on the hypotenuse of a right-angled triangle as diameter, passes through the vertex of the right angle.

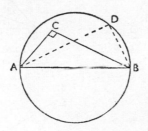

Given: △ABC right-angled at C and a circle ADB described on the hypotenuse AB as diameter.

Required: To prove that the circle ADB passes through C.

Construction: Take any point D on the circumference of the circle, on the same side of AB as C. Join AD, DB.

Proof: AD̂B = 1 rt. angle (∠ in a semi-circle).

But AĈB = 1 rt. angle (given)

∴ AĈB = AD̂B.

But these angles are subtended by a str. line AB at two points on the same side of AB

∴ A, C, D, B are concyclic

∴ circle on AB as diameter passes through C.

Exercises 39

1.

Prove that B, H, E, C are concyclic.

2.

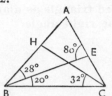

Prove that B, H, E, C are concyclic.

3.

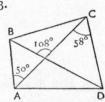

Prove that A, B, C, D are concyclic.

4.

Prove A, X, B, Y are concyclic.

5. Prove

(1) A, O, Q, P are concyclic.

(2) $O\hat{Q}A = O\hat{P}B$.

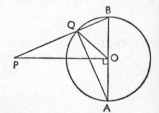

6. Find the centre of the circle passing through B, H, E, C. A circle is described on AK as diameter. Through which two points in the figure does it pass?

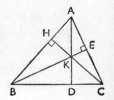

7. BN is the perpendicular from B to
   AC. M is the mid-point of AC.
   Show that BM and BN trisect $\hat{B}$.

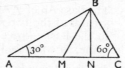

8. The segment APB is fixed and P moves
   on the arc of the circle. Find the locus
   of Q.

9. BE and CH are perpendiculars from the vertices B, C of
   △ABC to the opposite sides AC and AB respectively.
   Prove that $\widehat{BEH} = \widehat{BCH}$.

10. D, E, H are the mid-points of the sides BC, CA, AB respec-
    tively of △ABC. G is the foot of the perpendicular from
    A to BC. Prove that D, G, E, H are concyclic.

11. ABC is an isosceles triangle and D is any point in AB.
    DE is drawn parallel to BC meeting AC in E. Prove that
    B, C, E, D are concyclic.

12. AB is a fixed straight line. Find the locus of points at
    which AB subtends an angle equal to a given angle.

13. A triangle ABC has its base BC fixed, and its vertex A
    moves on the arc of a circle through B and C. Find the
    locus of the circumcentre of △ABC.

14. A triangle ABC has its base BC fixed, and its vertex A
    moves on the arc of a circle through B and C. If the
    bisectors of $\hat{B}$ and $\hat{C}$ meet in I, find the locus of I.

$$\left[\textit{Hint: Prove that } \widehat{BIC} = 90° + \frac{A}{2}. \right]$$

15. The base AB of △ABC is fixed and so also is $\widehat{C}$. From the greater of the two sides CA, CB, a part CP is cut off equal to the less. Prove that the locus of P, as C moves in a plane, is composed of two equal arcs of circles.

16. ABC is a triangle with BE and CH the perpendiculars from B and C to AC and AB respectively. D is the mid-point of BC. Prove that DH = DE.

17. In △ABC, AD and CE, the perpendiculars from A and C to the opposite sides, meet in O. X, Y, Z are the mid-points of BC, CA, AO. Prove that the circle on XZ as diameter passes through D and Y.

18. Prove that the circles described on the four sides of a rhombus as diameters have a common point.

19. AB is a diameter of a circle and AB bisects a chord XY. If XB is parallel to AY, prove that XY passes through the centre of the circle.

20. Two circles with centres P and Q intersect at X and Y. AXB and CYD are each drawn parallel to PQ and are terminated by the circumferences at A, B and at C, D. Prove that ABDC is a rectangle and that AY and CX both pass through P.

21. AB is any chord of a fixed circle, and P is any point at which it subtends a right angle. Prove that the sum of the squares on the lines joining the mid-point of the chord to P, and to the centre of the circle, respectively, is constant.

22. D is the foot of the perpendicular from the vertex C of a △ABC on the bisector AD of the angle CAB. DE is drawn parallel to BA and meets AC in E. Prove that E is the mid-point of AC.

23. X is the mid-point of the side QR of △PQR, and PY, the bisector of $Q\widehat{P}R$, meets QR in Y. The perpendicular from R to PY meets PY in Z. Prove XZ parallel to QP.

24. P, Q, R, S are four points in order on the circumference of a circle, such that PR and QS intersect at right angles at O. X is the mid-point of QR, and XO produced meets PS in Y. Prove that OY is perpendicular to PS.

THEOREM 26

(i) The opposite angles of a cyclic quadrilateral are supplementary.

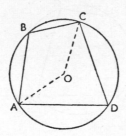

Given: Quadrilateral ABCD inscribed in a circle with centre O.

Required: To prove

(1) $\hat{B} + \hat{D} = 2$ rt. angles.

(2) $B\hat{A}D + B\hat{C}D = 2$ rt. angles.

Construction: Join AO and CO.

Proof: Reflex $A\hat{O}C = 2\hat{B}$ ($\angle$ at centre is twice $\angle$ at circ. standing on same arc).

$A\hat{O}C = 2\hat{D}$ (same reason)

∴ Reflex $A\hat{O}C + A\hat{O}C = 2\hat{B} + 2\hat{D}$.

But Reflex $A\hat{O}C + A\hat{O}C = 4$ rt. angles

∴ $\hat{B} + \hat{D} = 2$ rt. angles.

Similarly, by joining BO and OD it may be proved that

$B\hat{A}D + B\hat{C}D = 2$ rt. angles.

(ii) **An exterior angle of a cyclic quadrilateral is equal to the interior opposite angle.**

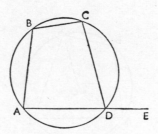

Given: Cyclic quad. **ABCD**, with **AD** produced to any pt. **E**.

Required: To prove **CD̂E = AB̂C**.

Proof: **AB̂C + CD̂A** = 2 rt. angles (opp. ∠s of a cyclic quad.).

But **CD̂E + CD̂A** = 2 rt. angles (adj. ∠s standing on a str. line **ADE**)

∴ **CD̂E = AB̂C**.

THEOREM 27

If a pair of opposite angles of a quadrilateral are supplementary, the quadrilateral is cyclic.

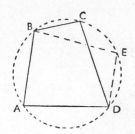

Given : Quad. ABCD with $\hat{A} + \hat{C} = 2$ rt. angles.

Required : To prove that ABCD is a cyclic quad.

Construction : Draw the circle through A, B, D.
Take E, any point on the circumference of the circle on the same side of BD as C.
Join BE, DE.

Proof : $\hat{A} + \hat{E} = 2$ rt. angles (opp. ∠s of a cyclic quad.).

But $\hat{A} + \hat{C} = 2$ rt. angles (given)

     ∴ $\hat{C} = \hat{E}$.

But $\hat{C}$ and $\hat{E}$ are subtended by BD at points C and E on the same side of BD

∴ B, C, E, D are concyclic

∴ C lies on the circle through A, B, D

∴ ABCD is a cyclic quad.

EXERCISES 40

1.

Find the remaining angles at B, C, D.

2.

Find BD̂C.

3.

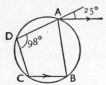

Find Ĉ.

4.

Find AB̂C.

5.

Find *x*.

6.

Prove ABCD a cyclic quadrilateral.

7.

Prove ABCD a cyclic quadrilateral.

8.

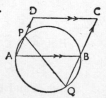

ABCD is a parm. Any circle through A and B cuts DA and CB produced at P and Q resp. Prove DCQP cyclic.

9. Find $\hat{B}$.

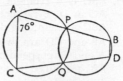

10. AFD and BFE are straight lines. Find $A\hat{C}E$.

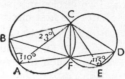

11. Find the number of degrees in each of the angles AFB, AEB, FBE.

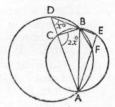

12. ABCD is a cyclic quadrilateral. EO and HO bisect $\hat{E}$ and $\hat{H}$ respectively. Find $D\hat{C}H$ and $D\hat{H}C$. Prove $E\hat{O}H = 90°$.

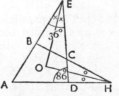

13. Prove that the opposite angles of a cyclic quadrilateral are supplementary, by drawing the diagonals of the quadrilateral.

14. ABC is an isosceles triangle with AB = AC. DE is a straight line parallel to BC, cutting AB, AC in D, E respectively. Prove that BCED is a cyclic quadrilateral.

15. Prove that if a parallelogram be inscribed in a circle, the parallelogram must be a rectangle.

16. ABC is a triangle. AD and BE are perpendiculars from the vertices A and B to the opposite sides. AD and BE intersect in O. Prove $O\hat{C}D = B\hat{A}D$.

17. ABC is a triangle. A circle through B and C cuts AB, AC in D, E respectively. Prove that triangles ADE and ABC are equiangular.

18. AB and CD are two intersecting chords of a circle. From A and C, perpendiculars AE and CH are drawn to CD and AB, produced if necessary. Prove EH parallel to BD.

19. Two circles intersect in X and Y. A straight line ABCD cuts the first circle in A and B and the second in C and D. Prove that $A\widehat{X}C + B\widehat{Y}D = 2$ right angles.

20. A, B, C, D, E, H are six points on the circumference of a circle, such that AB is parallel to ED, and BC is parallel to HE. Prove that CD is parallel to AH.

21. ABCD is a cyclic quadrilateral in which AB and DC produced meet in E, and BC and AD produced meet in H. Circles through B, C, E and through H, C, D intersect in C and K. Prove that E, H, K are collinear.

22. A circle is circumscribed to a triangle ABC. From P, any point on the circumference, perpendiculars PD, PE, PH are drawn to BC, CA, AB, produced if necessary. Prove that

    (1) $P\widehat{E}H = P\widehat{C}B$.
    (2) D, E, H are collinear.

23. PQRS is a parallelogram. Through Q, a straight line QX is drawn parallel to the diagonal PR, meeting SR produced at X. The circumcircle of △PQR meets PS, produced if necessary, at Y. Prove that R is the centre of the circle through X, Y, S.

24. ABC is an acute-angled triangle. L, M, N are points on BC, CA, AB respectively such that the circles through B, N, L and C, L, M intersect at a point O inside the triangle. Prove that AMON is a cyclic quadrilateral.

25. In a quadrilateral PQRS, PQ + RS = QR + SP. Points G, H, K, L are taken in PQ, QR, RS, SP respectively, such that PG = PL, QG = QH, RH = RK. Prove GHKL a cyclic quadrilateral.

26. ABCD is a cyclic quadrilateral. AP is the perpendicular from A to BC and P lies between B and C. AQ is the perpendicular from A to CD and meets CD produced at Q. Prove that

    (1) $P\widehat{A}B = Q\widehat{A}D$.
    (2) △BAD is equiangular to △PAQ.

27. **AB** is a diameter of a circle. **C** and **Q** are any two points on one of the semi-circles. **QF** is perpendicular to **AC** and **QE** is perpendicular to **AB**. If **QE** cuts the circle again in **R**, prove $Q\hat{E}F = Q\hat{R}C$. Prove also that **FE**, produced if necessary, bisects **QC**.

28. In triangle **ABC**, **AD** and **CE** are perpendicular respectively to **BC** and **AB**, and **CE** is produced to **G** so that **EG = HE**, where **H** is the point of intersection of **AD** and **CE**. Prove that

   (1) **AEDC** is a cyclic quadrilateral.

   (2) $B\hat{C}E = D\hat{A}B$, and **AGBC** is a cyclic quadrilateral.

29. **ABCD** is a cyclic quadrilateral in which **AD** > **BC**. **AB** and **DC** meet at **S**, and **AC** and **BD** meet at **O**. Prove the following pairs of triangles equiangular:

   (1) **SBC**, **SDA**;

   (2) **AOD**, **BOC**;

   (3) **SAC**, **SDB**.

   If **CD** is produced (through **D**) to **E**, and **BX**, the bisector of $A\hat{B}C$ meets the circumference of the circle circumscribing the quadrilateral, in **X**, prove that **XD**, produced if necessary, bisects $A\hat{D}E$.

30. **ABC** is a triangle in which the altitudes **AD** and **BE** meet in **H**. **O**, the mid-point of **CH**, is joined to **D**. Prove **A, E, D, B** are concyclic and $D\hat{O}C = 2A\hat{B}C$.

31. **PQR** is an acute-angled triangle. A circle is described on the side **QR** as diameter and cuts **PQ** and **PR** in **X** and **Y** respectively. **QY** and **RX** intersect in **Z**. Prove that $Q\hat{Z}R = P\hat{Q}R + P\hat{R}Q$.

32. Two circles **ACB** and **AOB** intersect in **A** and **B**, **O** being the centre of the circle **ACB**. If **X** is any point on the arc **AOB**, and **AX** cuts the circle **ACB** in **Y**, prove that **XB = XY**, and **OX** is perpendicular to **BY**.

THEOREM 28

The altitudes of a triangle are concurrent

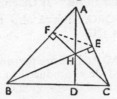

Given: △ABC.

Required: To prove that the altitudes of △ABC are concurrent.

Construction: Draw the altitudes BE and CF and let them meet in H.

Join AH and produce it to meet BC in D.

Proof: Join EF.

In quad. AFHE,

$$A\hat{F}H = A\hat{E}H = 1 \text{ rt. angle (constr.)}$$

∴ AEFH is a cyclic quad. (opp. ∠s supp.)

∴ $A\hat{E}F = A\hat{H}F$ (∠s in same seg.)

But $A\hat{H}F = D\hat{H}C$ (vert. opp. ∠s)

∴ $A\hat{E}F = D\hat{H}C$.

Also $B\hat{F}C = B\hat{E}C$ (each a rt. angle by constr.)

∴ BFEC is a cyc. quad. (BC subtends eq. ∠s at F and E)

∴ $F\hat{E}H = F\hat{C}B$ (∠s in same seg.),

i.e. $F\hat{E}H = H\hat{C}D$.

∴ $D\hat{H}C + H\hat{C}D = A\hat{E}F + F\hat{E}H = A\hat{E}H = 1 \text{ rt. angle}$
(constr.)

∴ $H\hat{D}C = 1 \text{ rt. angle (sum of ∠s of a } △ = 180°)$

∴ AD is perp. to BC.

But AD passes through H

∴ Altitudes of △ABC are concurrent.

[*Note:* The point H is called the **orthocentre** of the triangle.]

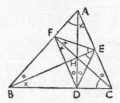

AD, BE, CF are the altitudes of △ABC and they are concurrent in H.

The triangle DEF formed by joining the feet of the altitudes is called the **pedal** triangle.

[*Note:* (1) There are two groups of three cyclic quadrilaterals in the figure, making six in all.

      (*a*) A group of three which together make up the complete figure ABC.
         These are AFHE, BFHD, CEHD.

      (*b*) A group of three, one standing on each of the three sides of the given triangle.
         These are BFEC, CDFA, AEDB.

    (2) There are three groups of four equal angles as shown in the figure.]

It follows from the figure that the altitudes of △ABC bisect the angles of the pedal triangle DEF.

Thus, the Orthocentre of a triangle is the Incentre * of its Pedal Triangle.

---

* Later, it will be proved that the point of concurrence of the bisectors of the angles of a triangle is the Incentre of the triangle.

EXERCISES 41

1. Two points E, F are taken on the circumference of a semi-circle whose diameter is AB. AE and BF produced meet in G. AF and BE meet in H. Prove GH perpendicular to AB.

2. ABC is a triangle with BE, CF two of its altitudes. K is the mid-point of BC. Prove that

(1) KB = KF = KE = KC.
(2) △AEF equiangular to △ABC.
(3) $K\widehat{E}F = K\widehat{F}E = \widehat{A}$.

3. ABC is a triangle with BE, CF two of its altitudes which meet in H. P is the mid-point of AH. Prove that

(1) PA = PF = PH = PE.
(2) $\widehat{F}PE = 2\widehat{A}$.

4. ABC is a triangle in which D, E, F are the feet of the altitudes from A, B, C to the opposite sides BC, CA, AB resp. H is the orthocentre. P, L, R, K are the mid-points of AH, AC, CH, CB respectively. Prove that

(1) L and R lie on the circle circumscribing the △PKD.
(2) E also lies on the circumference of this circle.

What other points must lie on the circumference of this circle ?

[*Note:* The above results are true for any triangle. The facts are usually stated as follows :

In any triangle, the mid-points of the sides, the feet of the perpendiculars from the vertices to the opposite sides, and the mid-points of the lines joining the orthocentre to the vertices, all lie on the circumference of a circle.

This circle is called the **nine point circle** and its centre, the **nine point centre** of the triangle.]

5. Show that in the figure for Theorem 28, A, B, C are the orthocentres of triangles BHC, CHA, AHB respectively.

6. In an acute-angled triangle ABC, the altitudes AD, BE, CF meet at H and when produced, meet the circumcircle of △ABC in P, Q, R respectively. Prove that HD = DP. Hence prove that the sides of △DEF are parallel to, and equal to half the corresponding sides of △PQR. Show also that H is the incentre of △PQR.

7. AD, BE, CF are the three altitudes of △ABC and are concurrent in H.

Circles are drawn on AH and BC as diameters. Prove that each of these circles passes through E and F. Show that the radii of these circles drawn to the point F contain a right angle.

8. H is the orthocentre of triangle ABC. AX is a diameter of the circumcircle. Prove that XH bisects BC.

9. P is the mid-point of the base BC of △ABC. If H is the orthocentre and S its circumcentre, prove that AH = 2SP.

Central Symmetry of the Circle

It has already been shown that a circle is symmetrical about any diameter.

There is a further type of symmetry possessed by the circle, called Central Symmetry.

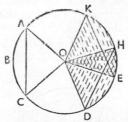

AC is a chord of a circle with centre O, and OA and OC are radii.

The figure bounded by the radii OA and OC, and the arc ABC intercepted by the radii, is called a **sector** of the circle.

The figure bounded by the chord AC and the arc ABC is called a segment of the circle.

Place a piece of tracing paper over the figure and pin it to the figure at O. Trace on the tracing paper the sector OABC and the chord AC and rotate the paper about O.

Owing to the central symmetry of the circle, the arc on the tracing paper always coincides exactly with an arc of the circumference of the circle.

Two positions of the rotating sector and segment are shown at **ODEH** and **OEHK**.

These sectors and the corresponding segments are identical since each is an exact copy of the original sector OABC and the segment ABC.

It follows that

$$\text{arc DEH} = \text{arc EHK} = \text{arc ABC},$$
$$\text{chord DH} = \text{chord EK} = \text{chord AC},$$
$$\text{D}\hat{\text{O}}\text{H} = \text{E}\hat{\text{O}}\text{K} = \text{A}\hat{\text{O}}\text{C}.$$

Angle–Chord–Arc Property of the Circle

It follows from considerations of symmetry that:

(1) If two angles at the centre of a circle are equal they stand on equal arcs.

(2) If two arcs of a circle are equal, the angles subtended by them at the centre of the circle are equal.

(3) If two chords of a circle are equal, the arcs cut off by them are equal, the major arc equal to the major arc, and the minor arc equal to the minor.

(4) If two arcs of a circle are equal, the chords which cut them off are equal.

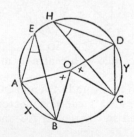

AÊB and CĤD are equal angles at the circumference, standing on the arcs AXB and CYD respectively.

But $\text{A}\hat{\text{O}}\text{B} = 2\text{A}\hat{\text{E}}\text{B}$ (angle at centre double angle at circumference)

and $\text{C}\hat{\text{O}}\text{D} = 2\text{C}\hat{\text{H}}\text{D}$ (same reason)

∴ $\text{A}\hat{\text{O}}\text{B} = \text{C}\hat{\text{O}}\text{D}$.

Hence the sectors OAXB and OCYD are congruent. What has been said above for angles at the centre of a circle is therefore also true for angles at the circumference. Again, the above facts which apply to one circle, will also apply to equal circles, since the one circle can be fitted exactly on to the other circle.

Hence it follows that:

(1) In equal circles, or in the same circle, if two angles, either at the centre or at the circumference, are equal, the arcs on which they stand are equal.

(2) In equal circles, or in the same circle, if two arcs are equal, the angles subtended by them, either at the centre or at the circumference, are equal.

(3) In equal circles, or in the same circle, if two chords are equal, the arcs cut off by them are equal, the major arc equal to the major arc and the minor equal to the minor.

(4) In equal circles or in the same circle, if two arcs are equal, the chords which cut them off are equal.

EXERCISES 42

1. AB and CD are parallel chords. Prove arc AC = arc BD.

2. BC = AD. Prove AB parallel to DC.

3. Â of △ABC is bisected by AD which meets the circumcircle in D. Prove △DBC isosceles.

4. ABCDEH is a regular hexagon and O the centre of its circumcircle. Find AÔH. What angle does CD subtend at each of the vertices A, B, E, H?

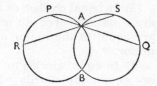

5. Circles are equal. PAQ and RAS are any lines through A. Prove that arc PR = arc QS.

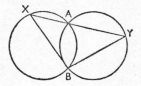

6. Circles are equal. XAY is any line through A. Prove △XBY isosceles.

7. △ABC is equilateral. P and S are mid-points of arcs AB and AC. Prove that PQ = QR = RS.

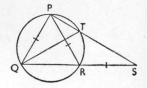

8. PQ = PR. QR is produced to S making RS = PR. PS cuts the circle in T. Prove that QT bisects PÔR.

9. Show how to bisect any arc of a circle.

10. Show how to divide the circumference of a circle into 5, 6, 8 equal arcs.

11. A rectangle PQRS is inscribed in a circle. ST is a chord of the circle, equal to RS. Prove that QT = PS.

12. ABC is an equilateral triangle inscribed in a circle. D and E are points on the arcs AC, BC respectively, so that AD = BE. If BD and EA cut at O, prove that CO produced bisects arc AB.

13. ABC is a triangle inscribed in a circle. AX bisects the arc BC, and BY, parallel to XA, meets the circle in Y. Prove that YX and AC are parallel and that XC = AY.

14. A square is inscribed in a circle. One of its vertices is the vertex of an equilateral triangle inscribed in the circle. Prove that the side of the triangle opposite this vertex is parallel to a diagonal of the square.

15. Two circles intersect at A and B. Two parallel straight lines PAQ and RBS are drawn through A and B, meeting the circles in P, R and in Q, S. Prove that PR = QS.
    [*Hint*: Prove each equal to AB.]

16. Two circles intersect at A and B, and C is a variable point on one of the circles.
    CA and CB when produced meet the other circle in D and E. Prove that, as C moves on the arc ACB, the length of the arc DE remains constant.

    [*Hint*: Prove that $D\widehat{A}E$ remains constant.]

17. AB is any chord of a circle. P is the mid-point of either arc AB and Q is any point on the other arc AB. Prove that P is equidistant from QA and QB.

18. ABCD is a cyclic quadrilateral in which $\widehat{A} = \widehat{D}$. Through B, a chord BE is drawn parallel to the diagonal AC, meeting the circle in E. Prove that AC bisects the angle EAD.

19. I is the point of concurrence of the bisectors of the angles of $\triangle ABC$. AI produced meets the circumcircle of $\triangle ABC$ in D. Prove DB = DI = DC.

20. AB and CD are two perpendicular chords of a circle intersecting at E inside the circle. Prove that the sum of the arcs AC and BD is equal to half the circumference of the circle.

Tangency

It has already been proved that a straight line cannot cut a circle in more than two points.

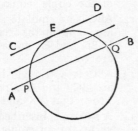

The line AB in the figure cuts the circle at P and Q and is called a **secant**.

If the line AB is moved parallel to itself, the points P and Q move along the circumference of the circle towards each other, and when AB reaches the position CD, the two points P and Q coincide at E.

CD is said to be a **tangent** to the circle, and E is called the **point of contact** of the tangent.

The word " tangent " means " touching ", and in defining a tangent, it is this property of touching that must be explained.

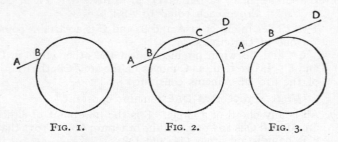

FIG. 1.   FIG. 2.   FIG. 3.

In Fig. 1, the line AB meets the circumference of the circle at B.

In Fig. 2, the line AB meets the circumference of the circle at B, but, when produced, cuts the circumference at B and again at C.

In Fig. 3, the line AB meets the circumference of the circle at B, and, when produced, does not cut the circumference, and we say that AD touches the circle at B, or is a tangent to the circle at B.

Definitions:

(1) A **tangent** to a circle is a straight line which meets the circumference of the circle and which, when produced, does not cut the circumference.

(2) A circle is said to be **inscribed** in a rectilineal figure when each side of the figure is a tangent to the circle. The circle is called the **incircle** and its centre is called the **incentre.**

The rectilineal figure may then be said to be **circumscribed** to the circle.

(3) A circle is said to be **escribed** to a triangle when it touches one side and the other two sides produced. The circle is called the escribed circle and its centre is called the **ex-centre.**

A triangle has thus three escribed circles and three ex-centres.

(4) In the figure, TAN is a tangent to the circle at A and AB is any chord drawn from the point of contact A.

The angle between the tangent and the chord is $\hat{BAN}$, or its supplement $\hat{BAT}$.

If we regard $\hat{BAN}$ as being the angle between the tangent and the chord, the segment ACB is referred to as the **alternate segment** and $\hat{ACB}$ as an angle in the alternate segment.

Similarly, if we regard $\hat{BAT}$ as being the angle between the tangent and the chord, then the segment ADB is the alternate segment.

The radius drawn to the point of contact of a tangent to a circle is perpendicular to the tangent.

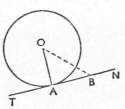

Since the point of contact is the only point which a tangent has in common with a circle, all points on the tangent, other than the point of contact, lie outside the circle.

In the figure, TN is a tangent to a circle with centre O. A is the point of contact of the tangent and B is any point on the tangent other than A.

∴ OA < OB.

This is true for all positions of the point B

∴ OA is the shortest distance from O to the line TN

∴ OA is perp. to TN.

∴ The radius of a circle drawn to the point of contact of a tangent to the circle is perpendicular to the tangent.

Conversely, the straight line drawn perpendicular to a radius at the point where it meets the circumference is a tangent to the circle.

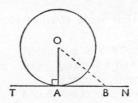

In the figure, OA is a radius and

$$O\hat{A}T = 1 \text{ right angle.}$$

We therefore have to show that all points on TN, other than A, lie outside the circle.

Let B be any point on TN other than A.

Then $O\hat{A}B = 1$ right angle.

∴ $O\hat{A}B > O\hat{B}A$ (sum of ∠s of a △ = 2 rt. angles

∴ OB > OA (greater side is opp. greater ∠)

and this is true for all positions of B.

But OA is a radius

∴ B lies outside the circle.

Hence all points on TN, other than A, lie outside the circle

∴ TAN is a tangent to the circle.

EXERCISES 43

1. AB is a diameter of the circle. PAQ and RBS are tangents to the circle at A and B. Prove PQ parallel to RS.

2. AB is a diameter of the circle, and TAN the tangent at A. XY is any chord parallel to TN. Prove AB bisects XY.

3. What is the locus of the mid-points of a system of parallel chords in a circle?

4. AT is the tangent at A to a circle with centre O. Find x in terms of y.

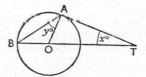

5.

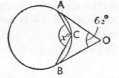

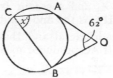

OA and OB are tangents to the circle. Find x in both cases.

6. I is the incentre of $\triangle$ABC and the incircle touches the sides at D, E, H. Find the angles of the triangle ABC.

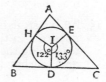

7. Show how to draw to a given circle a tangent which is
   (a) parallel to a given straight line,
   (b) perpendicular to a given straight line.

8. PQ is a diameter of a circle and X is any point on the
   circumference. PR is perpendicular to the tangent at X.
   Prove that PX bisects RP̂Q.

9. PM is the diameter of a circle. On the tangent at P, a
   point S is taken so that PS = PM. If the straight line
   SM cuts the circle at N, prove MN = NS = NP.

10. TA and TB are tangents to a circle from a point T, meeting
    the circle in A and B. Prove that TA = TB.

11. From a point P, outside a circle, two tangents PA, PB and
    a secant PQR are drawn to the circle. BC is the chord of
    the circle parallel to PQR, and AC meets PR in D.
        Prove that P, A, D, B lie on a circle which passes through
    O, the centre of the given circle, and that D is the mid-
    point of the chord QR.

12. A is any point on the diameter of a circle whose centre is O,
    and OB is the radius perpendicular to this diameter. If
    BA cuts the circle again in C, and the tangent at C meets
    OA produced at D, prove that DA = DC.

13. Tangents at points A and B of a circle with centre O meet
    in X, and a secant from X cuts the circle in Y and Z.
        If C is the mid-point of YZ prove that ACOX is a cyclic
    quadrilateral and that AĈX = AÔX.
        If AC produced meets the circle in D, prove DB parallel
    to ZY.

14. AB is a diameter of a circle. State and prove a con-
    struction for finding in AB produced, a point P, such that
    the angle between PA and a tangent from P to the circle
    may be 30°.

15. AB is a straight line and C a fixed point in it. D is a fixed
    point not in the line AB. State and prove a construction
    for finding the centre of the circle which passes through D
    and touches the line AB at the point C.

CONSTRUCTION 16

To draw a tangent to a circle from a point outside the circle.

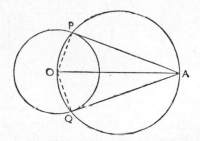

Given: Circle with centre O, and A a point outside the circle.

Required: To draw, from A, a tangent to the circle.

Construction: Join OA.
   On OA as diameter construct a circle and let it cut the given circle at P and Q.
   Join AP and AQ.
   Then AP and AQ are tangents to the given circle.

Proof: Join OP and OQ.
   OP̂A = 1 rt. angle (∠ in a semi-circle).
   But OP is a radius of the given circle
   ∴ AP is a tangent to the given circle.
   Similarly AQ is a tangent to the given circle.

Cor.: Tangents from an external point to a circle are equal.

Proof: In △s OPA and OQA
   1.   OP = OQ (radii of same circle).
   2.   OA is common.
   3.   OP̂A = OQ̂A (rt. angles).
   ∴ △OPA ≡ △OQA (rt. angle, hyp. and side)
      ∴ AP = AQ.

Two circles are said to touch one another when their circumferences meet, but do not cut, one another.

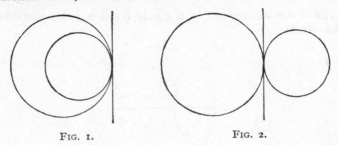

Fig. 1.   Fig. 2.

The point where they meet is called the point of contact. When one circle lies within the other, as in Fig. 1, the circles are said to touch one another internally, or to have internal contact.

When each of the circles is outside the other, as in Fig. 2, the circles are said to touch one another externally, or to have external contact.

When two circles touch, whether internally or externally, they necessarily have the same tangent at the point of contact.

The tangent is then called a common tangent to the two circles.

When two circles touch one another, their centres and the point of contact lie in the same straight line.

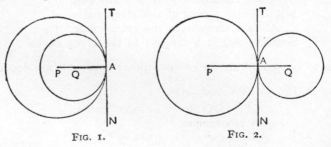

Fig. 1.   Fig. 2.

Draw the common tangent **TN** to the two circles at their point of contact **A**.

Then   P$\hat{A}$T = 1 rt. angle.   (Radius to pt. of contact perp.
to tangent.)

Also   Q$\hat{A}$T = 1 rt. angle. (Same reason.)

In Fig. 1. Since AP and AQ are each perp. to TAN
∴ AP and AQ lie in the same str. line.

In Fig. 2. Since P$\hat{A}$T and Q$\hat{A}$T are adjacent supplementary angles

∴ PAQ is a straight line.

Cor.—The distance between the centres of two circles which touch one another is equal to the difference or the sum of the radii, according as the circles touch internally or externally.

Exercises 44

1. The quadrilateral is circumscribed to the circle. Prove that
   AB + CD = BC + DA.

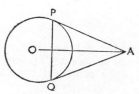

2. Find the length of the tangent from P to the circle.

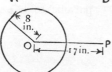

3. AP and AQ are tangents to the circle. Find x.

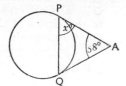

4. AP and AQ are tangents to the circle. Prove that OA bisects PQ perpendicularly.

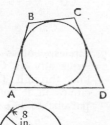

5. AP and AQ are tangents to the circle with centre O. PR is the diameter through O. Prove RQ parallel to OA.

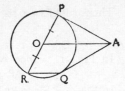

6. The circle is the inscribed circle of the △. If s = semi-perimeter of △ABC prove

AH = AE = s − a.
BH = BD = s − b.
CD = CE = s − c.

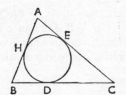

7. Circles, centres A and B, touch externally at O. POQ is any line through O, meeting the circles in P and Q. Prove AP parallel to BQ.

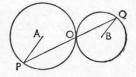

8. Circles touch externally at C. O is a point on the tangent to the circles at C. OD and OE are tangents.

Prove OD = OC = OE.
Prove x − y = 6.

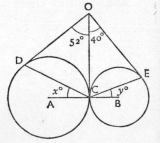

9. If the tangents drawn from a point to a circle of radius 1 in. are 2·5 in. long, find the distance of the point from the centre of the circle by measurement and check by calculation.

10. Draw a circle of radius 4·5 cm. Construct the tangents to this circle from a point 8·5 cm. from the centre. Measure the lengths of the tangents, and check by calculation.

11. Prove that the intercept made by any two parallel tangents to a circle on any third tangent subtends a right angle at the centre of the circle.

12. Tangents AB and AC are drawn to a circle from an external point A. DXE is the tangent at a point X on the arc BC, and cuts AB and AC in D and E respectively. Prove that the perimeter of $\triangle$ADE $= 2$AB.

13. Draw two parallel straight lines cut by a third straight line in A and B, and show that two circles can be drawn to touch all three lines. If AB meets the two circles in P and Q, prove that AP $=$ BQ. Show also that the distance between the centres is equal to AB.

14. B and C are points of contact of tangents from a point A to a circle with centre O. The tangent at any point D on the minor arc BC meets AB, AC in E and H respectively. Prove that, as D moves on the arc BC, the angle EOH remains constant.

15. The angle between two tangents to a circle from a point P is equal to the angle between the two tangents to the same circle, drawn from a point Q. Prove that P and Q are equidistant from the centre of the circle.

16. A straight line XY is a tangent to two circles touching them at X and Y respectively. Z is the mid-point of XY, and the perpendicular from Z to the line of centres is equal to half of XY. Prove that the circles touch each other.

17. Two circles touch each other internally or externally at a point P. Through P, a straight line is drawn meeting the circles again at A and B. Prove that the tangents to the circles at A and B are parallel.

18. Two circles touch one another externally at A, and the tangent at a point B on one of them cuts the other at C and D. Prove that AB bisects externally $\hat{CAD}$.

Theorem 29

The angles between a tangent to a circle and a chord drawn through the point of contact are respectively equal to the angles in the alternate segments of the circle.

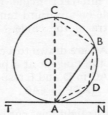

Given: Circle with centre **O**, and **TAN** the tangent at **A**. The chord **AB** divides the circle into two segments **ACB** and **ADB**.

Required: To prove that

      (1) $B\hat{A}N$ is equal to any angle in the segment **ACB**.

      (2) $B\hat{A}T$ is equal to any angle in the segment **ADB**.

Construction: (1) Draw the diameter **AC** through **A** and join **CB**.

           (2) Take any point **D** on the arc **ADB** and join **AD** and **DB**.

Proof: (1) $A\hat{B}C = 1$ rt. angle ($\angle$ in a semicircle)

    $\therefore$ $B\hat{A}C + \hat{C} = 1$ rt. angle (sum of $\angle$s of a $\triangle = 2$ rt. angles).

      But $C\hat{A}N = 1$ rt. angle. ($\angle$ between tangent and rad. to point of contact),

i.e. $C\hat{A}B + B\hat{A}N = 1$ rt. angle

  $\therefore$ $C\hat{A}B + B\hat{A}N = B\hat{A}C + \hat{C}$

      $\therefore$ $B\hat{A}N = \hat{C}$.

      But $\hat{C}$ is equal to any angle in the segment **ACB**.

      $\therefore$ $B\hat{A}N =$ any angle in the segment ACB ($\angle$s in the same segment of a $\odot$).

  (2) **ACBD** is a cyclic quad.

      $\therefore$ $A\hat{D}B =$ supplement of $\hat{C}$ (opp. $\angle$s of cyclic quad.).

But $B\hat{A}N = \hat{C}$ (proved)

$\therefore A\hat{D}B$ = supplement of $B\hat{A}N$

$\qquad = B\hat{A}T$ (TAN is a str. line).

But $A\hat{D}B$ = any angle in the segment ADB ($\angle$s in
same segment of a $\odot$)

$\therefore B\hat{A}T$ = any angle in the segment ADB.

THEOREM 30

If through an extremity of a chord, a straight line is drawn, making with the chord an angle equal to the angle in the alternate segment, then the straight line is a tangent to the circle.

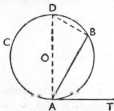

Given: Circle with centre O and a chord AB, and AT a line through A such that $B\hat{A}T$ = any angle in the segment ACB.

Required: To prove that AT is a tangent to the circle at A.

Construction: Draw through A, the diameter AD and join DB.

Proof: $A\hat{D}B$ is an angle in the segment ACB

$\qquad\qquad \therefore B\hat{A}T = A\hat{D}B.$

To each add $B\hat{A}D$

$\qquad \therefore B\hat{A}T + B\hat{A}D = A\hat{D}B + B\hat{A}D$

$\qquad\qquad \therefore D\hat{A}T = A\hat{D}B + B\hat{A}D.$

$\qquad$ But $A\hat{B}D = 1$ rt. angle ($\angle$ in a semi-circle)

$\therefore A\hat{D}B + B\hat{A}D = 1$ rt. angle (sum of $\angle$s of a $\triangle$
$\qquad\qquad\qquad\qquad\qquad\qquad = 2$ rt. angles)

$\qquad\qquad \therefore D\hat{A}T = 1$ rt. angle.

But DA is a diameter (constr.)

$\therefore$ AT is a tangent to the circle at A.

EXERCISES 45

1.

Find x.

2.

Find x.

3. △ABC is isos. with AB = AC. TN is the tangent at A. Prove TN parallel to BC.

4. Two parallel tangents touch a circle at A and B. Prove that AB is a diameter.

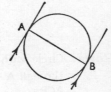

5. Tangent at D meets chord AB produced, in C. Prove that AD̂C = DB̂C.

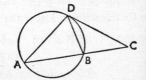

6. Inscribed circle of △ABC touches the sides at D, E, H. Find the angles of △DEH.

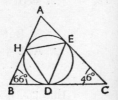

7. XY is the tangent at C. Prove XY parallel to DE.

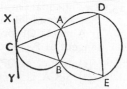

8. △ABC is right angled at A. AD = AC, and DE is perpendicular to BC. Prove DA is a tangent to circle BDE.

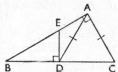

9. AB and AC are equal chords. D is any point on BC. AD produced meets circle in E. Prove CA is a tangent to the circle CDE.

10. BE and CH are altitudes of △ABC. TAN is the tangent at A to the circle ABC. Prove TAN parallel to HE.

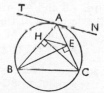

11. BC is a chord of a circle and when produced meets the tangent at a point A, in D. The bisector of AD̂B meets AB and AC in E and H respectively. Prove that AE = AH.

12. ABC is a triangle inscribed in a circle. D is any point on the tangent at A to the circle. Through D a line is drawn parallel to AC to meet BC, or BC produced, in E. Show that a circle can be drawn through A, B, D, E.

13. The tangent at A to the circumcircle of △ABC meets BC produced in D. A point E is taken in BD so that DE = DA. Prove that AE bisects BÂC.

14. The bisector of the exterior Â of △ABC meets the circle ABC in E, and BC produced in D. Prove that E is the mid-point of the arc BAC. Show that the triangle EBC is isosceles and that CE is the tangent at C to the circle ACD.

15. Two unequal parallel chords **AB** and **PQ** of a circle are such that **AQ** and **PB** meet inside the circle at **C**. The tangent at **A** meets **QP** produced in **R**, and **AR** is met at **S** by the tangent at **P**. Prove that

    (1) $R\widehat{S}P = 2A\widehat{Q}P$.

    (2) **SPCA** is a cyclic quadrilateral.

16. $\widehat{A}$ of $\triangle ABC$ is a right angle. The circle on **AB** as diameter cuts **BC** in **D**. If **E** is the mid-point of **AC**, prove that **ED** is a tangent at **D** to the circle **ABD**.

17. A quadrilateral **ABCD** is circumscribed to a circle, the points of contact of the sides being **E**, **H**, **K**, **L**.

    If $\widehat{A} = \widehat{B}$, prove that two of the sides of the quadrilateral **EHKL** are equal.

18. A circle touches a straight line **XY** at a point **A** and also touches another circle at a point **B**. If **AB** produced meets this circle again in **C**, prove that the diameter of this circle through **C** is perpendicular to **XY**.

19. **AB** and **AC** are tangents from a point **A** to a circle. **CE** is a chord of the circle, and a straight line **AOD**, parallel to **CE**, meets **BE** in **O** and the circle again in **D**. Prove that **A**, **B**, **O**, **C** are concyclic and that **AO** bisects $B\widehat{O}C$.

20. $\widehat{A}$ of $\triangle ABC$ is bisected by **AD** which meets **BC** in **D**. **E** is a point in **BC** produced, such that **DE** = **AE**. Prove that **AE** is the tangent at **A** to the circle **ABC**. When **AB** = **AC**, show that the tangent at **A** to circle **ABC** is parallel to **BC**.

21. $\triangle XYZ$, in which **XY** is greater than **XZ**, is right angled at **X**. **XB** and **XC** bisect the interior and exterior angles at **X**, and meet **YZ** and **YZ** produced at **B** and **C** respectively. If **A** is the mid-point of **YZ**, prove that **XA** is a tangent to the circumcircle of triangle **XBC**.

22. **ABC** is a triangle and **D** is any point in **BC**. Tangents at **B** and **C** to the circumcircles of $\triangle$s **ABD**, **ACD** meet in **E**. Prove that

    (1) **A**, **B**, **E**, **C** are concyclic.

    (2) $\triangle ABD$ is equiangular to $\triangle AEC$.

23. $\triangle ABC$ is inscribed in a circle and tangents at **A**, **B**, **C** are drawn to the circle forming the triangle **PQR**, the vertices **P**, **Q**, **R** lying opposite the vertices **A**, **B**, **C** respectively.

Prove that if $R\hat{P}Q = 2C\hat{A}B$, $\triangle PQR$ is a right-angled $\triangle$. If $\triangle ABC$ is itself a right-angled triangle, show that the triangle PQR does not exist.

24. Two circles intersect in A and B. BC is a tangent to the first circle and cuts the second in C.

DAE is any line through A cutting the circles in D and E respectively. Prove that DB is parallel to CE.

25. Two circles intersect at A and B, and CAD is any line through A meeting the circles in C and D. Tangents at C and D to the circles meet at E. Prove ECBD is a cyclic quadrilateral.

If BA produced passes through E, prove that BA bisects $C\hat{B}D$.

26. Two circles intersect at A and B. Tangents are drawn to both circles at A, meeting them again in C and D. If $C\hat{A}D = 90°$, prove that C, B, D are collinear.

27. Two circles intersect at A and B. Through A, a tangent is drawn to one of the circles meeting the other in C. CB produced meets the first circle again in D. Prove that AD is parallel to the tangent at C.

28. Two circles intersect in X and Y. Tangents at X to the circles meet the first circle in A and the second in B.

PXQ is any line through X, not lying within $A\hat{X}B$, meeting the circles in P and Q respectively.

PY and QY meet AX and BX in C and D respectively. Prove that XCYD is a cyclic quadrilateral and that if P is the mid-point of the arc APX, then

(1) PQ is a tangent to the circle CXDY.
(2) Q is the mid-point of the arc XQB.

29. AB is a tangent to one circle at A and touches a second circle at B. AD and BE are chords of the circles which meet, when produced, at C.

DE, produced both ways, cuts the first circle in P and the second in Q. PA and QB meet, when produced, in R. Prove that $P\hat{R}Q = A\hat{C}B$.

30. Two circles touch externally at a point A. Two common tangents BC and DE touch the first circle at B and D, and the second at C and E. Prove that

(1) $B\hat{A}C = 90°$.
(2) BC = DE.

Common Tangents to Two Circles

The number of common tangents which can be drawn to two circles depends on how the circles are placed.

The following figures show the various cases which arise.

Fig. 1.—One circle entirely within the other. No common tangent.

Fig. 2.—Circles touch internally. One common tangent.

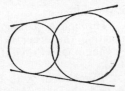

Fig. 3.—Circles intersect. Two common tangents.

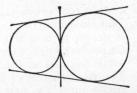

Fig. 4.—Circles touch externally. Three common tangents.

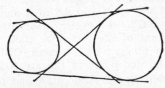

Fig. 5.—Each circle entirely outside the other. Four common tangents.

The common tangent drawn at the point of contact of two circles which touch has already been dealt with, as in Figs. 2 and 4.

In Fig. 3 the tangents are called **direct common tangents**. Figs. 4 and 5 have each a pair of direct common tangents. In Fig. 5, the remaining pair are called **transverse common tangents**.

CONSTRUCTION 17

To construct a direct common tangent to two circles

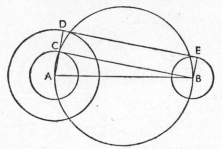

Given: Two circles with centres A and B.

Required: To draw a direct common tangent to the circles.

Construction: With centre A, and radius equal to the difference of the radii of the given circles, draw a circle. From B, draw a tangent BC to this circle.
Join AC and produce it to meet the circumference of given circle with centre A, at D.
Through B, draw BE parallel to AD, to meet the circumference of circle with centre B, at E.
Join DE.
Then DE is a direct common tangent.

Proof:
$$CD = AD - AC$$
$$= BE \text{ (constr.)}$$
Also CD ∥ BE (constr.).
∴ DCBE is a parallelogram (quad. with one pair of sides equal and parallel).
But $B\hat{C}A$ = 1 rt. angle (angle bet. tangent and rad.)
∴ $D\hat{C}B$ = 1 rt. angle (adj. ∠s. DC a str. line)
∴ DCBE is a rectangle
∴ $A\hat{D}E$ and $B\hat{E}D$ are right angles
∴ DE is a direct common tangent (str. line perp. to radii).

CONSTRUCTION 18

To draw a transverse common tangent to two given circles

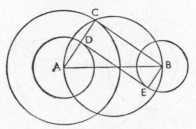

Given: Two circles with centres **A** and **B**.

Required: To draw a transverse common tangent to the circles.

Construction: With centre **A** and radius equal to the sum of the radii of the given circles, draw a circle.

From **B**, draw a tangent **BC** to this circle.

Join **AC** and let it cut the circumference of the given circle with centre **A**, at **D**.

Through **B**, draw **BE** parallel to **CA** to meet circumference of circle with centre **B**, in **E**. Join **DE**.

Then **DE** is a transverse common tangent to the two given circles.

Proof: CD = AC — AD
                     = BE (constr.).

     Also **CD** is parl. to **BE** (constr.)

     ∴ **CBED** is a parm. (one pair of sides eq. and parl.).

But $D\hat{C}B$ = 1 rt. angle ($\angle$ bet. tangent and rad.)

     ∴ **CBED** is a rectangle.

     ∴ $B\hat{E}D$ = 1 rt. angle ($\angle$ in a rect.)

and $A\hat{D}E$ = 1 rt. angle (supp. to $C\hat{D}E$).

     But **AD** and **BE** are radii of the circles

     ∴ **DE** is a tangent to both circles (str. line perp. to
                                        radii),

     i.e. **DE** is a transverse common tangent.

CONSTRUCTION 19

On a given straight line, to construct a segment of a circle containing an angle equal to a given angle

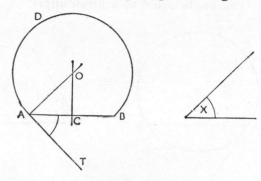

Given: Straight line AB and an angle X.

Required: To construct on AB, a segment of a circle containing an angle equal to $\hat{X}$.

Construction: From A draw a line AT making $B\hat{A}T = \hat{X}$.
Draw AO perpendicular to AT and let AO meet CO, the perpendicular bisector of AB, in O.
With centre O and radius OA draw the arc ADB.
Then any angle in the segment ADB is equal to $\hat{X}$.

Proof: CO is the perp. bisector of AB (constr.)
∴ CO is the locus of points equidistant from A and B
∴ OA = OB
∴ circle with centre O and radius OA passes through B.
Also OA is a radius and $O\hat{A}T = 1$ rt. angle.
∴ AT is a tangent.
∴ $B\hat{A}T$ = any angle in the alternate segment ADB
            (∠ bet. tangent and chord).
But $B\hat{A}T = \hat{X}$ (constr.)
∴ segment ADB contains an angle equal to $\hat{X}$.

CONSTRUCTION 20

From a given circle, to cut off a segment containing an angle equal to a given angle

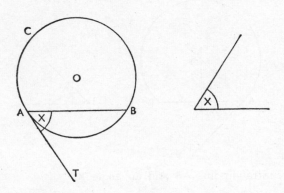

Given: Circle with centre O and $\hat{X}$.

Required: To cut off from the circle, a segment which will contain an angle equal to $\hat{X}$.

Construction: Let A be any point on the circle. Draw AT, the tangent at A.

At A, in AT, make $\hat{TAB} = \hat{X}$ and let AB meet the circle again at B.

Then the segment ACB of the circle contains an angle equal to $\hat{X}$.

Proof: AT is the tangent at A (constr.) and AB is a chord.

∴ $\hat{BAT}$ = any angle in the alternate segment ACB
(∠ bet. tangent and chord).

But $\hat{BAT} = \hat{X}$ (constr.)

∴ segment ACB contains an angle equal to $\hat{X}$.

CONSTRUCTION 21

To inscribe in a circle a triangle equiangular to a given triangle

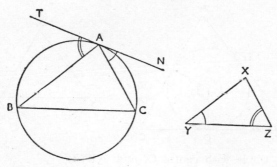

Given: A circle and a triangle XYZ.

Required: To inscribe in the circle a triangle ABC equiangular to triangle XYZ.

Construction: Take any point A on the circle and draw TAN the tangent at A.

At A in TAN, make $N\hat{A}C = \hat{Y}$ and $T\hat{A}B = \hat{Z}$ and let AC and AB meet the circle in C and B.
Join BC.
Then △ABC is equiangular to △XYZ.

Proof: Since TAN is the tangent at A (constr.) and AB and AC are chords

∴ $N\hat{A}C = \hat{B}$ and $T\hat{A}B = \hat{C}$ (∠ bet. tangent and chord).

But $N\hat{A}C = \hat{Y}$ and $T\hat{A}B = \hat{Z}$ (constr.)

∴ $\hat{B} = \hat{Y}$ and $\hat{C} = \hat{Z}$

∴ $B\hat{A}C = \hat{X}$ (sum of ∠s of a △)

∴ △ABC is equiangular to △XYZ.

CONSTRUCTION 22

To circumscribe about a circle a triangle equiangular to a given triangle

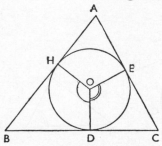
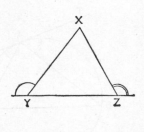

Given: Circle with centre **O**, and △XYZ.

Required: To circumscribe about the circle a triangle **ABC** equiangular to △XYZ.

Construction: Produce **YZ** in both directions to form the exterior angles at **Y** and **Z**.

Draw **OD** any radius of the circle.

At **O** in **OD**, make **DÔH** = the exterior ∠ at **Y** and **DÔE** = the exterior ∠ at **Z**

and let **OH** and **OE** meet the circle in **H** and **E**.

Draw the tangents to the circle at **D, E, H** to form the △ABC.

Then △ABC is the required triangle.

Proof: **OH** and **OD** are radii of the circle and **BH** and **BD** are tangents (constr.)

∴ **OĤB** = **OD̂B** = 1 rt. angle

∴ **OHBD** is a cyclic quad (opp. ∠s supp.)

∴ **B̂** is the supplement of **DÔH**

∴ **B̂** is the supplement of ext. **Ŷ**

∴ **B̂** = **XŶZ**.

Similarly **Ĉ** = **XẐY**. ∴ **Â** = **X̂** (sum of ∠s of a △)

∴ △ABC is equiangular to △XYZ.

CONSTRUCTION 23

To inscribe a circle in a given triangle

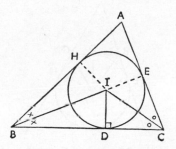

Given: △ABC.

Required: To inscribe a circle in △ABC.

Construction: Bisect AB̂C and AĈB and let the bisectors meet in I.
Draw ID ⊥ BC.
With centre I and radius ID draw a circle.   Then this circle is the required circle.

Proof: Draw IE and IH perp. to CA and AB respectively.
Since IB is the bisector of AB̂C
∴ ID = IH.
Similarly ID = IE
∴ ID = IE = IH
∴ Circle with centre I and radius ID passes through E and H.
Since ID is a radius of the circle and BC is perp. to ID
∴ BC is a tangent to the circle.
Similarly AB and AC are tangents to the circle
∴ circle HDE is the inscribed circle of the △ABC.

(The point I is the **In-centre** of the △ABC.)

CONSTRUCTION 24

To draw an escribed circle of a given triangle

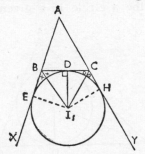

Given: △ABC with AB and AC produced to X and Y respectively.

Required: To draw the escribed circle touching BX, BC, CY.

Construction: Bisect XB̂C and BĈY by BI₁ and CI₁ respectively and let BI₁ and CI₁ meet in I₁.
Draw I₁D perp. to BC.
With centre I₁ and radius I₁D draw a circle.
This circle is the required circle.

Proof: Draw I₁E and I₁H perp. to AX and AY respectively.
Since BI₁ is the bisector of XB̂C (constr.)
∴ BI₁ is the locus of pts. equidistant from BX and BC
∴ I₁E = I₁D.
Similarly I₁D = I₁H
∴ I₁D = I₁E = I₁H
∴ circle with centre I₁ and radius I₁D passes through E and H.
Also I₁D̂B is a right angle (constr.).
But I₁D is a radius of the circle
∴ BC is a tangent to the circle.
Similarly BX and CY are tangents to the circle
∴ circle EDH is the escribed circle touching BX, BC, CY.

(The point I₁ is an **ex-centre** of △ABC.)

The Ex-Central Triangle

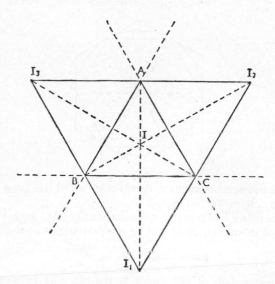

The ex-central triangle is the triangle formed by joining the three ex-centres of a triangle.

In the figure, ABC is the given triangle.

I is the incentre of $\triangle$ABC and I_1, I_2, I_3 are the three ex-centres.

$\triangle I_1 I_2 I_3$ is the ex-central triangle.

The following facts should be proved and noted:

(1) AII_1, BII_2, CII_3 are straight lines.

(2) I_1A is perp. to I_2I_3 and similarly for I_2B and I_3C.

(3) I is the orthocentre of $\triangle I_1 I_2 I_3$.

(4) $\triangle$ABC is the pedal triangle of $\triangle I_1 I_2 I_3$.

(5) The above figure is related to the figure showing that the altitudes of a triangle are concurrent (see p. 241).

To inscribe in a Circle, or circumscribe to a Circle, a Regular Figure of n Sides

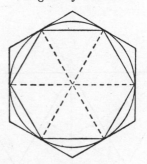

Since the figure is regular, its sides are all of the same length and its angles are all equal.

If the figure has n sides, when its vertices are joined to the centre of the circle, there will be n equal angles at the centre.

Each angle will be $\dfrac{360°}{n}$.

The construction of the figure is therefore as follows.

Draw radii to form the n equal angles at the centre. To inscribe the figure in the circle join the extremities of the radii.

To circumscribe the figure about the circle, draw tangents at the extremities of the radii.

The minimum value of n is 3.

The following table shows the values of $\dfrac{360}{n}$ for different values of n.

n	3	4	5	6	8	9	10	12	15
$\dfrac{360}{n}$	120	90	72	60	45	40	36	30	24

The figure shows an inscribed and circumscribed regular hexagon. What is the easy method for this construction?

EXERCISES 46

1. Draw a straight line 2·5 in. long. Construct a segment of a circle on this line as chord, the angle in the segment being (1) 56°, (2) 134°.

2. Construct a triangle ABC, given BC = 3 in., $\widehat{A}$ = 74°, median AD = 1·8 in.

3. Construct a triangle ABC, given BC = 3½ in., $\widehat{A}$ = 71°, perimeter = 8½ in.

[*Hint:* Construct, on base BC, segments of circles to contain angles equal to (*a*) the vertical angle, (*b*) half the vertical angle.]

4. A, B, C are three points in a straight line such that AB = 4 cm. and BC = 3 cm. Find a point D so that the angles subtended at D by AB and BC will each be 35°.

5. AB is a direct common tangent to the circles. Calculate AB.

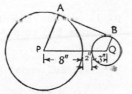

6. AB is a transverse common tangent to the circles. Calculate AB.

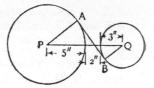

7. △ABC is isosceles with AB = AC. If $\widehat{B}$ = 2$\widehat{A}$, show that BC is the side of a regular pentagon inscribed in the circle.

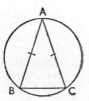

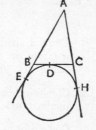

8. Circle is the escribed circle of the △. Prove that

    (1) AE = semi-perimeter s of △ABC.
    (2) Per. of △ABD = per. of △ACD.

9. Figure shows the inscribed and one escribed circle of △ABC. Evaluate BD, BE, CE, CD in terms of s, a, b, c and show that

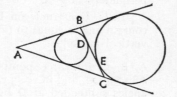

    (1) BD = CE.
    (2) BE = CD.
    (3) DE = AC − AB.

10. I is the incentre of △ABC. Circle BIC cuts AB in X. Prove that

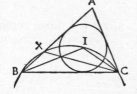

    (1) $\widehat{BIC} = 90° + \dfrac{A}{2}$.

    (2) △AXC is isosceles.

11. AC and BD are direct common tangents to two non-intersecting circles. PQ is a transverse common tangent which, when produced, meets AC and BD at points R and S respectively. The points of contact A, P, B lie on one circle and C, Q, D lie on the other and AR < RC. Prove that

    (1)   AC = BD.
    (2) RC − AR = BS − SD = PQ.
    (3)   AR = SD, and RC = BS.

12. Prove that (1) the direct common tangents, and (2) the transverse common tangents to two circles, intersect on the line of centres.

13. Draw two circles, radii 2·5 cm. and 3 cm. respectively, their centres being 7 cm. apart. Draw all the common tangents and calculate their lengths.

14. Prove that the sum of the diameters of the inscribed and circumscribed circles of a right-angled triangle is equal to the sum of the sides containing the right angle.

15. A circle inscribed in △ABC touches BC at D. Prove that BD + AC = AB + BC − BD.

16. A circle is inscribed in a △ABC, the sides BC, CA, AB touching the circle at D, E, F respectively. △DEF is drawn and DE, DF are produced to meet the parallel to BC through A, in G and H respectively. Prove that a circle can be drawn with A as centre, passing through H, F, E, G, and that △s DEF, DGH are equiangular.

17. I is the incentre of △ABC. The incircle touches AB and AC at P and Q. If AI meets the circle in L, show that L is the incentre of △APQ.

18. Two circles with centres A and B intersect in P and Q. AQ cuts the circle with centre B again in R, and AB cuts this circle in L and M. Prove that L and M are the centres of circles which touch the sides of △APR.

19. A circle inscribed in △ABC touches AB and AC at H and E respectively. If AB = AC, prove HE parallel to BC.

20. If r is the radius of the inscribed circle of △ABC, prove that the area of △ABC = r × semi-perimeter.

Construction of Circles

In order to construct a circle we must know (1) its centre, (2) the length of its radius.

(1) If we can draw two lines on each of which the centre is known to lie, their points of intersection will be possible positions of the centre.

(2) If we find the distance of any point on the circumference from the centre, we know the radius of the circle.

The following examples should be noted. In each case the proof is left as an exercise for the student.

1. Construct a circle to touch a given straight line at a given point, and to pass through another given point.

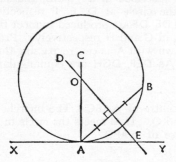

Given: Straight line XY and A a point in it, and a point B outside it.

Required: To construct the circle touching XY at A and passing through B.

Construction: Join AB.

        At A, draw AC perp. to XY.
        Draw DE the perp. bisector of AB.
        Let AC and DE cut at O.
        With centre O and radius OA draw a circle.
        This circle is the required circle.

2. Construct a circle to touch another circle and to touch a straight line at a given point.

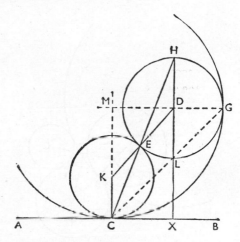

Given: Circle with centre **D**, and str. line **AB** with **C** a point in it.

Required: To construct a circle touching circle centre **D** and touching **AB** at **C**.

Construction: Draw **DX** perp. to **AB**.
Produce **XD** to meet the circumference of the given circle in **H**.
Join **HC** and let it cut the given circle in **E**.
Join **DE**.
Draw **CK** perp. to **AB** and let it meet **DE** produced in **K**. With centre **K** and radius **KC** draw a circle.
This circle has external contact with the given circle at **E**.

A second circle satisfying the conditions, and having internal contact with the given circle, may be obtained as follows.

Join **CL** and produce it to cut the given circle in **G**. Join **GD** and produce it to meet **CK** produced, in **M**. With centre **M** and radius **MC** draw a circle.

3. Construct a circle to touch a given circle at a given point and to touch another given circle.

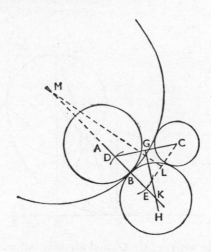

Given :   Circle with centre **A** and a point **B** on it and a second circle with centre **C**.

Required :   To construct a circle touching circle with centre **A** at **B**, and touching the circle with centre **C**.

Construction :   Join **AB** and produce it. With centre **B** and radius equal to that of the circle with centre **C**, draw arcs to cut **AB** and **AB** produced, at **D** and **E**. Join **CD** and **CE**.

     Draw **GK** and **LM** the perp. bisectors of **CD** and **CE**, and let them meet **AB** produced both ways in **K** and **M** respectively.

     With centre **K** and radius **KB** draw a circle. This is the required circle which has external contact with circle, centre **A**.

     With centre **M** and radius **MB** draw a circle. This circle also satisfies the conditions and has internal contact with circle, centre **A**.

Exercises 47

1. In each case, state the locus of the centres of circles which touch

    (1) a given straight line at a given point ;
    (2) a given circle at a given point ;
    (3) a given straight line and with a given radius ;
    (4) a given circle and with a given radius ;
    (5) two given intersecting straight lines.

2. **AB** is a straight line. A circle of radius 0·8 in. has its centre 1·8 in. from **AB**. Construct a circle of radius 0·6 in. to touch the straight line and the given circle.

3. Construct a circle to pass through two fixed points and having its centre on a given straight line.

4. Two circles are drawn, radii 1·5 cm. and 2 cm., their centres being 5·5 cm. apart. Construct a circle of radius 1·8 cm. to touch both circles.

5. Two circles are drawn, radii 1·5 cm. and 2 cm., their centres being 5·5 cm. apart. Construct a circle of radius 6 cm. with which each of the given circles has internal contact.

6. $B\hat{A}C = 55°$. Construct a circle touching **AB** and **AC** and having a radius 2·5 cm.

7. $B\hat{A}C = 55°$. Construct a circle touching **AB** and **AC**, the point of contact on **AB** being 2 in. from **A**.

8. **P** is a point 3 in. from the centre of a circle of radius 1 in. Construct two circles of radius $1\frac{1}{2}$ in. to touch the original circle and to pass through **P**.

9. Construct a circle to touch a given circle at a given point and also to touch a given straight line.

10. **C** is a point 2 in. from a straight line **AB**. Draw a circle of radius 1·2 in. to pass through **C** and to touch **AB**.

11. Draw a circle with centre **C** and radius 1 in. Take any point **A** on the circumference. Find a point **P** 2 in. from **C** and 1·2 in. from **A**. Draw the circle that passes through **P** and touches the first circle at **A**.

Revision Papers XXI–XXX

XXI

1. Two parallel chords of a circle whose diameter is 13 cm. are 12 cm. and 10·4 cm. long. Find the distance between them.

2.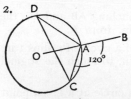

PS is parallel to AB.
Prove that PQ = RS.

3.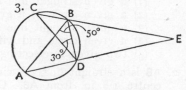

AB is a diameter.
Find $\hat{E}$ and $E\hat{B}D$.

4. In △ABC, the altitudes from B and C meet at H, and, when produced, meet the circumcircle in E and F respectively. Prove that AH = AE = AF.

5. Show how to find a point P inside a triangle ABC at which the three sides subtend equal angles.

XXII

1. Two circles of radii 3 cm. and 5·1 cm. cut at A and B. If their centres are 6·3 cm. apart, calculate the length of AB and its distance from each of the centres.

2.

Calculate $\hat{D}$.

3.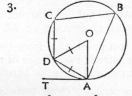

Calculate $\hat{B}$. If $D\hat{O}A = 2D\hat{A}T$, prove TA a tangent to the circle.

4. O is the centre of a circle. ACB and ADE are drawn from a point A outside the circle to meet it in C, B and D, E respectively, making $B\hat{C}E$ an acute angle. Prove that $B\hat{O}E = C\hat{O}D + 2C\hat{A}D$.

5. Show how to construct the △ABC, having given the vertical angle A and the segments BD and DC into which the base is divided by AD, the bisector of Â.

XXIII

1. A circle has a radius of 3 in. From a point distant 5 in. from its centre, two tangents are drawn to the circle. Find the length of the chord joining their points of contact.

2.

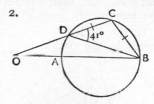

AB is a diameter.
Calculate Ô.

3.

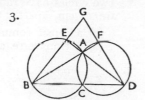

Prove AFGE a cyclic quadrilateral.

4. ABCD is a cyclic quadrilateral in which Â and D̂ are each 45°. The perpendicular from B on AD is produced to meet the circumference in E. Show that CE is a diameter of the circle and that it is parallel to the tangent at A.

5. Show how to describe a circle which will pass through a given point inside a given circle and touch the given circle at a given point.

XXIV

1. △ABC is right-angled at A and B̂ = 30°. AD is perpendicular to BC. If P is the mid-point of BC, prove that AP and AD trisect Â.

2.

Find the relation between x and y.

3.

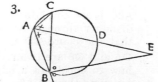

Prove that D is equidistant from B, E, C.

4. △ABC is right-angled at C and CN is perpendicular to AB. Points D, E are taken in AC, BC such that DE is bisected by CN. Prove that ADEB is a cyclic quadrilateral.

5. With the vertices of a given triangle as centres, construct three circles each of which touches the other two.

XXV

1. Two circles have radii 11 cm. and 3 cm. and their centres are 17 cm. apart. Calculate the lengths of
   (1) a direct common tangent to the circles,
   (2) a transverse common tangent to the circles.

2.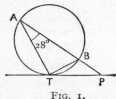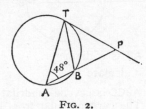

FIG. 1.   FIG. 2.

Fig. 1. AB is a diameter of the circle.
Fig. 2. AB is a chord equal in length to the radius.
If PT is a tangent to the circle, calculate in both cases the angles of the triangle BTP.

3. AÔC = 116°, AĈB = 24°.
   Find BÂC, OB̂A.

4. ABC is an equilateral triangle inscribed in a circle. The diameter through A meets the circle again in D. Prove that the chord BD is equal in length to the radius.

5. OA and OB are two radii of a circle with centre O. Show how to construct a circle touching OA and OB, and also touching the arc AB. Show also how to construct a circle touching OA and OB produced, and also touching the arc AB.

XXVI

1. Two concentric circles have radii 3·6 in. and 6 in. A chord **AB** of one circle touches the other at **T**. Find the length of **AB**.

2.

Calculate $\hat{\text{B}}$.

3.

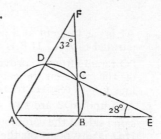

Calculate all the angles of the quadrilateral **ABCD**.

4. Tangents at **A** and **B** to a circle meet in **C**, and **H** is the mid-point of the minor arc **AB**. **AH** and **BH** produced meet **BC** and **AC** in **D**, **E** respectively. Prove that

   (1) **AEDB** is a cyclic quadrilateral.

   (2) **HC** bisects $\hat{\text{C}}$.

5. **AB** is a chord of a circle with centre **O**, and **P** is any point within the minor segment of the circle. Show how to draw through **P** a chord of the circle which will be bisected by **AB**.

XXVII

1. A square **ABCD** is inscribed in a circle with centre **O** and radius 2 in. Calculate the length of its side.
   If **P** is the mid-point of **AB**, and **AP** is produced to meet the circumference in **Q**, show that **BQ** is the side of a regular octagon inscribed in the circle. Find the length of **BQ**.

2. **E**, **H**, **K**, **L** are points of contact of sides of quad. **ABCD**. Calculate the angles of quad. **EHKL**.

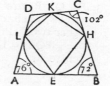

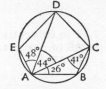

3. Calculate the angles of the pentagon.

4. **AT** is the tangent at a point **A** on a circle, and **PQ** is a chord parallel to **AT**. If **B** is a point on the circle on the side of **PQ** remote from **A**, prove that **BA** bisects $\widehat{PBQ}$. **C** is a point on the circle on the same side of **PQ** as **A**. Find how the line **CA** is related to the angle **PCQ**.

5. **ACB** and **ADB** are two segments of circles standing on the same side of the common chord **AB**, such that $A\widehat{C}B = 2A\widehat{D}B$. If **D** is any point on the arc **ADB**, and **AD** cuts the arc **ACB** in **C**, prove that **AC** + **CB** = **AD**.

   Hence devise a construction for finding a point **C** on the circumference of a circle of which **AB** is a chord, such that **AC** + **CB** is a given length.

XXVIII

1. **ABC** is an equilateral triangle inscribed in a circle. Show how to construct the equilateral triangle **DEH** circumscribing the circle, with its sides respectively parallel to those of △**ABC**. If the circle has radius 1 in., calculate the lengths of a side of each △ and show that **AB** = ½**DE**.

2. Two equal circles cut at **A** and **B**. If **AB** = 6 in. and **CD** = 2 in., calculate the radius.

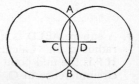

3. **P, Q, R** are the centres of three circles, each of which touches the other two. Prove that the perimeter of △**PQR** = Diameter of circle with centre **R**.

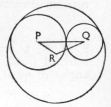

4. △ABC is inscribed in a circle and the tangents at A and C meet at D. If E is a point on BC produced such that BADE is a cyclic quadrilateral, prove that DE is parallel to AC. BA and ED produced meet at G, and BD and AE cut in H. Show that, when AB = BC, GHC is a straight line.

5. From a point P, tangents are drawn to a series of concentric circles with centre O. If T is the point of contact on one of these circles, and Q is a point on the perpendicular to PT through T, such that TQ = TP, find the locus of Q.

XXIX

1. A chord of length l is placed in a circle of radius r. The perpendicular distance from the centre to the chord is d. Show that $l = 2\sqrt{(r^2 - d^2)}$. Hence show that the nearer a chord is to the centre of the circle, the greater it is, and vice versa. What is the length of the greatest chord in the circle?

2. Circles are equal and touch at O. Prove that OA = OB.

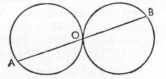

3. BÔA = 90° and OA = OB. Semi-circles on OA and OB as diameters cut at C. Prove A, C, B collinear. Show that the quadrant OAB is equal in area to twice the quadrant with radius OC.

4. AB is a diameter of a circle and GBH is the tangent to the circle at B. Any two chords AC, AD are drawn in the circle and produced to cut the tangent at B in G, H respectively. Prove that GCDH is a cyclic quadrilateral.

5. Show that the locus of the mid-points of equal chords in a circle is a circle concentric with the given circle. P is a point distant $2\frac{3}{4}$ in. from the centre of a circle of radius $1\frac{1}{4}$ in. Show how to draw through P, a secant, such that the chord intercepted on it by the circle shall be $1\frac{1}{2}$ in. long. Calculate the distance of the chord from the centre of the circle and check by measurement.

XXX

1. The inscribed circle of a triangle ABC touches the sides BC, CA, AB at D, E, H respectively. If s denotes the semi-perimeter of the triangle prove that $s =$ AH + BC. Hence show that if the sides BC, CA, AB are denoted by a, b, c, AH $= s - a$ and find similar expressions for BD and DC.

2. $\triangle$DEH is the pedal triangle of $\triangle$ABC. Calculate the angles of $\triangle$ABC.

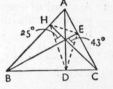

3. AC, AD are tangents to the circles at A. BE is the tangent at B to circle ABC. Prove that

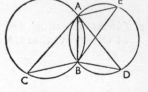

   (1) AE is parallel to CB.
   (2) $A\widehat{B}C = A\widehat{B}D$.

4. $\triangle$ABC is inscribed in a circle and the tangent at A meets BC produced, in T. AD bisects $B\widehat{A}C$ and meets BC, in D. TE bisects $\widehat{T}$ and meets AD, in E. Prove that

   (1) AE = ED.
   (2) TE is perpendicular to AD.

5. Three circles have radii r_1, r_2, r_3 and are such that each touches the other two externally. Find the lengths of the sides of the triangle formed by joining their centres. Hence find a construction for drawing three circles to touch each other, given that their radii are 1 in., 2 in., 3 in.

BOOK IV

RECTANGLES

Definitions:

(1) A rectangle is said to be contained by **any two** adjacent sides.

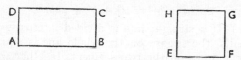

The rectangle ABCD is said to be contained by **AB** and **AD** and, as stated on page 150, is referred to as rect. **AB, AD** or **AB.AD**. Similarly the square **EFGH** is referred to as the sq. on **EF** or **EF²**.

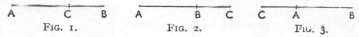

FIG. 1.　　　　　FIG. 2.　　　　　FIG. 3.

(2) If a point **C** is taken in a straight line **AB**, or in **AB** produced, then **C** is said to divide **AB** into two **segments** **AC** and **CB**. In all cases the segments are the distances of **C** from the ends of the line **AB**. In Fig. 1, **AB** is divided internally at **C**. In Fig. 2 and Fig 3, **AB** is divided externally at **C**.

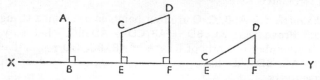

(3) From the point A, **AB** is drawn perp. to **XY**. **B** is the **projection** of A on **XY**.

From the ends **C** and **D** of the str. line **CD**, perpendiculars **CE** and **DF** are drawn to **XY**.

EF is the projection of **CD** on **XY**. In one figure **E** and **C** coincide.

APPLICATION OF ALGEBRA TO GEOMETRY

It has already been shown (pages 171–173) how we can illustrate algebraic identities by geometrical figures, and that there are geometrical theorems corresponding to the various algebraic identities. The following identities and corresponding geometrical theorems are used frequently in the solution of problems :

(1) $$(a + b)^2 \equiv a^2 + b^2 + 2ab.$$

Theorem.—If a straight line is divided internally into any two segments, the square on the whole line is equal to the sum of the squares on the two segments together with twice the rectangle contained by the segments.

(2) $$(a - b)^2 \equiv a^2 + b^2 - 2ab.$$

Theorem.—If a straight line is divided externally into any two segments, the square on the whole line is equal to the sum of the squares on the two segments diminished by twice the rectangle contained by the segments.

(3) $$a^2 - b^2 = (a + b)(a - b).$$

Theorem.—The difference of the squares on two straight lines is equal to the rectangle contained by the sum and difference of the two straight lines.

The following worked examples illustrate the application of Algebra to Geometry. They can, of course, be worked purely by Geometry.

Example 1.—A, B, C, D are four points in order on a straight line. Prove that $AC.BD = AB.CD + AD.BC$. Let x, y, z be the number of units of length in AB, BC, CD respectively. Then AC, BD, AD have $(x + y)$, $(y + z)$, $(x + y + z)$ units respectively.

$$\therefore AC.BD = (x + y)(y + z)$$
$$= xy + y^2 + xz + yz.$$

$$AB.CD + AD.BC = xz + (x + y + z)y$$
$$= xz + xy + y^2 + yz$$
$$\therefore AC.BD = AB.CD + AD.BC.$$

Example 2.—P, Q, R, S, T are five points taken in order on a straight line such that PQ = QR = RS. Prove that

$$PT^2 - ST^2 = 3(QT^2 - RT^2).$$

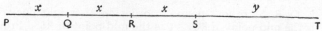

Let x be the number of units of length in PQ, QR and RS. Let y be the number of units of length in ST.

Then PT, QT, RT have $(3x + y)$, $(2x + y)$, $(x + y)$ units of length respectively,

$$\therefore PT^2 - ST^2 = (3x + y)^2 - y^2$$
$$= 9x^2 + 6xy + y^2 - y^2$$
$$= 9x^2 + 6xy.$$
$$3(QT^2 - RT^2) = 3[(2x + y)^2 - (x + y)^2]$$
$$= 3[4x^2 + 4xy + y^2 - x^2 - 2xy - y^2]$$
$$= 3[3x^2 + 2xy]$$
$$= 9x^2 + 6xy.$$
$$\therefore PT^2 - ST^2 = 3(QT^2 - RT^2).$$

Example 3.—ABC is an isosceles triangle with AB = AC and D is a point in BC. Prove that $AD^2 + BD.DC = AC^2$.

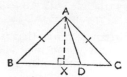

Draw AX perp. to BC.
△s ABX and ACX are congruent
∴ BX = XC.
$AC^2 = AX^2 + XC^2$ [Pythagoras' Th., △AXC]
$\quad = (AD^2 - XD^2) + XC^2$ [Pythagoras' Th., △AXD]
$\quad = AD^2 + XC^2 - XD^2$
$\quad = AD^2 + (XC + XD)(XC - XD)$
$\quad = AD^2 + (BX + XD)(DC)$ (BX = XC proved above)
$\quad = AD^2 + BD.DC.$

Exercises 48

1. A straight line AB is bisected at C and divided internally at X. Prove that $AX.XB = AC^2 - CX^2$.

2. A straight line AB is bisected at C and divided externally at X. Prove that $AX.XB = CX^2 - AC^2$.

3. P, Q, R, S are four points in order on a straight line. X is the mid-point of PQ. Y is the mid-point of RS. Prove that $2XY = PR + QS$.

4. A straight line PQ is trisected at X and Y (X nearer to P) and is produced to any point Z. Prove that
$$XZ^2 - XQ^2 = QZ(PZ + YQ).$$

5. A, B, C are three points in order on a straight line. AB is bisected at P, BC is trisected at Q and R (R nearer to C). Prove that $PR^2 - 3BQ^2 = AP.PC + RC.PQ$.

6. AB is a straight line divided internally at C and externally at D so that $\dfrac{AC}{CB} = \dfrac{AD}{DB}$. If O is the mid-point of AB, prove that $OC.OD = OB^2$.

7. A, B, C, D are four points in order on a straight line so that $AB = BC = CD$. AD is produced to any point X. Prove that $AX^2 - DX^2 = 3(BX^2 - CX^2)$.

8. ABC is an isosceles triangle with $AB = AC$ and D is a point in BC produced. Prove that $AD^2 - BD.DC = AC^2$.

9. In a right-angled triangle prove that, if a perpendicular is drawn from the right angle to the hypotenuse, the square on the perpendicular is equal to the rectangle contained by the segments of the hypotenuse.

- 10. In any right-angled triangle prove that the rectangle contained by the sum and difference of the hypotenuse and one side is equal to the square on the other side.

11. P and Q are two points in the side AB of the square ABCD such that $AP = QB$. Prove that rect. $AB.PQ = $ diff. of squares on PC and PD.

12. ABC is a triangle with $\hat{C} = 90°$. D is the mid-point of BC. Prove that the rectangle contained by the sum and difference of AB and $AD = 3BD^2$.

13. AC is a straight line divided internally at B so that AB = 3BC. AC is produced to D so that CD = AC. Prove that $2AB^2 + CD^2 = BD^2 + 9BC^2$.

14. PQ is a straight line bisected at R and produced to S. Prove that $PS^2 - QS^2 = 4PR.RS$.

15. If A, B, C, D are four points in order on a straight line such that AB = CD, prove that $AC^2 = AB^2 + AD.BC$.

16. ABC is a triangle with AD perpendicular to BC produced. If BC = CD prove that $AB^2 - AC^2 = 3CD^2$.

17. AB is a straight line bisected at C. If D is any point on AB, show that

    (1) AD.DB is a maximum,
    (2) $AD^2 + DB^2$ is a minimum,

when D is at C.

18. Prove that, if a square and a rectangle have equal perimeters, the square has the greater area.

Theorem 31

In an obtuse-angled triangle, the square on the side opposite the obtuse angle is equal to the sum of the squares on the other two sides, together with twice the rectangle contained by one of those sides and the projection of the other side upon it.

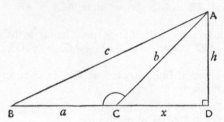

Given : △ABC with $\hat{C}$ an obtuse angle and AD drawn perp. to BC so that CD is the projection of CA on BC.

Required : To prove that $AB^2 = BC^2 + CA^2 + 2BC \cdot CD$.

Proof : Let the lengths of AB, BC, CA, CD, AD be c, a, b, x, h units respectively.

$$c^2 = (a + x)^2 + h^2 \quad \text{[Pythagoras' Th., } \triangle ABD]$$
$$= a^2 + x^2 + 2ax + h^2$$
$$= a^2 + (x^2 + h^2) + 2ax$$
$$= a^2 + b^2 + 2ax \quad \text{[Pythagoras' Th., } \triangle ACD]$$
$$\therefore AB^2 = BC^2 + CA^2 + 2BC \cdot CD.$$

Exercises 49

1. State whether the following triangles are right-angled or obtuse-angled.

    (1) $a = 8$ in., $b = 4$ in., $c = 5$ in.
    (2) $a = 3$ cm., $b = 4$ cm., $c = 5$ cm.
    (3) $a = 3$ cm., $b = 5$ cm., $c = 6$ cm.
    (4) $a = 3$ in. $b = 5$ in., $c = 3$ in.

2.

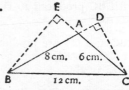

Calculate AD and AE.

3.

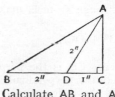

Calculate the altitude AD.

4.

Calculate AB and AC correct to 2 dec. pl.

5.

Find x in terms of a, b, c.

6. Prove that in an isosceles triangle whose vertical angle is 120°, the square on the base is equal to 3 times the square on either of the other sides.

7. The angle C of an isosceles triangle is obtuse. If $AB^2 = 3BC^2$, prove that the projection of AC on BC is half of BC.

8. △ABC has AB = 22 in., BC = 26 in., CA = 40 in. Show that △ABC is obtuse-angled.

If CD is the perpendicular from C to AB produced, find, by calculation,

(1) lengths of BD and CD,
(2) area of △ABC.

9. In △ABC, $a = 7$ in., $b = 9$ in., $c = 4$ in. From C, CD is drawn perpendicular to AB, and from B a perpendicular BE is drawn to AC. Find the lengths of AD and AE.

10. △ABC is an equilateral triangle. D is any point in BC produced. Complete the parallelogram ABDE. Prove that

$$BE^2 = BA^2 + BD^2 + BD \cdot DE.$$

11. ABC is an equilateral triangle with BC produced to D so that $BD \cdot CD = BC^2$. Prove that $AD^2 = 2BC^2$.

12. ABC is an equilateral triangle. BC and CA are produced to D and E respectively so that CD = AE.
If $BD \cdot DC = BC^2$, prove that DE = 2BC.

13. $\triangle ABC$ has an obtuse angle at B, and D is the mid-point of AB. Prove that $AC^2 + BC^2 = 2(AD^2 + CD^2)$.

14. $\triangle ABC$ is an acute-angled triangle in which the base BC is produced through B to D and through C to E, making DB = BC = CE. Prove that
$$AD^2 + AE^2 = AB^2 + AC^2 + DC^2.$$

15. $\widehat{A}$ of the isosceles $\triangle ABC$ is obtuse. CD is the perpendicular on BA produced, and AE is drawn perpendicular to AB and equal to AB. Prove that the difference of the squares on BC and BE is equal to four times the area of $\triangle ADE$.

THEOREM 32

In any triangle, the square on the side opposite an acute angle is equal to the sum of the squares on the other two sides diminished by twice the rectangle contained by one of those sides and the projection of the other side upon it.

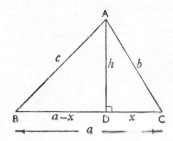 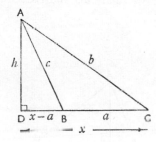

Given: △ABC with $\hat{C}$ an acute angle, and AD drawn perp. to BC, so that DC is the projection of AC on BC.

Required: To prove that $AB^2 = BC^2 + CA^2 - 2BC.CD$.

Proof: Let the lengths of AB, BC, CA, CD, AD be c, a, b, x, h units respectively.

$$c^2 = (a - x)^2 + h^2 \quad \text{[Pythagoras' Th., } \triangle ABD]$$
$$= a^2 + x^2 - 2ax + h^2$$
$$= a^2 + (x^2 + h^2) - 2ax$$
$$= a^2 + b^2 - 2ax \quad \text{[Pythagoras' Th., } \triangle ADC]$$
$$\therefore AB^2 = BC^2 + CA^2 - 2BC.CD.$$

EXERCISES 50

1. △ABC has its sides $a = 6$ in., $b = 8$ in., $c = 9$ in. Show that the △ is acute-angled.

2. AD is the altitude from A to BC. Calculate BD and DC.

4 in.   5 in.
B   D   C
6 in.

3.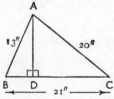

A
13″   20″
B   D   C
21″

Calculate the altitude AD.

4.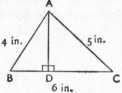

8″   x″
60°
6″

Find x correct to 2 dec. pl.

5. Find x and y in terms of a, b, c. Check that $x + y = a$.

A
c   b
B   x   D   y   C
a

6. In △ABC, AB = 13 in., AC = 14 in., BC = 15 in. Calculate

(1) projection of AB on AC,
(2) area of △ABC.

7. In $\triangle ABC$, the altitudes AD, BE, CF intersect in the orthocentre H.

If AB = 5 in., BC = 6 in., CA = 7 in., calculate the lengths of DC and AE.

Calculate also the length of AH correct to 1 dec. pl.

8. ABC is an acute-angled triangle and AD is the altitude from A to BC. E is the mid-point of BC. Prove that the difference between the squares on AB and AC is equal to twice the rectangle contained by BC and ED.

9. ABC is a triangle in which the median AD makes an angle of 60° with the base. Prove that the difference between the squares on AB and AC is equal to the rectangle contained by AD and BC.

10. The hypotenuse BC of a right-angled triangle ABC is trisected at D and E. Prove that $AD^2 + AE^2 = 5DE^2$.

11. If the base BC of $\triangle ABC$ is trisected at D and E, prove that $AB^2 + AC^2 = AD^2 + AE^2 + 4DE^2$.

12. In $\triangle ABC$, the angle A is an acute angle. On the sides AB and AC of the triangle, squares ABDE and ACFG are described outwards. P and Q are the feet of the perpendiculars from C on AB and from G on EA produced. Prove that

(1) $\triangle APC \equiv \triangle AQG$.
(2) $BC^2 + EG^2 = 2AB^2 + 2AC^2$.

13. ABCD is a trapezium having AB parallel to DC and the angles at A and B acute angles. E and F are the mid-points of AD and BC respectively. Prove that

(1) EF is parallel to DC.
(2) $AC^2 + BD^2 = AD^2 + BC^2 + 2AB.DC$.

14. If the sum of the squares on one pair of opposite sides of a quadrilateral is equal to the sum of the squares on the other pair, prove that the diagonals cut at right angles.

15. ABC is any triangle. BE and CH are the altitudes from B and C to AC and AB respectively.

Prove that rect. AH.AB = rect. AE.AC.

Theorem 33

In any triangle, the sum of the squares on any two sides is equal to twice the square on half the third side, together with twice the square on the median which bisects the third side. (Apollonius' Theorem.)

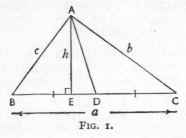

Fig. 1.

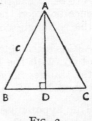

Fig. 2.

Given: △ABC with AD the median drawn from A to BC.

Required: To prove that $AB^2 + AC^2 = 2BD^2 + 2AD^2$.

Proof: Either $A\hat{D}B$ and $A\hat{D}C$ are unequal, one being obtuse and the other acute (Fig. 1),

or $A\hat{D}B$ and $A\hat{D}C$ are equal, both being rt. angles (Fig. 2).

(Fig. 1). If $A\hat{D}B$ is acute then $A\hat{D}C$ will be obtuse. Draw AE perp. to BC.

From the extensions of Pythagoras' Theorem to △ADB and to △ADC

$$AB^2 = BD^2 + DA^2 - 2BD.DE,$$
$$AC^2 = DC^2 + AD^2 + 2CD.DE.$$

But BD = DC

∴ adding, $AB^2 + AC^2 = 2BD^2 + 2AD^2$.

(Fig. 2). Let $A\hat{D}B$ and $A\hat{D}C$ be both rt. angles.

By Pythagoras' Theorem applied to △s ABD, ACD

$$AB^2 = BD^2 + AD^2,$$
$$AC^2 = DC^2 + AD^2.$$

But BD = DC

∴ adding, $AB^2 + AC^2 = 2BD^2 + 2AD^2$.

EXERCISES 51

1.

Calculate BC.

2.

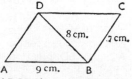

ABCD is a parallelogram. Find diagonal AC.

3.

Calculate x and y, correct to 1 dec. pl.

4.

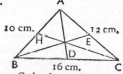

Calculate the medians AD, BE, CH, correct to 1 dec. pl.

5. The medians AD, BE, CH are respectively 12 in., 15 in., 9 in. Calculate the sides of $\triangle$ABC correct to 1 dec. pl.

6. BC = a.
CA = b.
AB = c.

Calculate the medians AD, BE, CH in terms of a, b, c.

7. Prove that the sum of the squares on the sides of a parallelogram is equal to the sum of the squares on its diagonals.

8. PQRS is a rectangle and X is any point within it. Prove that $XP^2 + XR^2 = XQ^2 + XS^2$.

[*Hint:* Join X to O, the pt. of intersection of the diagonals.]

9. Prove that the sum of the squares on the sides of any quadrilateral exceeds the sum of the squares on the diagonals by four times the square on the line joining the mid-points of the diagonals.

10. $\triangle ABC$ is right-angled at C, and AD and BE are medians meeting at G. Prove that
   (1) $4(AD^2 + BE^2) = 5AB^2$.
   (2) $9(AG^2 + BG^2) = 5AB^2$.

11. P is any point outside a parallelogram whose diagonals AC and BD meet at O. Prove that
   $PA^2 + PB^2 + PC^2 + PD^2 = 4PO^2 + \frac{1}{2}(AC^2 + BD^2)$.
   If ABCD is a rhombus, prove that
   $PA^2 + PB^2 + PC^2 + PD^2 = 4PO^2 + 2AB^2$.

12. In triangle ABC, AB = AC. BC is produced its own length to D. If P is any point on the circle with centre D and radius DA, prove that $AB^2 + BP^2 = 2CP^2$.

13. The angle B of $\triangle ABC$ is an acute angle and E is the mid-point of AC. If $\triangle ABC$ is right-angled at A, and if AN is the perpendicular from A to BC, prove that
   $$BC . BN = BE^2 - CE^2.$$

14. P is any point in the plane of a rectangle ABCD. Prove that $PA^2 + PC^2 = PB^2 + PD^2$.

15. ABCD is a parallelogram and P is any point in its plane. Prove that $PA^2 - PB^2 + PC^2 - PD^2$ is constant and equal to half the difference of the squares on the diagonals of ABCD.

16. ABCD is a quadrilateral and E, F, G, H are the mid-points of AB, BC, CD, DA respectively. EG and HF meet in O. If P be any point, prove that
   $PA^2 + PB^2 + PC^2 + PD^2 = \frac{1}{2}(AB^2 + CD^2 + 2EG^2) + 4PO^2$.
   If $PA^2 + PB^2 + PC^2 + PD^2$ has a constant value, find the locus of P.

17. A and B are any two fixed points on the circumference of a circle and P is a variable point also on the circumference. Find the position of P such that
   (1) $PA^2 + PB^2$ is a maximum.
   (2) $PA^2 + PB^2$ is a minimum.

18. PQ is a chord of a circle, parallel to a diameter AB. If X is any point in AB, prove that $PX^2 + XQ^2 = AX^2 + XB^2$.

19. If the medians of a triangle ABC meet at G, prove that $3(AG^2 + BG^2 + CG^2) = BC^2 + CA^2 + AB^2$.

20. Find the locus of a point which moves so that the sum of the squares of its distances from two fixed points is constant. What does the locus become if the point is not confined to a plane?

THEOREM 34

If two chords of a circle intersect, the rectangles contained by their segments are equal.

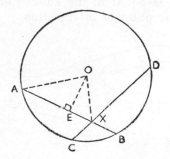

Given : Circle with centre O, and two chords AB and CD intersecting at X.

Required : To prove that $AX.XB = CX.XD$.

Construction : Draw OE perp. to AB.
Join OA and OX.

Proof : OE is the perp. drawn from the centre O to the chord AB

$$\therefore AE = EB$$
$$\therefore AX.XB = (AE + EX)(EB - EX)$$
$$= (AE + EX)(AE - EX)$$
$$= AE^2 - EX^2$$
$$= (AO^2 - OE^2) - (OX^2 - OE^2)$$
[Pythagoras' Th., $\triangle$s. AEO, XEO]
$$= AO^2 - OE^2 - OX^2 + OE^2$$
$$= AO^2 - OX^2$$
$$= r^2 - OX^2 \text{ (where } r = \text{radius of circle).}$$

Similarly $CX.XD = r^2 - OX^2$
$$\therefore AX.XB = CX.XD.$$

For alternative proof, see p. 384.

Theorem 35

If two chords of a circle intersect when produced, the rectangles contained by their segments are equal, and each rectangle is equal to the square on the tangent drawn from the point of intersection.

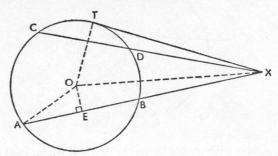

Given: Circle, centre O, and two chords AB, CD which intersect when produced at X, and XT the tangent drawn from X.

Required: To prove that AX.XB = CX.XD
$$= XT^2.$$

Construction: Draw OE perp. to AB.
                    Join OA, OX, OT.

Proof: OE is the perp. drawn from the centre O to the chord AB

      ∴ AE = EB

∴ AX.XB $= (EX + AE)(EX - EB)$
                $= (EX + AE)(EX - AE)$
                $= EX^2 - AE^2$
                $= (OX^2 - OE^2) - (OA^2 - OE^2)$
                     [Pythagoras' Th., △s OEX, OAE]
                $= OX^2 - OE^2 - OA^2 + OE^2$
                $= OX^2 - OA^2$
                $= OX^2 - r^2$ (where r = radius of circle)

For alternative proof, see pp. 384, 386.

Similarly $CX.XD = OX^2 - r^2$

∴ $AX.XB = CX.XD$.

Since TX is a tangent and OT a radius

∴ $O\hat{T}X$ is a rt. angle

∴ $XT^2 = OX^2 - OT^2$ [Pythagoras' Th., $\triangle OTX$]

$= OX^2 - r^2$

∴ $AX.XB = CX.XD = XT^2$.

[*Note:* These two theorems may be combined and stated as follows :

(1) If two chords of a circle intersect, internally or externally, the rectangle contained by the segments of the one is equal to the rectangle contained by the segments of the other.

(2) If, from a point outside a circle, a secant and a tangent are drawn, the rectangle contained by the whole secant and the part outside the circle is equal to the square on the tangent.]

EXERCISES 52

1.

Find BX.

2.

If CD = 8·5 in., find CO and OD.

3.

Find OP.

4.

O is the centre of the circle. Find OP.

5.

O is the centre. Find OC.

6.

Find AT, and OA (correct to 1 dec. pl.).

7. Prove that
$$h^2 + 2rh - d^2 = 0.$$
Show that if h is measured in feet and $r = 3960$ miles, then
$$d = \sqrt{\frac{3h}{2}} \text{ miles (approx.).}$$

8. Radius of arch $= r$,
           span $= 2d$.
Find h in terms of r and d.

9. The three altitudes AP, BQ, CR of △ABC meet at O. Prove that

    (1) AO.OP = BO.OQ = CO.OR.
    (2) AR.AB = AQ.AC.

10. The median AD of △ABC meets the circumcircle of △ABC in E. Prove that $AB^2 + AC^2 = 2AD.AE$.

11. AB is a diameter of a circle and C is a point on AB such that $BC = \frac{1}{3}AB$. If PQ is the chord through C perpendicular to AB, prove that
$$PQ^2 = 2AC^2.$$
Hence show that PQ is equal to the diagonal of the square described on AC.

12. ABC is a triangle inscribed in a circle with centre O and is such that AB bisects the angle between AC and the tangent to the circle at A.
    If BO, or BO produced, meets AC at D, prove that

    (1) BD is perpendicular to AC.
    (2) $2BD.BO = AB^2$.

13. $\triangle$ABC is right-angled at C and the perpendicular from C to AB meets AB in D.

G is any point in CD and AG produced meets the circumcircle of $\triangle$ABC in H.

Show that, for all positions of G, the rect. AG.AH is constant in area.

14. Two circles intersect; prove that their common chord produced bisects their common tangents.

If two circles touch one another externally, state how the bisector of the two direct common tangents is related to the circles.

15. Circles are drawn through two fixed points A and B. Prove that the points of contact of tangents, drawn to these circles from a fixed point O in AB produced, lie on a circle.

16. Two circles, the second of which passes through the centre B of the first, intersect at a point P. The line of centres of the circles, when produced, cuts the first at A and C and the second at B and D, and PE is the perpendicular from P to AD. Prove that DC.DA = DB.DE.

17. Two concentric circles have centre O, and A and B are any two points on the outer circle.

From A and B, secants AXY and BPQ are drawn to the inner circle. Show that for all positions of A and B

$$AX.AY = BP.BQ.$$

18. C is the mid-point of a straight line AB and BCDE is the square on BC. A circle with centre B and radius BD cuts AB at H and AB produced at K. Prove that

(1) Rect. HC.CK = AC².
(2) Rect. AH.AK = 2AC².

19. A, B, C, D are four points in order on a straight line. Find a point O in the line such that

rect. AO.OC = rect. BO.OD.

20. Two circles cut at A and B, and P is a point on BA produced. PQ and PR are the tangents to the circles from P. The tangents at A to the circles meet PQ and PR in D and E respectively. Prove that the perimeters of triangles PAD and PAE are equal.

THEOREM 36

If two straight lines cut one another so that the rectangle contained by the segments of the one is equal to the rectangle contained by the segments of the other, the four extremities of the straight lines are concylic.

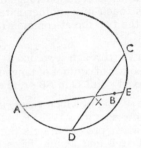

Given: Two straight lines AB and CD intersecting at X and AX.XB = CX.XD.

Required: To prove that A, B, C, D are concyclic.

Proof: If the circle through A, C, and D does not pass through B let it cut AB (or AB produced) at E

Then AX.XE = CX.XD (rectangle property of circle).

But AX.XB = CX.XD (given)

∴ AX.XE = AX.XB

∴ XE = XB.

This is impossible because XB is only a part of XE

∴ the circle through A, C, D must pass through B,

i.e. A, B, C, D are concyclic.

For alternative proof, see p. 385.

Theorem 37

If two straight lines AB and CD are both produced to meet at X, and if the rectangle XA, XB is equal to the rectangle XC, XD, then the four points A, B, C, D are concyclic.

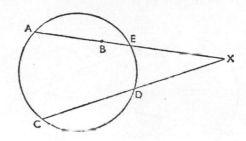

Given: Two straight lines **AB** and **CD** both produced to meet at **X**, and rect. **XA, XB** = rect. **XC, XD**.

Required: To prove that **A, B, C, D** are concyclic.

Proof: If the circle through **A, C, D** does not pass through **B** let it cut **XA** (or **XA** produced) at **E**.

Then **XE.XA = XD.XC** (rect. property of circle).

But **XB.XA = XD.XC** (given)

∴ **XE.XA = XB.XA**

∴ **XE = XB**.

This is impossible because **XE** is only a part of **XB**

∴ the circle through **A, C, D** must pass through **B**, i.e. **A, B, C, D** are concyclic.

For alternative proof, see p. 385.

Theorem 38

If from a point outside a circle two straight lines are drawn, one of which cuts the circle and the other meets it, and if the rectangle contained by the secant and the part of it outside the circle is equal to the square on the line which meets the circle, then the line which meets the circle is a tangent to it.

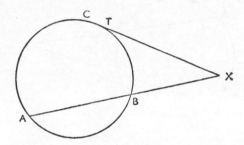

Given: Two straight lines drawn to a circle from an external point X, XBA cutting the circle at A and B, and XT meeting the circle at T, and XA.XB = XT².

Required: To prove that XT is a tangent to the circle.

Proof: If XT is not a tangent let it meet the circle again at a second point C.

Then XA.XB = XT.XC (rect. property of circle).

But XA.XB = XT² (given)

∴ XT.XC = XT²

∴ XC = XT,

i.e. C and T coincide

∴ XT cannot meet the circle at any point other than T

∴ XT is a tangent to the circle.

For alternative proof, see p. 387.

EXERCISES 53

1.

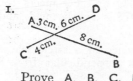

Prove A, B, C, D concyclic.

2.

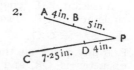

Prove A, B, D, C concyclic.

4.

3.

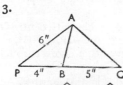

Prove $P\hat{A}B = A\hat{C}B$.

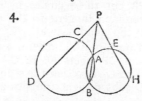

Prove C, D, H, E concyclic.

5. $BD^2 = AD.OD$. Prove that

(1) BD is a tangent to circle AOB.

(2) D is the mid-pt. of arc BDC.

6. △ABC is right-angled at A. A straight line through P, perpendicular to BC, bisects AC at Q. Prove that

(1) $BP^2 - CP^2 = AB^2$.

(2) $2CP.CB = CA^2$.

7. ABCD is a rectangle in which BC = 2AB. The perpendicular bisector of the diagonal AC cuts AD and AC in F and G respectively.

(1) Prove $AF.AD = AG.AC$.

(2) If AB = x in., show that FD = $\frac{3}{4}x$ in. and also that $\cos F\hat{C}D = \frac{4}{5}$.

8. Triangle XYZ is right-angled at Y and P is any point on YZ. YQ and YR are perpendicular to XP and XZ respectively. Prove that

(1) $XY^2 = XP.XQ$.

(2) P, Q, R, Z are concyclic.

9. PQ and PR are tangents from P to a circle with centre O. OP meets QR in X. Prove that $PQ^2 = PX.PO$.

A secant PST lying between PQ and PO meets the circle in S and T. Prove that XOTS is a cyclic quad., and that $S\hat{X}P = O\hat{X}T$.

10. P is any point on the circumference of a circle whose diameter is QR, and PA is the perpendicular from P to QR.

Circles are drawn on AQ and AR as diameters, and PQ and PR cut these circles in B and C. Prove that BC is a common tangent to the two circles and that QBCR is a cyclic quadrilateral.

11. Tangents PA and PB are drawn to a circle with centre O, and OP meets AB in C. Prove that $OC.CP = AC^2$.

Prove also that the segments of any other chord through C subtend equal angles at P.

12. Two circles intersect in A and B and P is any point in AB. Through P, a straight line CPD is drawn, cutting one of the circles in C and D, and through P, another straight line GPH is drawn, cutting the other circle in G and H. Prove that C, G, D, H are concyclic.

13. Two circles intersect in Q and R and P is any point in RQ produced. From P a tangent PA is drawn to one circle and a secant PBC is drawn to the other. Prove that PA is a tangent to the circle through the points A, B, C.

14. Two circles intersect in A and B and P is a point in BA produced. From P, two secants PCD and PGH are drawn to the circles meeting them in C, D and in G, H.

DG and CH intersect in K, prove that
$$CK.KH = DK.KG.$$
Show also that the tangents from P to all circles through A and B are equal.

15. PQ is a straight line bisected at A. AB is the perpendicular to PQ. Through C, a point in AB, PC is drawn and produced to point D so that $PC.PD = 2AQ^2$.

Prove that $P\hat{D}Q$ is a rt. angle.

16. A is the centre of two concentric circles. Two straight lines ABC and ADE cut the smaller circle at B and D and the larger at C and E respectively. BE and CD intersect at X. Prove that $BX.XE = DX.XC$.

The following constructions illustrate applications of the previous theorems.

(1) Construct a circle to pass through two given points and touch a given straight line.

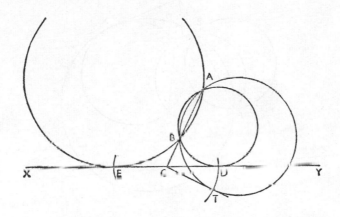

Let A, B be the given points and XY the given straight line.

Draw any circle through A and B.

Join AB and produce it to meet XY in C.

Draw CT the tangent to the circle touching it at T. With centre C, and radius CT, draw arcs to cut XY at D and E.

The circles ABD and ABE are required circles. The proof should be supplied.

[*Note.*—The above construction fails when AB is parl. to CD. What construction could be used in this case?]

(2) Construct a circle to pass through two given points and touch a given circle.

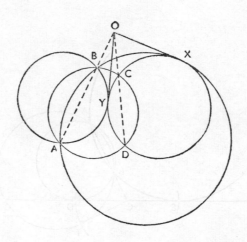

Let **A**, **B** be the given points and **XCYD** the given circle. Draw any circle through **A** and **B** cutting the given circle at **C** and **D**.

Join **AB** and **DC** and produce them to meet in **O**. Draw from **O**, the tangents **OX**, **OY** to the given circle touching it at **X** and **Y**.

The circles **ABY** and **ABX** are the required circles. The proof should be supplied.

(3) Construct a circle to pass through a given point and touch two given intersecting straight lines.

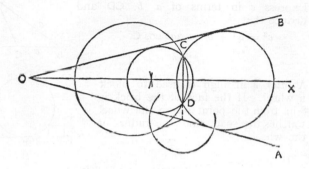

Let C be the given point, OA and OB the given straight lines intersecting at O.

Draw OX the bisector of AÔB.

Let D be the image of C in OX.

Draw the circle through C, D and touching OA (use the method of construction 1 on p. 313).

The proof should be supplied.

Revision Papers XXXI–XL

XXXI

1. Two points C and D divide a line AB internally so that $AC.CB = AD.DB$. Prove that $AC = DB$.

2. Express c in terms of a, b, CD and deduce that
$$c^2 = a^2 + b^2 - 2ab \cos C.$$

3. A brick 4 in. high is used to block a wheel. If the face of the brick is 8 in. from the point where the wheel touches the road, find the radius of the wheel.

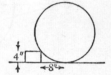

4. ABC is an acute-angled triangle inscribed in a circle of centre O. The perpendicular bisector of AB meets AC and BC, produced if necessary, in P and Q. Prove that $OP.OQ = OC^2$.

   If the perpendicular bisector of BC meets BA and CA, produced if necessary, in R and S, prove that P, Q, R, S are concyclic.

5. Show how to construct a triangle ABC with an area of 12 sq. in., if the base BC is 6 in. in length and
$$AB^2 + AC^2 = 68 \text{ sq. in.}$$

XXXII

1. C is the mid-point of a straight line AB, and D is any other point in AB, or in AB produced. Prove that
$$AD^2 + DB^2 = 2AC^2 + 2CD^2.$$

2. Express c in terms of a, b, CD and deduce that

$$c^2 = a^2 + b^2 - 2ab \cos C.$$

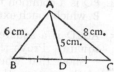

3. Calculate the lengths of the medians from B and C. Prove that $\widehat{A}$ is a rt. angle.

4. O is the centre, and OA a radius of a circle. On OA as diameter a circle is drawn. A chord BC of the first circle cuts the second in D and E. Prove that

$$BD.DC = AD^2.$$
$$BE.EC = AE^2.$$

5. In $\triangle$ABC, AB $>$ AC. Show how to find a point P in BC produced, such that $PA^2 = PB.PC$.

Show also how to find a point Q in BC such that $AQ^2 = BQ.QC$. Distinguish between the cases in which there are one and two solutions to this problem. In what exceptional case does the problem not admit of any solution?

XXXIII

1. ABC is an isosceles triangle, right-angled at A, and D is any point on BC. Prove that $BD^2 + DC^2 = 2AD^2$.

Hence show that the triangle which has as its sides BD, DC and the diagonal of the square on AD, will be right-angled.

2.

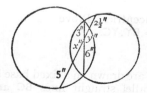

Find x and y.

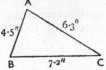

3. Prove that $\widehat{B} = 60°$.

4. PQ is a common tangent to two circles with centres A and B, which touch externally at C. Prove that $PQ^2 = 4AC.CB$.

5. ABCD is a square, and P is any point in the plane of the square. Prove that $PA^2 + PC^2 = PB^2 + PD^2$.

Show that when $PA^2 + PC^2$ is equal to twice the area of the square, the locus of P is the circumscribing circle of the square. If the locus of P is the inscribed circle of the square, find the value of $PA^2 + PC^2$.

XXXIV

1. E is a point in the side CD of a rectangle ABCD and F is the mid-point of EC. Prove that

$$AC^2 - AE^2 = 4CF.DF.$$

Hence show how to find a point G in DC such that

$$BD^2 = 4DG.GC.$$

2. AD and CD are tangents to the circle at A and E respectively. Find the lengths of AD and CE.

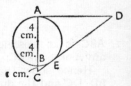

3. Circles are concentric. Prove
$$AX.XB = BY.YC.$$

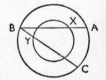

4. Triangles ABC are drawn on a fixed base BC and lie between two fixed parallel straight lines BC and XY. Find the position of the vertex A when $AB^2 + AC^2$ is a minimum.

5. Draw two intersecting circles having their centres on the same side of the common chord, and draw any diameter of the smaller circle. Show how to describe a circle within the area common to the circles, which shall touch both circles, and have its centre on the given diameter. Distinguish between the cases in which the problem admits of one or two solutions.

XXXV

1. A straight line **AB** is divided internally at **C**, and **D** and **E** are the mid-points of **AC** and **CB** respectively. Prove that $AE^2 + 3EB^2 = BD^2 + 3AD^2$.

2. An airman is flying over the sea at a height of 2,400 ft. How far away, at any time, is the sea horizon?

i.e. $AB = 2,400$ ft.
$\qquad OB = 3960$ ml.

Find **AD**.

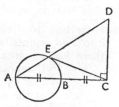

3. AB is a diameter and CE the tangent to the circle from C. Prove that

$$AE \cdot AD = CE^2.$$

If the diameter of the circle is 6 cm., evaluate the area of the rectangle **AE . AD**.

4. In a trapezium ABCD, AB is parallel to DC and equal to twice DC in length. Prove that

$$AC^2 + BD^2 = AD^2 + BC^2 + AB^2.$$

5. P is a point 3 cm. distant from the centre O of a circle of radius 4 cm., and APB is any chord of the circle through **P**. Find the area of the rectangle **AP, PB**.

Show how to draw, from **P**, a line terminated by the circumference, such that the square on it is equal to the area of the rectangle **AP, PB**.

XXXVI

1. D is any point in the base BC of an isosceles triangle ABC. Prove that $AB^2 - AD^2 = BD.DC$.

   If D lies in BC produced, show that
   $$AD^2 - AB^2 = BD.DC.$$

2. Calculate PS.

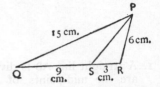

3. Calculate DC and hence find the area of $\triangle ABC$.

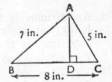

4. AD is an altitude of $\triangle ABC$. E is a point on AD produced, and the circle on AE as diameter cuts BC in H.

   If HD^2 is equal to $\triangle ABC$ prove that $DE = \frac{1}{2}BC$.

5. Show how to divide a straight line 8 cm. long, internally, into two segments, such that the rectangle contained by them has an area of 13 sq. cm.

   [Use Pythagoras' Theorem to find the side of a square whose area is 13 sq. cm.].

   Show that the number of units of length in the segments of the line are roots of the quadratic equation
   $$x^2 - 8x + 13 = 0.$$

XXXVII

1. A rectangle measures 5 cm. by 3 cm. Use the theorem about intersecting chords of a circle to construct a rectangle, equal in area to the given rectangle and standing on a base 5·6 cm. long. Measure the height of the rectangle.

2. Calculate **EB** and hence find the area of the trapezium.

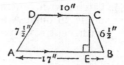

3.

Prove that $AX^2 + BX^2 + CX^2 + DX^2 =$ square on the diameter of the circle.

4. In $\triangle ABC$, $AB > AC$. AD is the median from A and AE is perpendicular to BC. Prove that $AB^2 - AC^2 = 2BC \cdot DE$. If BC is fixed and A moves so that $AB^2 - AC^2$ is constant, what is the locus of A?

5. Show how to divide a straight line 8 cm. long, externally, into two segments, such that the rectangle contained by them has an area of 13 sq. cm.

[Use Pythagoras' Theorem to find the side of a square of area 13 sq. cm.]

Show that the numbers of units of length in the segments of the line are roots of the quadratic equation

$$x^2 - 8x - 13 = 0.$$

XXXVIII

1. A rectangle measures 5 cm. by 3 cm. Use the theorem on intersecting chords of a circle to construct a square equal in area to it. Measure its side.

2. A and B are fixed points on the circumference of a circle.

P is a variable point on the circumference. Find the position of P, if $PA^2 + PB^2$ has its maximum value.

3. Circle, with centre P, and points A and B are fixed. Any circle through A and B cuts the fixed circle at C. Circle, with centre Q, passes through A and B and touches the

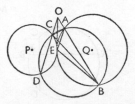

fixed circle at E. DC and BA produced meet in O. Prove OE a common tangent to circles with centres P and Q. Prove also that of all angles subtended by AB at points on the circle with centre P, A$\hat{\text{E}}$B is the greatest.

4. PA and PB are tangents to a circle with centre O. PO cuts the circumference at C, and PO, produced, cuts it again at D. AB cuts PO at G. Prove that PC.PD = PG.PO.

Any other secant PXY cuts the circumference at X and Y. Prove that XGOY is a cyclic quadrilateral.

5. A is a fixed point on the circumference of a fixed circle. Through A a variable chord AB is drawn. The chord is produced to C such that the rectangle AB, AC is equal to the square on a given line XY.

Find the locus of C.

XXXIX

1. AB is a chord of a circle. Show how to construct a rectangle equal in area to the square on AB, and having one side equal in length to the diameter.

2. Prove that $xy = h^2$.

Evaluate x and y in terms of b, c, h and prove that

$$\frac{1}{b^2} + \frac{1}{c^2} = \frac{1}{h^2}.$$

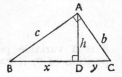

3. Circles intersect at A and B. PQ is a common tangent and

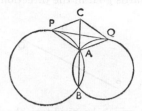

PAQC is a parallelogram. Prove that

(1) BAC is a str. line.
(2) P, C, Q, B are concyclic.

4. In △ABC, AB is produced to a point D. BE bisects $C\hat{B}D$ and meets AC produced in E.

The circumcircle of △ABC cuts EB produced in G. Prove that $G\hat{A}B = B\hat{E}A$.

Hence prove that G lies on the perpendicular bisector of AC.

5. Two fixed circles with centres A and B intersect in X and Y, and XY cuts AB in D. PQ and PR are tangents to the circles from a point P, and the perpendicular from P to AB meets AB, or AB produced, at C. Show that

$$PQ^2 - PR^2 = 2AB \cdot CD.$$

If $PQ^2 - PR^2 =$ constant, find the locus of P, and deduce the locus of P for the particular case in which the value of the constant is zero.

XL

1. A plane rises from a beach and flies out to sea at a height of 54 ft. above sea level, and is observed by a man 6 ft. tall, standing by the water's edge. How far will the plane be from the observer when it just disappears over the horizon?

2. If D is a point in the side BC of △ABC such that 3BD = 2DC, prove that

$$3AB^2 + 2AC^2 = 3BD^2 + 2DC^2 + 5AD^2.$$

3. **A** and **B** represent the goal posts on a soccer pitch. A player runs towards goal in the direction **P** to **Q**. Find the

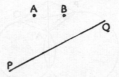

point on **PQ** at which he ought to shoot to have the best chance of scoring.

4. △ABC is isosceles with **AB** = **AC**. The perpendicular bisector of **AB** meets **BC**, or **BC** produced, in **D**. Prove that $AB^2 = BC.BD$.

[*Hint:* Drop perp. from mid-pt. of **AB** on to **BC**.]

5. **AB**, **CD** are any two perpendicular chords passing through a fixed point **R** in a circle with centre **O**. Prove that $AB^2 + CD^2 = $ constant. Circles on **AB** and **CD** as dia-

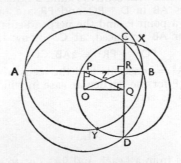

meters and with centres **P**, **Q** intersect in **X** and **Y**. **OR** and **PQ** intersect in **Z**. Prove that **ZX** = **ZY** = constant.

[*Hint:*—Use Apollonius' Theorem with △PXQ.]

Deduce the locus of points of intersection of circles which have as diameters any pair of perpendicular chords drawn through **R**.

BOOK V

PROPORTION SIMILARITY

The word " ratio " has already been defined in the section dealing with the sine, cosine, and tangent of an angle.

In the ratio $\frac{a}{b}$, a is called the **antecedent** and b is called the **consequent**.

The ratio $\left(\frac{a}{b}\right)^2$ or $\frac{a^2}{b^2}$ is called the **duplicate ratio** of $\frac{a}{b}$.

When two ratios $\frac{a}{b}$ and $\frac{c}{d}$ are equal, we write $a : b :: c : d$ or $a : b = c : d$ or $\frac{a}{b} = \frac{c}{d}$ and we read this as " a is to b as c is to d."

The four quantities a, b, c, d are then said to be in **proportion**.

a and d are called the **extremes** and b and c the **means** of the proportion.

d is called the **fourth proportional** to a, b, c.

Three quantities a, b, c are in **continued proportion** when $\frac{a}{b} = \frac{b}{c}$.

b is then a **mean proportional** between a and c and c is the **third proportional** to a and b.

Proofs of the following facts may be found in any textbook on algebra.

If $\frac{a}{b} = \frac{c}{d}$, then

(1) $ad = bc.$

(2) $\frac{b}{a} = \frac{d}{c}.$

(3) $\frac{a}{c} = \frac{b}{d}.$

(4) $\dfrac{a \pm b}{b} = \dfrac{c \pm d}{d}$.

(5) $\dfrac{a}{a \pm b} = \dfrac{c}{c \pm d}$.

(6) $\dfrac{a + b}{a - b} = \dfrac{c + d}{c - d}$.

If $\dfrac{a}{b} = \dfrac{c}{d} = \dfrac{e}{f}$, then each ratio is equal to $\dfrac{a + c + e}{b + d + f}$.

When two quantities have a common measure we can express the ratio between them as a ratio of two whole numbers. Thus the ratio of the lengths 3·24 in. and 1·89 in. is

$$\frac{3 \cdot 24}{1 \cdot 89} = \frac{324}{189} = \frac{36}{21} = \frac{12}{7}.$$

Here the common measure is $\dfrac{1}{100}$ in. and the lengths are said to be commensurable.

In a right-angled isosceles triangle where the sides containing the right angle are each 1 in. long, the ratio of any one of the sides containing the right angle to the hypotenuse is $\dfrac{1}{\sqrt{2}}$.

$\sqrt{2}$ cannot be expressed as a terminating decimal. Hence it is impossible to express the ratio $\dfrac{1}{\sqrt{2}}$ as the ratio of two integers. By taking successive approximations to $\sqrt{2}$, i.e. 1·4, 1·41, 1·414 and so on, we get successive approximations $\dfrac{10}{14}$, $\dfrac{100}{141}$, $\dfrac{1000}{1414}$ to the ratio $\dfrac{1}{\sqrt{2}}$, and indeed we could find two integers such that the ratio between them differed from $\dfrac{1}{\sqrt{2}}$ by an amount as small as we please.

The lengths of these two sides of the above triangle are **incommensurable,** having no common measure.

Theorems and exercises in this book will deal with commensurable quantities only and it will be assumed that they are true for incommensurable quantities.

THEOREM 39

(1) **The areas of triangles of equal altitude are to one another as their bases.**

(2) **The areas of triangles on equal bases are to one another as their altitudes.**

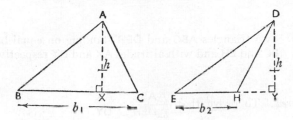

(1)

Given : Two triangles ABC and DEH with equal altitudes AX and DY, standing on bases BC and EH respectively.

Required : To prove that $\dfrac{\triangle ABC}{\triangle DEH} = \dfrac{BC}{EH}$.

Proof : Let b_1 and b_2 be the number of units of length in the bases BC and EH respectively, and let h be the number of units of length in the altitudes AX and DY.

Then area of $\triangle ABC = \frac{1}{2}b_1 h$ sq. units,

area of $\triangle DEH = \frac{1}{2}b_2 h$ sq. units.

$\therefore \dfrac{\triangle ABC}{\triangle DEH} = \dfrac{\frac{1}{2}b_1 h}{\frac{1}{2}b_2 h} = \dfrac{b_1}{b_2} = \dfrac{BC}{EH}$.

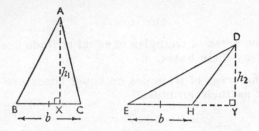

(2)

Given: Two triangles ABC and DEH standing on equal bases
BC and EH and with altitudes AX and DY respectively.

Required: To prove that $\dfrac{\triangle ABC}{\triangle DEH} = \dfrac{AX}{DY}$.

Proof: Let b be the number of units of length in the equal
bases BC and EH, and let h_1 and h_2 be the number of
units of length in the altitudes AX and DY respectively.

Then area of $\triangle ABC = \frac{1}{2}bh_1$ sq. units,

area of $\triangle DEH = \frac{1}{2}bh_2$ sq. units.

$$\therefore \frac{\triangle ABC}{\triangle DEH} = \frac{\frac{1}{2}bh_1}{\frac{1}{2}bh_2} = \frac{h_1}{h_2} = \frac{AX}{DY}.$$

Since the area of a Rectangle, or Parallelogram, is equal to
Base × Altitude, a similar form of proof can be used to
show that

**(1) The areas of rectangles, or parallelograms, of
equal altitude, are to one another as their bases.**

**(2) The areas of rectangles, or parallelograms, on
equal bases, are to one another as their altitudes.**

The commonest application of the case in which the altitudes are equal, occurs when the bases of the triangles are in one straight line and the triangles have the same vertex.

Here, $\dfrac{\triangle ABD}{\triangle ADC} = \dfrac{BD}{DC}$.

Similarly $\dfrac{\triangle ABD}{\triangle ABC} = \dfrac{BD}{BC}$ and $\dfrac{\triangle ABC}{\triangle ADC} = \dfrac{BC}{DC}$.

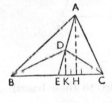

Fig. 1

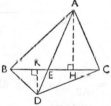

Fig. 2

The commonest application of the case in which the bases are equal, occurs when the triangles are on the same side, or on opposite sides, of a common base.

Here $\dfrac{\triangle ABC}{\triangle DBC} = \dfrac{AH}{DK}$.

From our earlier exercises on similarity

$\triangle$s AEH and KED are equiangular

$$\therefore \ \frac{AH}{DK} = \frac{AE}{ED} *.$$

Hence $\dfrac{\triangle ABC}{\triangle DBC} = \dfrac{AE}{ED}$.

* This fact will be proved later.

Worked Examples

Example I.—D and E are points in the sides **AB** and **AC** respectively, of $\triangle$ABC, such that $\frac{AD}{DB} = \frac{1}{2}$ and $\frac{CE}{EA} = \frac{3}{2}$. What fraction of $\triangle$ABC is the quadrilateral **BDEC**?

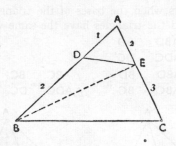

Join **BE**.

$$\frac{\triangle ADE}{\triangle ABE} = \frac{AD}{AB} \quad (\triangle s \text{ of eq. alt. prop. to their bases})$$

$$= \frac{1}{3} \left(\frac{AD}{DB} = \frac{1}{2} \ \therefore \ \frac{AD}{AB} = \frac{AD}{AD + DB} = \frac{1}{1 + 2} = \frac{1}{3} \right).$$

$$\frac{\triangle ABE}{\triangle ABC} = \frac{AE}{AC} \quad (\triangle s \text{ of eq. alt. prop. to their bases})$$

$$= \frac{2}{5} \left(\frac{AE}{EC} = \frac{2}{3} \ \therefore \ \frac{AE}{AC} = \frac{AE}{AE + EC} = \frac{2}{2 + 3} = \frac{2}{5} \right).$$

$$\therefore \ \frac{\triangle ADE}{\triangle ABE} \cdot \frac{\triangle ABE}{\triangle ABC} = \frac{1}{3} \cdot \frac{2}{5},$$

$$\text{i.e. } \frac{\triangle ADE}{\triangle ABC} = \frac{2}{15}$$

$$\therefore \ \triangle ADE = \frac{2}{15} \ \triangle ABC$$

$$\therefore \ \text{quad. } BDEC = \frac{13}{15} \ \triangle ABC.$$

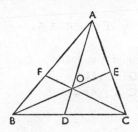

Example 2.—O is any point inside the triangle ABC. AO, BO, CO are joined and produced to meet the opposite sides BC, CA, AB in D, E, F respectively. Prove that

$$\frac{AO}{AD} + \frac{BO}{BE} + \frac{CO}{CF} = 2.$$

$$\frac{AO}{AD} = \frac{\triangle ABO}{\triangle ABD} = \frac{\triangle ACO}{\triangle ACD} \text{ (} \triangle\text{s of eq. alt. prop. to their bases)}$$

$$= \frac{\triangle ABO + \triangle ACO}{\triangle ABD + \triangle ACD} = \frac{\triangle ABO + \triangle ACO}{\triangle ABC}.$$

Similar values may be found for $\frac{BO}{BE}$ and $\frac{CO}{CF}$

$$\therefore \frac{AO}{AD} + \frac{BO}{BE} + \frac{CO}{CF}$$

$$= \frac{\triangle ABO + \triangle ACO}{\triangle ABC} + \frac{\triangle BAO + \triangle BCO}{\triangle ABC} + \frac{\triangle CAO + \triangle CBO}{\triangle ABC}$$

$$= \frac{2(\triangle ABO + \triangle BCO + \triangle CAO)}{\triangle ABC}$$

$$= \frac{2 \triangle ABC}{\triangle ABC}$$

$$= 2.$$

EXERCISES 54

1. Find the values of the ratios

$$\frac{\triangle ABD}{\triangle ADE}; \quad \frac{\triangle ABD}{\triangle AEC}; \quad \frac{\triangle ADE}{\triangle ABC}.$$

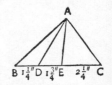

2. ABCD is a parallelogram. Find the ratio of the area of BFDG to that of the parm. ABCD.

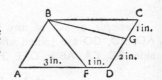

3. ABCD is a parallelogram.

$$\frac{AF}{FD} = \frac{3}{5} \text{ and } \frac{DG}{GC} = \frac{2}{3}.$$

Find ratio $\dfrac{\text{fig. BFDG}}{\text{parm. ABCD}}$.

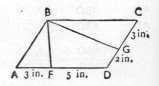

4. $\dfrac{AD}{DB} = \dfrac{1}{3}$ and $\dfrac{AE}{EC} = \dfrac{1}{2}$.

Find the ratios $\dfrac{\triangle ADE}{\triangle ADC}$ and $\dfrac{\triangle ADC}{\triangle ABC}$.

What fraction of $\triangle ABC$ is $\triangle ADE$?

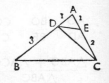

5. $\dfrac{AD}{DB} = \dfrac{AE}{EC} = \dfrac{1}{2}$.

What fraction of the whole triangle is quad. BDEC?

6.

D, E; F, G; H, K are points of trisection of the three sides. What fraction of $\triangle ABC$ is the figure DEFGHK?

7. AD, BE, CH are medians.

Prove $\dfrac{\triangle AHG}{\triangle ABC} = \dfrac{1}{6}$

and $\dfrac{\triangle DEH}{\triangle ABC} = \dfrac{1}{4}$.

8. O is any point inside $\triangle ABC$. AO, BO, CO, when produced, meet the sides in D, E, H respectively. Prove that

$$\frac{BD}{DC} = \frac{\triangle ABD}{\triangle ADC} = \frac{\triangle OBD}{\triangle ODC} = \frac{\triangle AOB}{\triangle AOC}.$$

Hence prove that

$$\frac{AH}{HB} \cdot \frac{BD}{DC} \cdot \frac{CE}{EA} = 1.$$

This is known as Ceva's Theorem.

9. P, Q, R are points in the sides of $\triangle ABC$ such that BP = $\frac{1}{3}$BC, CQ = $\frac{1}{3}$CA, AR = $\frac{1}{3}$AB. Prove that, in area, triangles ARQ, BPR, CQP are all $\frac{2}{9}$ of $\triangle ABC$ and that $\triangle PQR$ is $\frac{1}{3}$ $\triangle ABC$.

10. ABCD is a square and P is a point in AC such that $\dfrac{AP}{PC} = \tfrac{1}{3}$.

BP produced meets AD in Q. Prove

$$\triangle APB = \tfrac{1}{8} \text{ sq. ABCD.}$$
$$\triangle APB = \triangle CPQ.$$
$$\frac{\triangle APB}{\triangle APQ} = \frac{3}{1}.$$
$$\triangle ABQ = \tfrac{1}{6} \text{ sq. ABCD.}$$

11. In $\triangle ABC$, P is a point in AB such that $\dfrac{AP}{PB} = \dfrac{x}{y}$, and Q a point in AC such that $\dfrac{AQ}{QC} = \dfrac{y}{x}$. Express the ratio $\dfrac{\triangle APQ}{\text{quad. BPQC}}$ in terms of x and y.

12. ABCD is a quadrilateral with AC and BD intersecting at O. Prove that $\dfrac{\triangle AOB}{\triangle AOD} = \dfrac{\triangle BOC}{\triangle COD}$.

13. D and E are the points of trisection, nearest to A, of the sides AB and AC, respectively, of $\triangle ABC$. BE and CD are joined. Show that

$$\frac{AD}{DB} = \frac{\triangle ADE}{\triangle DBE}.$$

Hence show that DE is parallel to BC.

14. I is the incentre of $\triangle ABC$. Prove that

$$\triangle IBC : \triangle ICA : \triangle IAB = BC : CA : AB.$$

15. The medians AD and BE of a $\triangle ABC$ intersect at G. Find the ratios $\triangle ABG : \triangle GDE : \triangle ABC$.

16. Find a point O within a triangle ABC such that

$$\triangle BOC : \triangle COA : \triangle AOB = 4 : 2 : 1.$$

17. Through a point O within a triangle, straight lines are drawn from A, B, C cutting the opposite sides in D, E, F respectively. Show that

$$\frac{OD}{AD} + \frac{OE}{BE} + \frac{OF}{CF} = 1.$$

Division of a Line in a Given Ratio

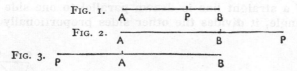

FIG. 1.
A   P   B

FIG. 2.
A   B   P

FIG. 3.
P   A   B

If AB is any straight line and P is a point in AB, as in Fig. 1, or in AB produced, as in Fig. 2 or in BA produced, as in Fig. 3, the line AB is divided in all cases into two segments AP and PB.

We say that P divides the line AB in the ratio $\frac{AP}{PB}$.

In Fig. 1, P divides AB internally in the ratio $\frac{AP}{PB}$.

In Fig. 2 and Fig. 3, P divides AB externally in the ratio $\frac{AP}{PB}$.

In Fig. 1, the ratio $\frac{AP}{PB}$ is small when P is near A and becomes larger when P approaches B. When P is the mid-point of AB, the value of the ratio $\frac{AP}{PB}$ is 1.

In Fig. 2, the ratio $\frac{AP}{PB}$ is always greater than 1, since AP is always greater than PB. When P is near B, the ratio has very large values, and, as P moves farther to the right, $\frac{AP}{PB}$ becomes smaller and approaches the value 1, as P moves to the right along AB produced.

In Fig. 3, the ratio $\frac{AP}{PB}$ is always less than 1, since AP is always less than PB. When P is near A, the ratio has very small values, and, as P moves farther to the left, $\frac{AP}{PB}$ becomes greater and approaches the value 1, as P moves to the left along BA produced.

Theorem 40

If a straight line is drawn parallel to one side of a triangle, it divides the other sides proportionally.

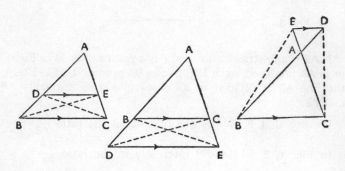

Given: △ABC with DE drawn parallel to BC, meeting AB and AC, or these lines produced, in D and E respectively.

Required: To prove that $\dfrac{AD}{DB} = \dfrac{AE}{EC}$.

Construction: Join BE and DC.

Proof: In all figures

$$\frac{AD}{DB} = \frac{\triangle ADE}{\triangle DEB} \quad (\triangle s \text{ of eq. alt. prop. to their bases}).$$

$$\frac{AE}{EC} = \frac{\triangle ADE}{\triangle DEC}.$$

But △DEB = △DEC (on same base and bet. same parls.)

$$\therefore \frac{\triangle ADE}{\triangle DEB} = \frac{\triangle ADE}{\triangle DEC}.$$

$$\therefore \frac{AD}{DB} = \frac{AE}{EC}$$

$\therefore$ DE divides AB and AC proportionally.

Conversely :

If a straight line divides two sides of a triangle proportionally, it is parallel to the third side.

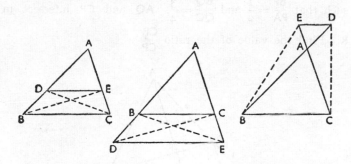

Given : △ABC with D and E points on AB and AC or on these sides produced, such that $\dfrac{AD}{DB} = \dfrac{AE}{EC}$.

Required : To prove that DE is parallel to BC.

Construction : Join BE and CD.

Proof : $\dfrac{AD}{DB} = \dfrac{\triangle ADE}{\triangle BDE}$ (△s of eq. alt. prop. to their bases).

$\dfrac{AE}{EC} = \dfrac{\triangle ADE}{\triangle DEC}$ (same reason).

But $\dfrac{AD}{DB} = \dfrac{AE}{EC}$ (given)

∴ $\dfrac{\triangle ADE}{\triangle BDE} = \dfrac{\triangle ADE}{\triangle DEC}$

∴ △BDE = △DEC.

But these triangles stand on the same base DE and lie on the same side of DE

∴ they lie between the same parallels

∴ DE is parl. to BC.

N.C.G.—12

WORKED EXAMPLES

Example 1.—P and Q are points in the sides AB, BC of △ABC such that $\dfrac{BP}{PA} = \dfrac{1}{2}$ and $\dfrac{BQ}{QC} = \dfrac{3}{4}$. AQ and CP intersect in R. Find the value of the ratio $\dfrac{CR}{CP}$.

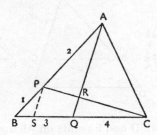

Through P draw PS parallel to AQ to meet BC in S.
In △ABQ, PS is parl. to AQ

$$\therefore \frac{BP}{PA} = \frac{BS}{SQ}, \text{ i.e. } \frac{BS}{SQ} = \frac{1}{2}$$

$$\therefore \frac{BS + SQ}{SQ} = \frac{1 + 2}{2}$$

$$\therefore \frac{BQ}{SQ} = \frac{3}{2}.$$

But $\dfrac{CQ}{BQ} = \dfrac{4}{3}$

$$\therefore \frac{CQ}{BQ} \cdot \frac{BQ}{QS} = \frac{4}{3} \cdot \frac{3}{2} = \frac{2}{1}$$

$$\therefore \frac{CQ}{QS} = \frac{2}{1}.$$

In △CPS, RQ is parl. to PS

$$\therefore \frac{CR}{RP} = \frac{CQ}{QS} = \frac{2}{1}$$

$$\therefore \frac{CR}{CP} = \frac{CR}{CR + RP} = \frac{2}{2 + 1} = \frac{2}{3}.$$

Example 2.—Q and R are points on the sides AB and AC respectively of △ABC, such that AQ = AR. QR produced meets BC produced, in P. Prove that

$$\text{rect. BP.CR} = \text{rect. BQ.CP.}$$

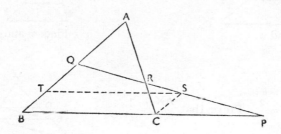

Given: As in question.

Required: To prove rect. BP.CR = rect. BQ.CP.

Construction: Draw CS parl. to BA to meet PQ in S and draw ST parl. to PB to meet AB in T.

Proof: AQ = AR (given) ∴ AQ̂R = AR̂Q (base ∠s of isos. △).
But AQ̂R = RŜC (alt. ∠s. AB, SC parl.)
and AR̂Q = SR̂C (vert. opp.)
∴ SR̂C = RŜC ∴ CR = CS.
Also BTSC is a parm. (opp. sides parl.)
∴ CS = BT (opp. sides of parm.) ∴ BT = CR.
In △BQP, CS is parl. to BQ

$$\therefore \frac{BC}{CP} = \frac{QS}{SP} \quad \therefore \frac{BC + CP}{CP} = \frac{QS + SP}{SP} \quad \therefore \frac{BP}{CP} = \frac{QP}{SP}.$$

But $\dfrac{QP}{SP} = \dfrac{QB}{TB}$ (TS is parl. to BP)

$$\therefore \frac{BP}{CP} = \frac{QB}{TB} = \frac{QB}{CR} \quad \text{i.e.} \quad \frac{BP}{CP} = \frac{QB}{CR}$$

∴ rect. BP.CR = rect. BQ.CP.

EXERCISES 55

1.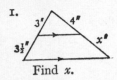

Find x.

2.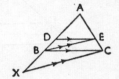

Find x and y.

3. $\dfrac{AD}{DB} = \dfrac{2}{1}$. Prove that $\dfrac{AX}{XB} = \dfrac{3}{1}$.

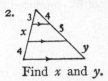

4. E is the mid-point of AB. D divides BC in the ratio 2 : 3.

Find ratio $\dfrac{CH}{CE}$.

[*Hint:* Draw EG parl. to AD to meet BC in G.]

5. E is the mid-point of the median AD. Prove that $\dfrac{AH}{AC} = \dfrac{1}{3}$.

6. $\dfrac{AD}{DB} = \dfrac{2}{1}$. Prove that each of the ratios $\dfrac{BX}{XE}$ and $\dfrac{CX}{XD}$ equals $\dfrac{3}{2}$.

7. P is any point in the common base BC of △s ABC, DBC. PQ and PR are parl. to BA and BD respectively. Prove QR parl. to AD.

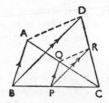

8. $\dfrac{AP}{PB} = \dfrac{3}{4}.$

$\dfrac{AR}{RC} = \dfrac{3}{2}.$

PR produced meets BC produced, in Q. Prove that C is the mid-point of BQ.

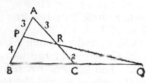

Check that $\dfrac{AP}{PB} \cdot \dfrac{BQ}{CQ} \cdot \dfrac{CR}{RA} = 1.$

9. In △ABC, P and Q are points in BC and CA respectively so that $\dfrac{BP}{PC} = \dfrac{1}{2}$ and $\dfrac{CQ}{QA} = \dfrac{1}{4}.$

QP produced meets AB produced, in R.

Calculate the ratio $\dfrac{RP}{PQ}.$

10. P and Q are points on the sides BC and AD respectively of parallelogram ABCD, such that $\dfrac{BP}{PC} = \dfrac{DQ}{QA} = \dfrac{2}{1}.$ Find the ratio in which BD is divided by AP and QC. Find also the ratio in which AP is divided by the diagonal BD.

11. Triangle XYZ is isosceles and right-angled at Y. A and B are points in XY and XZ respectively dividing these sides in the ratio 2 to 1.

Compare the perimeters of △XAB and the quad. AYZB.

12. Two straight lines OX and OY intersect at O. If P, Q, R are three points in order on OX, and S, T are two points on OY such that PS is parallel to QT and QS is parl. to RT, prove that $\dfrac{OP}{OQ} = \dfrac{OQ}{OR}$.

13. P is any point in the side BC of $\triangle$ABC. PQ, parallel to CA, meets AB in Q, and QR, parallel to BC, meets AC in R. Prove that $\dfrac{BP}{PC} = \dfrac{CR}{RA}$.

14. In triangle ABC, P is any point in the side BC. Through P, PQ and PR are drawn parallel to BA and CA meeting AC and AB in Q and R respectively. Prove that $\triangle$ARQ is a mean proportional between $\triangle$BPR and $\triangle$CPQ.

15. Two equal circles touch externally at a point B, and AB is the diameter of one of the circles. The tangent AT from A to the other circle cuts the first circle again in C. Prove that AC = 2CT.

16. Two circles of radii r_1 and r_2 touch externally at A, and PA, a diameter of the circle of radius r_1, meets the other circle again in Q. The tangent PX from P to the second circle cuts the first circle at B, and the tangent QY from Q to the first circle cuts the second circle again in C.

Express the ratio $\dfrac{PB}{BX}$ in terms of r_1 and r_2, and show that rect. PB.CQ = 4BX.CY.

17. ABCD is a trapezium and E and F are the mid-points of the oblique sides AC and BD respectively. Prove EF parallel to AB.

18. From any point E in the side CD of a parallelogram ABCD, a straight line EG is drawn parallel to the diagonal CA, meeting AD in G. Through E and G, EK and GH are drawn parallel to the diagonal DB, meeting BC and BA in K and H respectively. Prove HK parallel to AC.

19. Through a point O, three straight lines OAB, OCD, OFG are drawn so that $\dfrac{OA}{OB} = \dfrac{OC}{OD} = \dfrac{OF}{OG}$.

Prove that the triangles ACF and BDG are equiangular.

20. P and Q are points in the base BC of $\triangle$ABC such that BP = QC. PR, parallel to BA, meets AC in R, and QS, parallel to CA, meets AB in S. Prove SR parallel to BC.

CONSTRUCTION 25

To divide a straight line in a given ratio

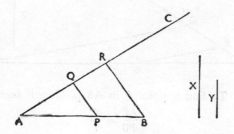

(1) *Internal Division*

Given : Straight line AB and two straight lines, whose lengths X and Y are in the given ratio.

Required : To find a point P in AB such that $\dfrac{AP}{PB} = \dfrac{X}{Y}$.

Construction : From A draw a straight line AC making any angle with AB.

From AC, cut off AQ equal to X and QR equal to Y. Join BR, and through Q draw QP parallel to RB, to meet AB in P.

Then $\dfrac{AP}{PB} = \dfrac{X}{Y}$.

Proof : In $\triangle$ABR,

QP is parl. to RB (constr.)

$\therefore \dfrac{AP}{PB} = \dfrac{AQ}{QR}$ (str. line parl. to one side of $\triangle$ divides other sides proportionally)

$\qquad = \dfrac{X}{Y}$ (constr.).

(2) *External Division*

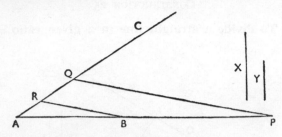

Required: To find a point **P** in **AB** produced, such that

$$\frac{AP}{PB} = \frac{X}{Y}.$$

Construction: From **A** draw a str. line **AC** making any angle
   with **AB**.
   From **AC** cut off **AQ** equal to **X** and from **QA** cut off
   QR equal to **Y**.
   Join **RB**, and through **Q** draw **QP** parallel to **RB**, to
   meet **AB** produced, in **P**.

   Then $\dfrac{AP}{PB} = \dfrac{X}{Y}.$

Proof: In △**ARB**, **QP** is drawn parallel to **RB** meeting **AR**
   and **AB** produced in **Q** and **P** respectively

$$\therefore \frac{AP}{PB} = \frac{AQ}{QR}$$

$$= \frac{X}{Y}.$$

In this case, the ratio $\dfrac{X}{Y}$ is greater than **1** since **X** is greater
than **Y**, and the point **P** lies to the right of **AB**, the segment
AP being greater than the segment **PB**. If the ratio $\dfrac{X}{Y}$ is less
than **1** then the segment **AP** must be less than the segment **PB**.
Hence **P** must lie on the side of **A** remote from **B**.

The form which the figure takes when $\dfrac{X}{Y} < 1$ is shown below.

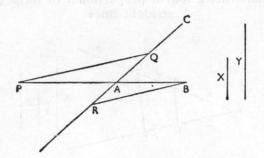

Construction: From A draw a str. line AC making any angle with AB.

From AC cut off AQ equal to X

Produce QA, and from QA produced cut off QR equal to Y

Join RB, and through Q draw QP parl. to BR, to meet BA produced, at P.

Then $\dfrac{AP}{PB} = \dfrac{X}{Y}$.

Proof: In $\triangle$ARB, QP is drawn parl. to BR, meeting RA and BA produced, in Q and P respectively

$$\therefore \; \dfrac{AP}{PB} = \dfrac{AQ}{QR}$$

$$= \dfrac{X}{Y}.$$

CONSTRUCTION 26

To construct a fourth proportional to three given straight lines

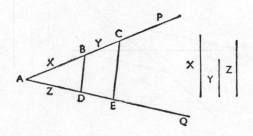

Given: Three straight lines **X, Y, Z.**

Required: To find a fourth proportional to **X, Y, Z.**

Construction: Draw two straight lines **AP** and **AQ** containing
      any angle.
      From **AP** cut off **AB = X** and **BC = Y.**
      From **AQ** cut off **AD = Z.**
      Join **BD,** and through **C** draw **CE** parl. to **BD,** meeting
      AQ in **E.**
      Then **DE** is the fourth proportional to **X, Y, Z.**

Proof: In $\triangle$**ACE,**
      BD is parl. to **CE**
$$\therefore \frac{AB}{BC} = \frac{AD}{DE},$$
    i.e. $\dfrac{X}{Y} = \dfrac{Z}{DE}$

      $\therefore$ **DE** is the fourth proportional to **X, Y, Z.**

[*Note.*—If the line **Z** is equal in length to the line **Y,** then
in the above construction, **AD = BC,** and **DE** becomes the
third proportional to **X** and **Y.**]

EXERCISES 56

1. Divide a straight line 2·5 in. long internally and externally in the ratio 7 : 3. Measure the segments and check the results.

2. Divide a straight line 2·5 in. long internally in the ratio 3 : 4 : 5.

3. Find, geometrically, a fourth proportional to 3, 4, 5.

4. Find, geometrically, a third proportional to 3, 4.

5. $A\hat{B}C$ is an angle and D a point within it. Construct a straight line XDZ passing through D, with its ends on AB and BC, so that XD : DZ = 3 : 2.

6. Draw a straight line 10 cm. long.

$$\frac{X}{Y}$$
$$\frac{Z}{}$$

Divide it in the ratio X : Y : Z.

7. Construct a triangle ABC whose perimeter is 6 in. and whose sides AB, BC, CA are in the ratio X : Y : Z (Exercise 6).

8. Find x geometrically, if $\frac{3}{x} = \frac{5}{8}$.

9. Find, geometrically, the value of $\frac{2\cdot3 \times 3\cdot6}{4\cdot1}$.

10. Find, geometrically, the value of $\frac{(2\cdot6)^2}{3\cdot1}$.

THEOREM 41

The internal and external bisectors of the vertical angle of a triangle divide the opposite side in the ratio of the sides containing the vertical angle.

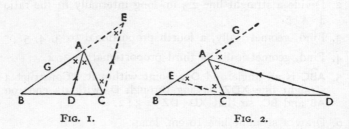

FIG. 1.   FIG. 2.

Given: $\triangle$ABC with AD bisecting the interior BÂC in Fig. 1, and the exterior GÂC in Fig. 2.

Required: To prove that $\dfrac{BD}{DC} = \dfrac{BA}{AC}$.

Construction: Through C draw CE parl. to DA to meet BA, or BA produced if necessary, in E.
  In Fig. 1 let a point G be taken in AB.

Proof: GÂD = AÊC (corresp. ∠s. DA, CE parl.)
  and DÂC = AĈE (alt. ∠s. DA, CE parl.).
  But GÂD = DÂC (given)
  ∴ AÊC = AĈE
    ∴ AE = AC (sides of a $\triangle$ opp. equal angles).
    In $\triangle$BEC, since DA is parl. to CE
  ∴ $\dfrac{BD}{DC} = \dfrac{BA}{AE}$
  ∴ $\dfrac{BD}{DC} = \dfrac{BA}{AC}$.

Conversely :

If the base of a triangle is divided internally or externally into two segments proportional to the other sides of the triangle, the line joining the point of section to the vertex bisects the vertical angle internally or externally.

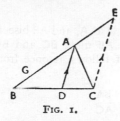
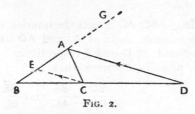

FIG. 1.   FIG. 2.

Given: △ABC with D a point in BC in Fig. 1, and in BC produced in Fig. 2, such that $\dfrac{BD}{DC} = \dfrac{BA}{AC}$.

In Fig. 1, G is any point in AB, and in Fig. 2, BA is produced to any point G.

Required: To prove that GÂD = DÂC.

Construction: Through C, draw CE parl. to DA to meet BA, or BA produced if necessary, in E.

Proof: In △BCE, since DA is parl. to CE

$$\therefore \frac{BA}{AE} = \frac{BD}{DC}.$$

But $\dfrac{BD}{DC} = \dfrac{BA}{AC}$ (given)

$$\therefore \frac{BA}{AC} = \frac{BA}{AE}$$

∴ AC = AE

∴ AĈE = AÊC (base ∠s of isos. △).

But AĈE = DÂC (alt. ∠s DA, CE parl.)

and AÊC = GÂD (corresp. ∠s DA, CE parl.)

∴ GÂD = DÂC.

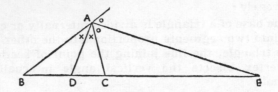

In $\triangle ABC$, AD bisects the interior angle at A, and AE bisects the exterior angle at A, and AD and AE meet BC and BC produced, at D and E respectively. It follows at once from the previous theorem, that

$$\frac{BD}{DC} = \frac{BA}{AC} \text{ and } \frac{BE}{EC} = \frac{BA}{AC}$$

$$\therefore \frac{BD}{DC} = \frac{BE}{EC},$$

i.e. the straight line BC is divided internally and externally in the same ratio at D and E. The straight line BC is said to be divided **harmonically** at D and E.

Note: (i) $D\hat{A}E = 1$ rt. angle.

(ii) $\dfrac{BA}{AC} = \dfrac{BD}{DC} = \dfrac{BE}{EC}.$

For any given value of the ratio $\dfrac{BA}{AC}$, the ratios $\dfrac{BD}{DC}$ and $\dfrac{BE}{EC}$ are fixed.

Suppose $\dfrac{BA}{AC} = \dfrac{3}{2}$, then $\dfrac{BD}{DC} = \dfrac{3}{2}$ $\therefore \dfrac{BD}{BC} = \dfrac{3}{5}$ or $BD = \dfrac{3}{5}BC$.

The point D is therefore a fixed point. So also is E a fixed point.

Hence, if B and C are fixed points, and A moves in such a way that $\dfrac{AB}{AC} = \dfrac{3}{2}$, then since D and E are fixed points and $D\hat{A}E$ is a right angle, the locus of A will be a circle on DE as diameter.

The circle is called Apollonius' Circle. For different values of the ratio $\dfrac{AB}{AC}$ the positions of D and E will vary. Hence the locus of A, for different values of the ratio $\dfrac{AB}{AC}$, consists of a system of circles.

EXERCISES 57

Find x.

2.

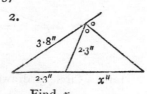

Find x.

3. Find x.

4. I is the incentre of $\triangle ABC$. AI, BI, CI produced meet the sides at D, E, H. Calculate the segments of AB, BC, CA.

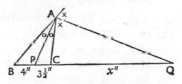

5. AD is the median from A. DE and DH bisect $A\hat{D}B$ and $A\hat{D}C$. Prove EH parallel to BC.

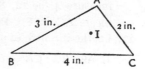

6. AD bisects $B\hat{A}C$. BE = BD and CH = CD. Prove EH parallel to BC.

7. Circles touch at **A**. Tangent at **C** to inner circle meets outer circle at **B** and **D**. Prove $\dfrac{AB}{AD} = \dfrac{BC}{CD}$.

8. **P** and **Q** divide **AB** internally and externally in the same

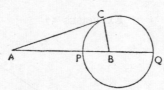

ratio. Circle is drawn on **PQ** as diameter. If **C** is any point on this circle, prove that $\dfrac{AC}{CB} = \dfrac{AP}{PB}$.

[*Hint:* Through **B** draw lines parallel to PC and QC.]

9. In △ABC, **AD** and **AE**, the internal and external bisectors of $\widehat{A}$, meet **BC** and **BC** produced, in **D** and **E** respectively. If **BE** = 7·02 in., **EC** = 2·7 in., **AE** = 3·6 in., find **AD**.

10. **ABCD** is a quadrilateral whose sides **AB**, **BC**, **CD**, **DA** measure 4, 6, 12, 8 cm. respectively. **BE** bisects $\widehat{B}$ and meets **AC** in **E**. Prove that **DE** bisects $\widehat{D}$.

11. **I** is the incentre of △ABC and **AI** produced meets **BC** in **D**. If **AB** : **BC** : **CA** = 6 : 5 : 4, prove that $\dfrac{AI}{ID} = \dfrac{2}{1}$.

12. **ABCD** is a rectangle in which $\dfrac{AB}{BC} = \dfrac{4}{3}$. The bisector of $A\widehat{C}B$ meets **AB** in **E**. If **AB** is 1 in. long, calculate **AE** and prove that **BE** is half of **BC**.

13. Show how to construct a triangle whose base is 2·2 in. long, whose vertical angle is 42° and whose sides are in the ratio 3 : 2.

14. Angles **A** and **D** of parallelogram **ABCD** are bisected by **AP** and **DQ**, which meet the diagonals **BD** and **AC** in **P** and **Q** respectively. Prove that **PQ** is parallel to **AD**.

15. I is the incentre of $\triangle$ABC and AI produced meets BC in D. Prove that $\dfrac{AI}{ID} = \dfrac{AB + AC}{BC}$.

16. Prove that the radius of the circle inscribed in an isosceles triangle has the same ratio to the altitude of the triangle as the base of the triangle has to its perimeter.

17. ABCD is a cyclic quadrilateral with AB = AD. The diagonals of the quadrilateral intersect at O. Prove that $\dfrac{BC}{CD} = \dfrac{BO}{OD}$.

18. If the bisectors of one pair of opposite angles of a quadrilateral meet on one diagonal, the bisectors of the other pair must meet on the other diagonal.

19. In triangle ABC, AB $>$ AC. The bisector AP of $\hat{A}$ meets BC in P and is produced to Q so that BQ = BP. BQ and AC, when produced, meet at R. Prove that
$$\frac{AR}{AC} = \frac{QR}{PC}.$$

20. AB is a chord of a circle and CD is the diameter perpendicular to it. P is any point on AB. CP and DP, when produced, meet the circle again in E and H respectively. Prove that $\dfrac{AE}{EB} = \dfrac{AH}{HB}$.

21. PQ and PR are tangents to a circle with centre O, and A is any point on QR. PB is the perpendicular from P to OA produced, and meets it at B. Prove that the points O, Q, B, P, R are concyclic. If QR, or RQ produced, meets PB produced, at C, prove that QR is divided harmonically at A and C.

22. P, Q, R are three points on the circumference of a circle such that PQ = QR. QS is the diameter through Q. A is any point on the tangent at P, and a straight line ABCD through A meets PQ, PR, PS in B, C, D respectively. Prove that $\dfrac{AB}{BC} = \dfrac{AD}{CD}$.

23. Two circles, centres P and Q, touch externally at O. A straight line parallel to PQ cuts the first circle in A and B, and the second in C and D. AP and DQ meet in R. Prove OR bisects $A\hat{R}D$.

24. AB is a diameter of a circle and C is the mid-point of the arc AB. CA is produced its own length to D, and DB cuts the circle at E. DGH is perpendicular to DC and meets CE and AE produced, at G and H. Prove that

(1) $\triangle HAD \equiv \triangle BCD$.

(2) $\dfrac{DG}{GH} = \dfrac{DE}{EH}$.

25. In $\triangle ABC$, $AB > AC$. The bisector of $B\hat{A}C$ meets the circumcircle in P. The diameter through P meets AB in Q, the circle again in R, and, when produced, meets CA produced, in S. Prove that $\dfrac{SR}{RQ} = \dfrac{SP}{PQ}$.

26. In $\triangle ABC$, $AB > AC$. The internal and external bisectors of $\hat{A}$ meet BC in P, and BC produced in Q. QR and QS are parallel to AB and CA, and meet AC and AB produced, in R and S respectively. Prove that

(1) ASQR is a rhombus.

(2) $\dfrac{BS}{CR} = \dfrac{AB^2}{AC^2}$.

27. In $\triangle ABC$, $AC = 2BC$. AB is produced its own length to D. CE, perpendicular to CD, meets AB in E. Prove that E is a point of trisection of AB.

Similar Figures

Similar figures may be described as figures which have the same shape, e.g. :

a map of a district and the district itself,

a picture on a film and its projection on a screen,

a photograph and an enlargement of the photograph,

a model of a ship and the ship itself.

For one figure to be a faithful reproduction of another figure with regard to shape, all angles in the one must be exactly equal to the corresponding angles in the other and all lengths in the one must be the same fraction of the corresponding lengths in the other, i.e. if two roads meet at an angle of 60° then the roads on a map of the district must also meet at an angle of 60°.

If three places A, B, C are such that the distance from A to B is 9 miles and from B to C, 6 miles, then on a map on which the distance from A to B is 3 in., the distance from B to C must be 2 in. All distances must be reduced in the same ratio, the scale of the map.

Similar figures must therefore satisfy two conditions:

(1) The angles of the one must be equal to the corresponding angles of the other.

(2) The sides of the one must be proportional to the corresponding sides of the other.

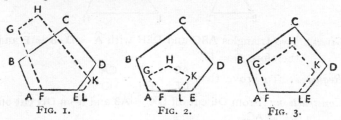

FIG. 1.   FIG. 2.   FIG. 3.

Both conditions are necessary as may be seen from the above figures.

In Fig. 1, the two pentagons are equiangular, but the sides are obviously not in proportion, and the pentagons are clearly of different shapes and are not similar figures.

In Fig. 2, each side of the pentagon FGHKL is half the corresponding side of the pentagon ABCDE, but the pentagons are obviously not equiangular and again are not of the same shape. They are, therefore, not similar figures.

In Fig. 3, the two pentagons are equiangular, and each side of FGHKL is three-quarters of the corresponding side of the pentagon ABCDE, i.e. both conditions are satisfied.

The pentagons are clearly of the same shape and are therefore similar figures.

It is found that when the figures concerned have four or more sides, the above conditions must both be satisfied in order that the figures should be similar.

In the three theorems which follow, similarity of triangles is dealt with, and these theorems show that in the case of two triangles the above conditions are not independent of each other, and that, when either is satisfied, the other is also satisfied.

THEOREM 42

If two triangles are equiangular, their corresponding sides are proportional.

Given: Two triangles ABC and DEH with $\hat{A} = \hat{D}$, $\hat{B} = \hat{E}$ and therefore $\hat{C} = \hat{H}$.

Required: To prove that $\dfrac{AB}{DE} = \dfrac{BC}{EH} = \dfrac{CA}{HD}$.

Construction: From DE cut off DK = AB and from DH cut off DL = AC.

Join KL.

Proof: In △s ABC and DKL

    1. AB = DK (constr.).

    2. AC = DL (constr.).

    3. $\hat{A} = \hat{D}$ (given).

∴ △ABC ≡ △DEH (two sides and incl. ∠)

∴ $\hat{ABC} = \hat{DKL}$.

But $\hat{ABC} = \hat{E}$ (given)

∴ $\hat{DKL} = \hat{E}$

∴ KL is parl. to EH (corresp. ∠s equal).

In △DEH, since KL is parl. to EH

∴ $\dfrac{DK}{KE} = \dfrac{DL}{LH}$

∴ $\dfrac{DK}{DK + KE} = \dfrac{DL}{DL + LH}$,

i.e. $\dfrac{DK}{DE} = \dfrac{DL}{DH}$.

But DK = AB and DL = AC (constr.)

∴ $\dfrac{AB}{DE} = \dfrac{AC}{DH}$.

Similarly it can be proved that $\dfrac{AB}{DE} = \dfrac{BC}{EH}$

$$\therefore \dfrac{AB}{DE} = \dfrac{BC}{EH} = \dfrac{CA}{HD}.$$

It follows immediately from the above theorem that equiangular triangles are necessarily similar.

Exercises 58

1. $\hat{B} = \hat{E}$ and $\hat{C} = \hat{H}$. Complete the following statements:

(1) $\dfrac{AB}{DE} = \dfrac{BC}{\text{——}}$.

(2) $\dfrac{AC}{BC} = \dfrac{\text{——}}{EH}$.

(3) $\dfrac{AB}{\text{——}} = \dfrac{DE}{DH}$.

2. △s ABC and DEH are equiangular. Find DH and EH.

3. △s ABC and DEH are equiangular. Find AB and DH.

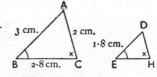

4. AB is a tangent and ACD a secant to the circle. Prove △s ABC and ADB equiangular.

Complete the following:

(1) $\dfrac{AB}{AD} = \dfrac{BC}{\text{——}}$.

(2) $\dfrac{AB}{AD} = \dfrac{AC}{\text{——}}$.

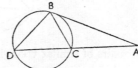

5. **ED is parallel to AC. Find EA and the**

value of the ratio $\dfrac{ED}{AC}$.

6. AB and CD are two chords intersecting
   at X. Prove △s ACX and DBX
   similar. Deduce that

$$AX . XB = CX . XD.$$

7. DE is parallel to BC and $\dfrac{AD}{DB} = \dfrac{4}{3}$. Prove

   (1) △s ADE and ABC similar.

   (2) △s DXE and CXB similar.

   (3) $\dfrac{DX}{XC} = \dfrac{4}{7}$.

8. FB bisects $\widehat{P}$ and A is the mid-point of PQ. RC is parallel

to PQ and meets AB produced, at C. Write down the

value of the ratio $\dfrac{QB}{BR}$ in two different ways and show that

$RC = \frac{1}{2}PR.$

9. PA and PB are tangents and PQR is a secant. Name two

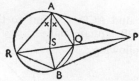

pairs of similar triangles. Prove that $\dfrac{AR}{AQ} = \dfrac{BR}{BQ}$. Hence

show that if AS bisects $R\widehat{A}Q$ then BS bisects $R\widehat{B}Q$.

10. AP is the tangent at A to ⊙ABC and meets BC produced,

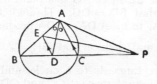

at P. AD bisects BÂC and DE is parl. to CA. From the similar triangles write down the value of the ratio $\dfrac{AP}{PB}$.

Prove that PE bisects $\widehat{P}$.

11. △ABC is right-angled at A and AD is the perpendicular from A to BC.

If $\dfrac{AB}{AC} = \dfrac{12}{5}$ find the ratio $\dfrac{BD}{DC}$.

12. ABCD is a trapezium in which AB is parallel to DC. If the sides AB, BC, CD, DA measure respectively 8, 5, 4, 6 cm and if AD and BC, when produced, meet in E, calculate EC and ED.

13. In triangle ABC, the side AB is twice the side AC. AD bisects $\widehat{A}$ and meets BC in D, and DE parallel to BA meets AC in E.

Find the ratios $\dfrac{AE}{EC}$ and $\dfrac{AB}{DE}$.

14. D and E are points on the sides AB and AC of △ABC such that $\dfrac{AD}{DB} = \dfrac{AE}{EC} = \dfrac{1}{2}$. BE and DC intersect in H. Find the ratio $\dfrac{DH}{HC}$. Express the areas BDC, BDH, AEHD as fractions of △ABC and verify that △BHD = quad. AEHD.

15. In triangle PQR, the angle P is bisected by PX which meets QR in X. Y is a point in QR produced, such that PY = XY. Prove that the triangles PRY and QPY are similar, and show that XY is a mean proportional between QY and RY.

16. AD is the bisector of the vertical angle A of $\triangle$ABC and meets the base BC in D. G is a point in DC, or DC produced, such that BD = DG. Through G, GH is drawn parallel to CA, to meet DA, or DA produced, in H. Find the ratio $\dfrac{GH}{CA}$ and deduce that GH = AB.

17. PA and PB are tangents to a circle, and Q is any other point on the circumference. QC and QD are perpendicular to PA and AB respectively, meeting them in C and D. Prove $\dfrac{QC}{QD} = \dfrac{QA}{QB}$.

18. In triangle ABC, AB is a tangent at A to a circle which passes through C, and AC is a tangent at A to a circle which passes through B. If these circles intersect at a second point P, prove that $AP^2 = BP.PC$.

19. Triangle ABC, in which AC > CB, is right-angled at C. The tangent at C to the circle ABC meets AB produced, at D, and DE, which is perpendicular to AD, meets AC produced, at E. Prove that DC = DE and $\dfrac{BC}{DC} = \dfrac{AB}{AE}$.

20. AB and CD are two chords of a circle and C is the mid-point of the arc ACB. AB and CD intersect in E, and EH, parallel to DA, meets the tangent at A in H. Prove the triangles AEH and DAB similar, and deduce that AH = EB.

21. PA and PB are tangents to a circle with centre O. PO cuts the circle in C, and PO produced cuts it again at D. If AB and PD intersect at E, prove that $PC.PD = PO.PE$.

22. A straight line DE is drawn parallel to the base BC of a triangle ABC and meets AB and AC in D and E respectively. BE and DC meet in O, and AO cuts DE in P and BC in Q. Prove that $\dfrac{AP}{AQ} = \dfrac{PO}{OQ}$, and that if AD = $\frac{1}{3}$AB then O is the mid-point of AQ.

23. ABCD is a cyclic quadrilateral such that the tangents at A and C meet on the diagonal BD produced. Prove that rect. AB.CD = rect. AD.BC.

[*Hint:* Prove $\triangle$s OAD and OBA similar and find the ratio which equals $\dfrac{AB}{AD}$.]

24. Two circles intersect at A and B and PQ is a common tangent to the circles at P and Q. If QA and PB meet at R, and PA and QB meet at S, prove that the triangles ARB and QSP are similar. Find a second pair of similar triangles and prove that AR.RP = AS.SQ.

25. Two circles intersect at A and B and the tangent at A to one of them meets the other in C. A straight line through A cuts circle ABC in D and the other in E. Prove that rect. AB.BD = rect. BE.BC.

26. XY is a chord of a circle and P any point on the circumference. Tangents to the circle at X and Y meet at Z. PL, PM, PN are the perpendiculars from P to XZ, XY, YZ respectively. Prove that $PM^2 = PL.PN$.

27. P is a fixed point within the acute angle XOY, and any line through P meets OX and OY at points A and B respectively. AC and BD are perpendiculars from A and B on OY and OX respectively, and Q is a point on CD such that $Q\hat{O}C = A\hat{O}P$. Prove

   (1) $\triangle$s AOP and COQ similar.

   (2) $OQ = OP \cos X\hat{O}Y =$ constant.

   Hence show that Q is a fixed point.

28. ABC is a given triangle. AB and AC are produced to P and Q respectively so that PQ is parallel to BC. R is a point in PQ such that $\dfrac{PR}{RQ} = \dfrac{BP}{CQ}$. AR cuts BC in S. Prove that

   (1) $\dfrac{BS}{SC} = \dfrac{PR}{RQ}$.

   (2) S is a fixed point.

   What is the locus of R as PQ varies in position?

29. State and prove a construction for finding two points D, E on the sides AB, BC of a triangle ABC, such that $\triangle$DBE may be similar to $\triangle$ABC and BD + DE may equal a given length.

30. P and Q are two fixed points. AB and CD are two fixed parallel straight lines. Prove that if M is any point in AB and if QN is drawn parallel to PM to cut CD at N, then $\dfrac{PM}{QN}$ is constant for all positions of M. Hence prove that MN passes through a fixed point.

THEOREM 43

If two triangles have the sides of the one proportional to the sides of the other, the triangles are equiangular, those angles being equal which are opposite corresponding sides.

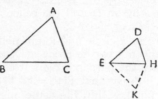

Given: Two triangles ABC and DEH with

$$\frac{AB}{DE} = \frac{BC}{EH} = \frac{CA}{HD}.$$

Required: To prove △ABC equiangular to △DEH.

Construction: On the side of EH remote from D, draw EK and HK so that HÊK = $\hat{B}$ and EĤK = $\hat{C}$.

Proof: In △s ABC and KEH

$$A\hat{B}C = K\hat{E}H \text{ (constr.)},$$

$$A\hat{C}B = K\hat{H}E \text{ (constr.)},$$

∴ $\hat{A} = \hat{K}$ (sum of ∠s of a △ = 180°)

∴ △s ABC and KEH are equiangular

∴ $\dfrac{AB}{KE} = \dfrac{BC}{EH} = \dfrac{CA}{HK}.$

But $\dfrac{AB}{DE} = \dfrac{BC}{EH}$ (given)

∴ $\dfrac{AB}{DE} = \dfrac{AB}{KE}$

∴ DE = KE.

Similarly DH = KH.

In △s DEH and KEH

1. EH is common.
2. DE = KE (proved).
3. DH = KH (proved).

$\therefore \triangle DEH \equiv \triangle KEH$ (three sides)

$\therefore$ D$\hat{E}$H = K$\hat{E}$H and D$\hat{H}$E = K$\hat{H}$E

$\therefore$ A$\hat{B}$C = D$\hat{E}$H and A$\hat{C}$B = D$\hat{H}$E (constr.)

$\therefore \hat{A} = \hat{D}$ (sum of $\angle$s of $\triangle$ = 180°)

$\therefore \triangle ABC$ is equiangular to $\triangle DEH$.

EXERCISES 59

1.

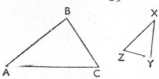

In $\triangle$s ABC and XYZ, $\dfrac{AB}{XY} = \dfrac{BC}{YZ} = \dfrac{CA}{ZX}$. Name the equal angles.

2. ACE is a straight line.   Prove BC parallel to DE.   BD produced meets AC produced, in H.   Calculate EH.

3. D is any point in BC.   F and G are midpoints of BD and DC.   HF = ½AB and HG = ½AC.   Prove AH produced passes through D.

4. $\triangle$s ABC and CAD are drawn on opposite sides of AC such that AB : BC : CA = CA : AD : DC. Prove DC parallel to AB.

5. $\triangle$s ABD and ACE are placed so that CAD is a straight line.   Prove that E$\hat{A}$B = 1 rt. angle.

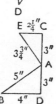

THEOREM 44

When two triangles have one angle of the one equal to one angle of the other, and the sides about the equal angles proportional, the triangles are similar.

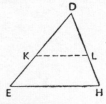

Given: Two triangles ABC and DEH with

$$\hat{A} = \hat{D} \text{ and } \frac{AB}{DE} = \frac{AC}{DH}.$$

Required: To prove that △ABC is similar to △DEH.

Construction: From DE cut off DK = AB, and from DH cut off DL = AC.

Join KL.

Proof: In △s ABC and DKL

1.   AB = DK (constr.).
2.   AC = DL (constr.).
3. $\hat{A} = \hat{D}$ (given).

∴ △ABC ≡ △DKL (2 sides and incl. ∠)

∴ $\hat{B} = D\hat{K}L$ and $\hat{C} = D\hat{L}K$.

But $\dfrac{AB}{DE} = \dfrac{AC}{DH}$ (given)

∴ $\dfrac{DK}{DE} = \dfrac{DL}{DH}$ (AB = DK and AC = DL constr.)

∴ $\dfrac{DK}{DE - DK} = \dfrac{DL}{DH - DL}$

∴ $\dfrac{DK}{KE} = \dfrac{DL}{LH}$,

i.e. KL divides the sides DE and DH of △DEH proportionally

∴ KL is parl. to EH

∴ DK̂L = Ê and DL̂K = Ĥ (corresp. ∠s KL, EH parl.).

But DK̂L = B̂ and DL̂K = Ĉ (proved)

∴ B̂ = Ê and Ĉ = Ĥ

∴ △ABC is equiangular to △DEH

∴ corresponding sides are proportional

∴ △ABC is similar to △DEH.

EXERCISES 60

1.

AD = ⅓AB ; AE = ⅓AC. Prove BEDC a cyclic quadrilateral.

2.

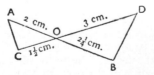

Find the ratio $\dfrac{AC}{BD}$ and prove AC parallel to BD.

3.

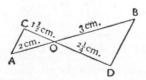

Find the ratio $\dfrac{AC}{BD}$ and prove A, C, B, D concyclic.

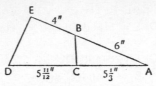

Prove quad. EBCD cyclic. Find the ratio $\dfrac{BC}{DE}$.

5.

BD bisects $\widehat{B}$. AG = AD and CH = CD. Calculate BG, BH, GH, if AB = 12 in., BC = 9 in., CA = 7 in.

6. D and E are points in AB and AC such that BD = $\frac{1}{2}$DA and CE = $\frac{1}{2}$EA. BE and CD intersect in F. Show that DF = $\frac{2}{3}$FC.

7. Two circles intersect at A and B, and P is a point on BA produced. PCD is a secant to one circle and PT a tangent to the other. Prove that △s CPT and TPD are similar.

8. Triangles ABC and DEH are similar and BC and EH are corresponding sides. Prove that the radii of the circumcircles of triangles ABC and DEH are in the ratio $\dfrac{BC}{EH}$, and also that the radii of the circumcircles are in the ratio of the perimeters of the triangles.

9. Two circles of radii r_1 and r_2 intersect in A and B. The tangents at A to the circles meet the circles of radii r_1 and r_2 in C and D respectively. Prove that

$$\frac{AC}{AD} = \frac{r_1}{r_2}.$$

10. ABC is an isosceles triangle with AB = AC. P is a point within the triangle ABC such that $PQ^2 = PR.PS$, where Q, R, S are the feet of the perpendiculars from P on BC, CA, AB respectively. Prove that the triangles SPQ and QPR are similar, and that AB and AC are tangents at B and C to the circle through B, P, C.

11. ABCD is a square. P and Q are points on BC and CD such that BP = 3PC and CQ = QD. Prove that

$$AQ = 2PQ \text{ and } A\hat{P}Q = C\hat{P}Q.$$

12. D is a point in the side BC of triangle ABC such that $\dfrac{BD}{DC} = \dfrac{AB}{AC}$. AD is produced to E so that $\dfrac{AB}{AE} = \dfrac{AD}{AC}$. Prove that $\triangle BEC$ is isosceles.

13. Triangle ABC is inscribed in a circle and AT is the tangent at A to the circle. CT is drawn on the side of CA remote from B, making $A\hat{C}T = A\hat{C}B$. P and Q are the mid-points of AB and AT respectively. Prove that

   (1) $\triangle BCP$ is similar to $\triangle ACQ$.

   (2) $\dfrac{BC}{BA} = \dfrac{CP}{PQ}$.

14. ABCD is a cyclic quadrilateral having AB.CD = BC.AD. DA is produced to P so that AP = AD. Prove $A\hat{B}P = D\hat{B}C$. If CB is produced to Q so that BQ = BC, and if AQ and BP intersect at R, prove AR = RB.

15. Triangle ABC is an isosceles triangle with AB = AC and $\hat{A}$ is a right angle. A rectangle BCDE is described on the side of BC remote from A, such that BC = 2CD. If H is the mid-point of AC, prove that $B\hat{H}D = 90°$.

16. Triangle ABC is inscribed in a circle and the tangent at A meets BC produced, at D. Prove that

$$\frac{BD}{CD} = \frac{AB^2}{AC^2}.$$

17. A straight line AB is divided at C and D so that $\dfrac{AB}{AC} = \dfrac{AC}{AD}$. AE is another straight line equal to AC. Show that $B\hat{E}D$ is bisected by EC.

18. ABCD is a parallelogram with XY a straight line parallel to AB, cutting AD, BC in X, Y respectively. H and K are points in XY, and AH and BK produced meet in P, and DH and CK produced meet in Q. Prove that PQ is parallel to BC.

Theorem 45

If a perpendicular is drawn from the right angle of a right-angled triangle to the hypotenuse, the triangles on each side of the perpendicular are similar to the whole triangle and to each other.

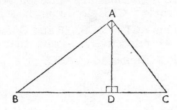

Given: △ABC right-angled at A, with AD the perp. to BC from A.

Required: To prove that △s ABD and ADC are similar to △ABC and to each other.

Proof: In △s DBA and ABC

     $\hat{B}$ is common,

     $A\hat{D}B = C\hat{A}B$ (each is a rt. angle),

∴ $B\hat{A}D = B\hat{C}A$ (sum of ∠s of a △ = 180°)

∴ △DBA is equiangular to △ABC

∴ corresponding sides are proportional

∴ △DBA is similar to △ABC.

Similarly △DAC is similar to △ABC

∴ △s DBA and DAC are similar,

i.e. △s DBA, DAC, ABC are similar triangles.

Mean Proportionals

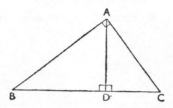

Three important results follow at once from the similar triangles in the above figure of the right-angled triangle ABC, with AD the perpendicular from the right angle to the hypotenuse.

(1) △s DBA and ABC are similar

$$\therefore \frac{BD}{BA} = \frac{BA}{BC} \text{ or } BA^2 = BD.BC,$$

i.e. AB is a mean proportional between BD and BC.

(2) △s DAC and ABC are similar

$$\therefore \frac{CD}{CA} = \frac{CA}{CB} \text{ or } CA^2 = CD.CB,$$

i.e. CA is a mean proportional between CD and CB.

Results 1 and 2 show that the square on any one of the sides containing the right angle is equal to the rectangle contained by the hypotenuse and that segment of the hypotenuse which is adjacent to the side.

(3) △s DBA and DAC are similar

$$\therefore \frac{BD}{DA} = \frac{DA}{DC} \text{ or } AD^2 = BD.DC$$

∴ AD is a mean proportional between BD and DC

or The square on the perpendicular is equal to the rectangle contained by the segments of the hypotenuse.

CONSTRUCTION 27

To construct a mean proportional to two given straight lines

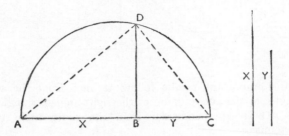

Given: Two straight lines X and Y.

Required: To construct a mean proportional between X and Y.

Construction: Draw a straight line AB equal in length to the given line X, and produce AB to C, making BC equal in length to the given line Y. On AC as diameter, describe a semicircle. At B draw BD perpendicular to AC and let it meet the semicircle at D. Then BD is a mean proportional between X and Y.

Proof: Join AD and DC.
　　AD̂C is a rt. angle (∠ in a semicircle).
　　DB is perp. to AC (constr.).
　　∴ △ABD is similar to △DBC
　　∴ $\dfrac{AB}{BD} = \dfrac{BD}{BC}$,
　　i.e. $\dfrac{X}{BD} = \dfrac{BD}{Y}$.

　　∴ BD is a mean proportional between X and Y.

Alternative Method

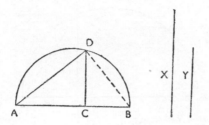

Construction: Draw AB equal to X and from AB cut off AC equal to Y.

On AB as diameter draw a semicircle.

At C make CD perp. to AB and let it cut the semicircle at D. Join AD.

Then AD is a mean proportional between AB and AC.

Proof: Join BD.

AD̂B is a rt. angle ($\angle$ in a semicircle).

DC is perp. to AB (constr.)

$\therefore$ $\triangle$ABD is similar to $\triangle$ADC

$\therefore$ $\dfrac{AB}{AD} = \dfrac{AD}{AC}$

$\therefore$ AD is a mean proportional between AB and AC, i.e. between X and Y.

CONSTRUCTION 28

To construct a square equal in area to a given rectangle

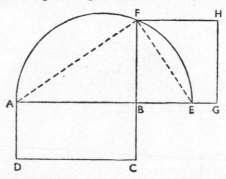

Given : Rectangle ABCD.

Required : To construct a square equal in area to the rect. ABCD

Construction : Produce AB to E, making BE equal to BC.
On AE describe a semicircle and produce CB to meet the semicircle in F.
On BF construct the square BFHG.
Then sq. BFHG = rect. ABCD.

Proof : Join AF, FE.

$\quad$ A$\widehat{F}$E = 1 rt. angle (angle in a semicircle).

$\quad$ Also F$\widehat{B}$A = 1 rt. angle since it is the supplement of A$\widehat{B}$C

$\quad\therefore$ △s AFB and FEB are similar

$\quad\therefore \dfrac{AB}{BF} = \dfrac{BF}{BE}$

$\quad\therefore BF^2 = AB \cdot BE$

$\qquad\quad = AB \cdot BC$ (constr.)

$\qquad\quad = $ rect. ABCD.

$\quad$ But $BF^2 = $ sq. BFHG (constr.)

$\therefore$ sq. BFHG = rect. ABCD.

EXERCISES 61

1.

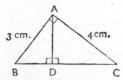

Calculate BC, AD, BD, DC, given that BÂC = 90° and AD is perp. to BC.

2. TA and TB are tangents from T to circle with centre O.

Prove that
(1) TA² = TC.TO.
(2) OA² = OC.OT.

3. AD is the perp. from the rt. angle A to the opp. side BC.

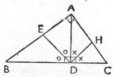

DE and DH bisect AD̂B and AD̂C. Prove that

$$\frac{BE}{EA} = \frac{AH}{HC}.$$

4. AB is a diameter. AC and BD are tangents. E is any

point on the circle, and CED is the tangent at E. Prove that rect. CE.ED = sq. on OE.

5. Triangle ABC is right-angled at A. A straight line parallel to AC meets AB at D, and BC at E. If DE is a mean proportional between BD and DA, prove that AE is a mean proportional between BE and EC.

6. Given that the sum of two straight lines is 13 cm., and that the mean proportional between the lines is 6 cm., find the lengths of the lines.

7. AB is divided at P so that $AB \cdot BP = AP^2$. BC is drawn at right angles to AB and equal to AP. CQ is drawn at right angles to AC, to meet AB produced, at Q. Prove that $BP = BQ$.

8. A semicircle is described on the radius OA of a given circle, and the perpendicular to OA, drawn through the centre of the semicircle, meets the semicircle in B. Prove that the circle with centre O and radius OB is half the area of the given circle.

9. PQ is a common tangent to two circles which touch externally at A. Prove $P\hat{A}Q = 1$ rt. angle. PR and QS are diameters through P and Q, meeting the circles again in R and S. Prove that PQ is a mean proportional to PR and QS.

10. Triangle ABC is right-angled at A. AD is the perpendicular from A to BC, DE the perpendicular from D to AB, EH the perpendicular from E to BC and so on.
Show that the perpendiculars CA, AD, DE, EH, etc., form a Geometric Series.

11. Find, geometrically, a mean proportional between 4 and 8.

12. Find, geometrically, a mean proportional between 3 and 6.

13. A square has a side 1 in. long. A rectangle equal in area to the square has one side 2·1 in. long. Find, geometrically, the length of the adjacent side of the rectangle.

14. A square has a side 1 in. long. The perimeter of a rectangle equal to it in area is 6 in. Find the dimensions of the rectangle, leaving answers in surd form.

15. A square has a side 1 in. long. Construct a rectangle with twice the area and twice the perimeter of the square. What are its dimensions? Give answers in surd form.

THEOREM 46

The areas of similar triangles are proportional to the squares on corresponding sides.

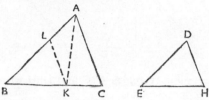

Given: Two similar triangles ABC and DEH with BC and EH corresponding sides.

Required: To prove $\dfrac{\triangle ABC}{\triangle DEH} = \dfrac{BC^2}{EH^2}$.

Construction: From BC and BA cut off BK and BL equal respectively to EH and ED. Join KL and KA.

Proof: In $\triangle$s BLK and EDH

    1.   BK = EH (constr.).

    2.   BL = ED (constr.).

    3. $\hat{B} = \hat{E}$ (corresp. $\angle$s in similar $\triangle$s).

$\therefore$ $\triangle$BLK $\equiv$ $\triangle$EDH (2 sides and incl. $\angle$)

$\therefore$ $\dfrac{\triangle ABC}{\triangle DEH} = \dfrac{\triangle ABC}{\triangle BLK} = \dfrac{\triangle ABC}{\triangle ABK} \cdot \dfrac{\triangle ABK}{\triangle BLK}$

$\qquad = \dfrac{BC}{BK} \cdot \dfrac{AB}{BL}$ ($\triangle$s of equal altitude are prop. to their bases)

$\qquad = \dfrac{BC}{EH} \cdot \dfrac{AB}{ED}$.

But $\dfrac{AB}{ED} = \dfrac{BC}{EH}$ ($\triangle$s ABC and DEH are similar)

$\therefore$ $\dfrac{\triangle ABC}{\triangle DEH} = \dfrac{BC^2}{EH^2}$.

Similarly $\dfrac{\triangle ABC}{\triangle DEH} = \dfrac{CA^2}{HD^2} = \dfrac{AB^2}{DE^2}$.

The Theorem may also be proved as follows:

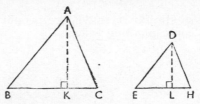

Given: Two similar triangles **ABC** and **DEH** with **BC** and **EH** corresponding sides.

Required: To prove $\dfrac{\triangle ABC}{\triangle DEH} = \dfrac{BC^2}{EH^2}$.

Construction: From **A** and **D**, drop perpendiculars **AK** and **DL** to **BC** and **EH** respectively.

Proof: Since the area of a triangle is given by

$$\tfrac{1}{2}\text{Base} \times \text{Altitude}$$

$$\frac{\triangle ABC}{\triangle DEH} = \frac{\frac{1}{2}BC.AK}{\frac{1}{2}EH.DL} = \frac{BC}{EH}.\frac{AK}{DL}.$$

In triangles **ABK** and **DEL**

$$\hat{B} = \hat{E} \text{ (from sim. } \triangle\text{s ABC, DEH)}.$$
$$A\hat{K}B = D\hat{L}E \text{ (constr.)}.$$
$$\therefore B\hat{A}K = E\hat{D}L \text{ (sum of } \angle\text{s of a } \triangle)$$
$$\therefore \triangle ABK \text{ is equiangular to } \triangle DEL$$

$$\therefore \frac{AK}{DL} = \frac{AB}{DE}.$$

But $\dfrac{AB}{DE} = \dfrac{BC}{EH}$ ($\triangle$s ABC, DEH similar)

$$\therefore \frac{\triangle ABC}{\triangle DEH} = \frac{BC}{EH}.\frac{BC}{EH} = \frac{BC^2}{EH^2}.$$

Similarly $\dfrac{\triangle ABC}{\triangle DEH} = \dfrac{AB^2}{DE^2} = \dfrac{CA^2}{HD^2}.$

[*Note:* This theorem may also be proved using the formula Area of $\triangle = \frac{1}{2}$ ab tin C.]

EXERCISES 62

1.

BC and EH are corresponding sides of similar triangles ABC, DEH.   Find area of △DEH.

2.

AB and XY are corresponding sides of similar triangles ABC, XYZ.   Find XY.

3.

DE is parl. to BC. $\dfrac{AD}{DB} = \dfrac{2}{1}$.   △ADE = 8 sq. in.   Find area BDEC.

4. What fraction is the quad. DEGH of the whole triangle ?

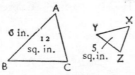

5. AC is a diagonal.   What fraction is APQR of ABCD ?

6. DE, parallel to BC, divides AB in the ratio 5 : 3.

Find the ratio $\dfrac{\triangle DEH}{\triangle CBH}$.

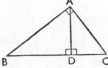

7.

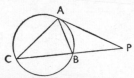

$\widehat{A} = 90°$. AD is perp. to BC. Express the ratio $\dfrac{\triangle ABD}{\triangle CAD}$ in four different ways. Prove that $\dfrac{BD}{DC} = \dfrac{AB^2}{AC^2}$.

8.

PA is a tangent and PBC a secant. Prove that
$$\dfrac{PB}{PC} = \dfrac{PB^2}{PA^2}.$$

9. △s ABC and PQR are similar and AD and PS are perpendiculars from A and P to corresponding sides BC and QR.

Prove that $\dfrac{\triangle ABC}{\triangle PQR} = \dfrac{AD^2}{PS^2}$.

10. Prove that similar triangles are proportional to the squares on
   (1) corresponding medians,
   (2) the radii of their inscribed circles,
   (3) the radii of their circumscribed circles.

11. P is a point in the side AB of △ABC such that $\dfrac{AP}{PB} = \dfrac{1}{3}$. PQ, parallel to BC, meets AC in Q, and QR, parallel to AB, meets BC in R. Prove that $BPQR = \frac{3}{8}\triangle ABC$.

12. ABC is a triangle and DE, parallel to BC, cuts AB, AC, in D and E respectively. BE and DC intersect in H.
If $\dfrac{AD}{DB} = \dfrac{1}{3}$ and $\triangle ABC = 64$ sq. cm.,
find areas of $\triangle$s ADE, BDE, DHE.

13. Triangle ABC is right-angled at A and AD is perpendicular to BC. The bisector of $B\hat{A}C$ meets BC in E. Prove that
$$\dfrac{BD}{DC} = \dfrac{BE^2}{EC^2}.$$

14. Triangles ABC and CAD are drawn on opposite sides of AC such that AB : BC : CA = CA : AD : DC. Prove that
$$\dfrac{BC^2}{AD^2} = \dfrac{AB}{DC}.$$

15. ABC is a triangle with AC > AB. A straight line BD is drawn, meeting AC at D, and making $A\hat{B}D$ equal to $A\hat{C}B$. Prove that $\dfrac{BD^2}{BC^2} = \dfrac{AD}{AC}.$

16. PQR is an equilateral triangle and A is a point on RQ produced. B is a point on QR produced, such that $A\hat{P}B = 120°$. Prove that
    (1) $\triangle$s PAQ and PBR are similar.
    (2) AQ.RB = QR².
    (3) $\dfrac{AQ}{RB} = \dfrac{PA^2}{PB^2}.$

17. Triangle ABC is inscribed in a circle. Through the vertex C a line CD is drawn, parallel to the tangent at A, to meet AB in D. Prove that the triangles ABC and ACD are similar and that $\dfrac{AB}{AD} = \dfrac{BC^2}{CD^2}.$

18. ABCD is a quadrilateral in which the diagonals intersect at E. If $B\hat{A}D = D\hat{B}C$ and if DB bisects $A\hat{D}C$, prove that
$\dfrac{AE}{EC} = \dfrac{AB^2}{BC^2}.$

19. Triangle **ABC** is inscribed in a circle. Straight lines are drawn through **B** and **C**, parallel to **CA** and **BA** respectively, to meet the tangent at **A** in **D** and **E**. Prove that

$$\frac{DA}{AE} = \frac{AB}{EC} = \frac{AB^2}{AC^2}.$$

20. The sides **AB** and **DC** of a cyclic quadrilateral meet when produced at **E**. The circle through **B**, **E**, **D** cuts **AD**, or **AD** produced, again in **H**. Prove that

(1) $\dfrac{\triangle ABH}{\triangle ADE} = \dfrac{AB^2}{AD^2}.$

(2) $AB . BE = BH . BC.$

21. **AX**, **BY**, **CZ** are the perpendiculars from the vertices **A**, **B**, **C** to the opposite sides of $\triangle ABC$. Prove that

(1) $\triangle ABC : \triangle XBZ = AB^2 : BX^2.$

(2) Quad. $AZXC : \triangle XBZ = AX^2 : BX^2.$

22. **AB** is the diameter of a circle, and **P** is any point on the circumference. **AP** produced meets the tangent at **B**, in **C**. **PD** is the perpendicular from **P** on **AB**. Prove that

$$\frac{AB^2}{BC^2} = \frac{AD}{DB}.$$

23. **P** is the mid-point of the side **AB** of $\triangle ABC$, and **Q** is a point on **AB**, such that **AQ** is a mean proportional between **AP** and **AB**. Prove that a straight line through **Q**, parallel to **BC**, bisects the area of the triangle.

24. The base **BC** of triangle **ABC** is divided at **D** so that $BD = 2DC$. On **BC**, on the side remote from **A**, a semicircle is drawn. Through **D**, draw **DE** at right angles to **BC**, to cut the semicircle in **E**. From **BC**, cut off a part **BP** equal to **CE**, and draw **PQ** parallel to **CA**, to cut **BA** in **Q**. Prove that $\triangle BPQ = \frac{1}{3}\triangle ABC.$

25. **ABC** is a triangle whose vertical angle $\widehat{A}$ is $45°$. **E** and **H** are the feet of the perpendiculars from **B** and **C** on the opposite sides **AC** and **AB** respectively, and **D** is the mid-point of the side **BC**. Prove that

(1) $AB = \sqrt{2} . AE.$

(2) $\triangle AEH = \frac{1}{2}\triangle ABC.$

(3) $H\widehat{D}E = 90°.$

Similar polygons may be divided up into the same number of similar triangles.

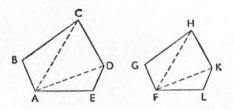

The polygons ABCDE and FGHKL are similar polygons with AB and FG corresponding sides.

By joining AC and AD in polygon ABCDE, and FH and FK in polygon FGHKL, each figure is divided into 3 triangles, and it can be proved that each of the 3 triangles which make up the polygon ABCDE is similar to the corresponding triangle in polygon FGHKL.

(1) △ABC is similar to △FGH.

For $\dfrac{AB}{FG} = \dfrac{BC}{GH}$ (corresponding sides of similar figures).

Also $\hat{B} = \hat{G}$ (corresponding angles of similar figures).

∴ △ABC is similar to △FGH (sides about eq. ∠s prop.).

(2) △ACD is similar to △FHK.

Here $B\hat{C}D = G\hat{H}K$ (corresp. ∠s in sim. figures).

$B\hat{C}A = G\hat{H}F$ (corresp. ∠s in sim. △s).

∴ By subtraction $A\hat{C}D = F\hat{H}K$.

Also $\dfrac{AC}{FH} = \dfrac{BC}{GH}$ (corresp. sides of sim. △s).

But $\dfrac{CD}{HK} = \dfrac{BC}{GH}$ (corresp. sides of sim. figures).

∴ $\dfrac{AC}{FH} = \dfrac{CD}{HK}$

∴ △ACD is sim. to △FHK (sides about eq. ∠s proportional).

(3) △ADE is similar to △FKL. (Proof similar to (1).)
   The method of division of the figures is quite arbitrary.

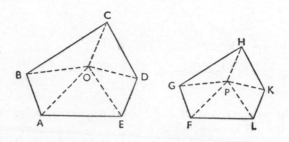

   Take any point O inside the polygon ABCDE and join O to
each of the vertices.

   AE and FL are corresponding sides of the polygons. At F
make LF̂P = EÂO and F̂LP = AÊO, and let FP and LP intersect
in P.

   △s AOE and FPL are therefore similar since they are equiangular by construction.
   Join PG, PH, PK.

   It can be proved very easily that, of the remaining four
triangles in ABCDE standing on the sides AB, BC, CD, DE, each
is similar to that triangle which stands on the corresponding
side of the polygon FGHKL.

Similar figures are to one another as the squares on corresponding sides.

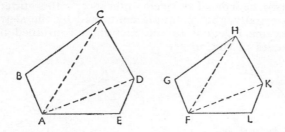

We have already shown that in the similar polygons ABCDE and FGHKL

$$\triangle ABC \text{ is similar to } \triangle FGH.$$
$$\triangle ACD \text{ is similar to } \triangle FHK.$$
$$\triangle ADE \text{ is similar to } \triangle FKL.$$

$$\frac{\triangle ABC}{\triangle FGH} = \frac{AB^2}{FG^2} \quad \text{(similar } \triangle s \text{ are prop. to sqs. on corresp. sides).}$$

$$\frac{\triangle ACD}{\triangle FHK} = \frac{CD^2}{HK^2} \text{ (same reason).}$$

$$\frac{\triangle ADE}{\triangle FKL} = \frac{AE^2}{FL^2} \text{ (same reason).}$$

But $\dfrac{AB}{FG} = \dfrac{CD}{HK} = \dfrac{AE}{FL}$ (corresp. sides of similar figures).

$$\therefore \frac{AB^2}{FG^2} = \frac{CD^2}{HK^2} = \frac{AE^2}{FL^2}$$

$$\therefore \frac{\triangle ABC}{\triangle FGH} = \frac{\triangle ACD}{\triangle FHK} = \frac{\triangle ADE}{\triangle FKL}.$$

Each of these ratios $= \dfrac{\triangle ABC + \triangle ACD + \triangle ADE}{\triangle FGH + \triangle FHK + \triangle FKL}$

$$= \frac{\text{Fig. ABCDE}}{\text{Fig. FGHKL}}$$

$$\therefore \frac{\text{Fig. ABCDE}}{\text{Fig. FGHKL}} = \frac{AB^2}{FG^2}.$$

Alternative Proof for Theorems 34, 35

If two chords of a circle intersect, either internally or externally, the rectangle contained by the segments of the one is equal to the rectangle contained by the segments of the other.

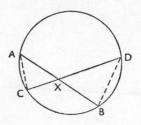

FIG. 1.   FIG. 2.

Given: A circle with two chords AB and CD intersecting at X, internally in Fig. 1 and externally in Fig. 2.

Required: To prove that AX.XB = CX.XD.

Construction: Join AC and BD.

Proof: In △s ACX and DBX

$$A\hat{X}C = D\hat{X}B \quad \left(\begin{array}{l} \text{Vert. opp., Fig. 1.} \\ \text{Common } \angle, \text{ Fig. 2.} \end{array} \right)$$

$$C\hat{A}X = B\hat{D}X \left(\begin{array}{l} \text{Angles in same segment, Fig. 1.} \\ \text{Ext. } \angle = \text{int. opp. } \angle \text{ of cyclic} \\ \text{quad., Fig. 2.} \end{array} \right)$$

∴ $A\hat{C}X = D\hat{B}X$ (sum of ∠s of △ = 180°)

∴ △s ACX and DBX are equiangular.

∴ △ACX is similar to △DBX

∴ $\dfrac{AX}{XD} = \dfrac{CX}{XB}$

∴ AX.XB = CX.XD.

Alternative Proof for Theorems 36, 37

If two straight lines AB and CD intersect in X in such a way that rect. AX.XB = rect. CX.XD, then the four points A, B, C, D are concyclic.

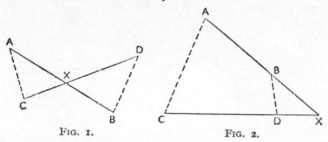

FIG. 1.   FIG. 2.

Given: Two straight lines AB and CD intersecting in X, in Fig. 1 internally and in Fig. 2 externally, in such a way that rect. AX.XB = rect. CX.XD.

Required: To prove that the four points A, B, C, D are concyclic.

Construction: Join AC and BD.

Proof: In △s AXC and DXB

$$A\hat{X}C = D\hat{X}B \begin{pmatrix} \text{Fig. 1, vert. opp.} \\ \text{Fig. 2, common angle.} \end{pmatrix}$$

$$\frac{AX}{XC} = \frac{DX}{XB} \text{ (AX.XB = CX.XD given).}$$

∴ △AXC is similar to △DXB (sides about eq. ∠s prop.).

Fig. 1.

∴ $C\hat{A}X = B\hat{D}X$ (corresp. ∠s in sim. △s).
But these angles are subtended by BC at two points on the same side of BC
∴ A, C, B, D are concyclic.

Fig. 2.

$C\hat{A}X = B\hat{D}X$ (corresp. ∠s in sim. △s).
∴ ABDC is a cyclic quad. (ext. ∠ = int. opp. ∠).

Alternative Proof for Second Part of Theorem 35

If from a point outside a circle, a secant and tangent are drawn, the rectangle contained by the whole secant and the part outside the circle is equal to the square on the tangent.

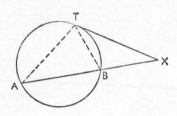

Given: Circle with **X** a point outside it, and **XT** and **XBA** a tangent and secant to the circle.

Required: To prove that $XT^2 = XB.XA$.

Construction: Join **AT, BT**.

Proof: In $\triangle$s **XBT** and **XTA**

$\hat{X}$ is common.

$X\hat{T}B = X\hat{A}T$ (angle bet. tangent and chord equals
$\angle$ in alt. seg.).

$\therefore$ $X\hat{B}T = X\hat{T}A$ (sum of $\angle$s of $\triangle$ = 180°)

$\therefore$ $\triangle$s **XBT** and **XTB** are equiangular

$\therefore$ corresponding sides are in proportion

$\therefore$ $\dfrac{XB}{XT} = \dfrac{XT}{XA}$

$\therefore$ $XT^2 = XA.XB$.

Alternative Proof for Theorem 38

If from a point outside a circle a secant is drawn to the circle and another straight line is drawn to meet the circumference, and if the rectangle contained by the whole secant and the part outside the circle is equal to the square on the other line, that line is a tangent to the circle.

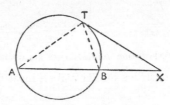

Given: Circle with a point X outside it. XBA is a secant and XT meets the circumference at a point T such that XA.XB = XT².

Required: To prove that XT is a tangent to the circle at T.

Construction: Join AT, BT.

Proof: XA.XB = XT² (given)

$$\therefore \frac{XA}{XT} = \frac{XT}{XB}.$$

In △s AXT and TXB

A$\hat{X}$T = T$\hat{X}$B (common angle).

$$\frac{XA}{XT} = \frac{XT}{XB} \text{ (proved).}$$

∴ △s AXT and TXB are similar (sides about eq. ∠s prop.)

∴ T$\hat{A}$X = B$\hat{T}$X (opp. corresp. sides),

i.e. T$\hat{A}$B = B$\hat{T}$X.

But BT is a chord of the circle

∴ TX is the tangent at T (converse of tangent-chord theorem.)

[*Note:* For exercises on the previous four theorems see Exercises 52 and 53.]

Construction of Similar Figures

(1) On a given straight line, to construct a rectilineal figure similar to a given rectilineal figure.

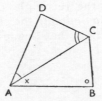

Given: Rectilineal figure **ABCD** and straight line **EH**.

Required: To construct on **EH** a rectilineal figure similar to **ABCD**.

Construction: Join **AC**.

At **E**, make $H\hat{E}K = B\hat{A}C$.

At **H**, make $E\hat{H}K = \hat{B}$.

At **K**, make $E\hat{K}L = A\hat{C}D$.

At **E**, make $K\hat{E}L = C\hat{A}D$.

Then **EHKL** is the required figure.

Proof: Since $D\hat{A}C = L\hat{E}K$ and $C\hat{A}B = K\hat{E}H$ (constr.)

∴ $D\hat{A}B = L\hat{E}H$.

Similarly $D\hat{C}B = L\hat{K}H$

and $\hat{B} = \hat{H}$ (constr.)

∴ **ABCD** and **EHKL** are equiangular (sum of ∠s of quad. = 4 rt. angles).

Since △s **ABC** and **EHK**, also △s **ACD** and **EKL**, are equiangular (constr.)

∴ $\dfrac{AB}{EH} = \dfrac{BC}{HK} = \dfrac{AC}{EK} = \dfrac{CD}{KL} = \dfrac{DA}{LE}$

∴ the corresponding sides of **ABCD** and **EHKL** are prop.

∴ **EHKL** is similar to **ABCD** and has been described on **EH**.

(2) To construct a rectilineal figure similar to a given rectilineal figure, on a line of a given length.

1st Method:

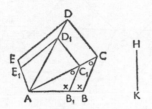

Given: Rectilineal figure ABCDE and HK the given length.

Required: To construct, on a side equal to HK, a figure similar to ABCDE.

Construction: From AB cut off AB_1 equal to HK.

Join AC and AD.

Through B_1 draw B_1C_1 parl. to BC to meet AC in C_1.

Through C_1 draw C_1D_1 parl. to CD to meet AD in D_1.

Through D_1 draw D_1E_1 parl. to DE to meet AE in E_1.

Then $AB_1C_1D_1E_1$ is the required figure.

Proof: $A\widehat{C_1}B_1 = A\widehat{C}B$ (corresp. $\angle$s, B_1C_1 and BC parl.).

$A\widehat{C_1}D_1 = A\widehat{C}D$ (corresp. $\angle$s, C_1D_1 and CD parl.).

$\therefore B_1\widehat{C_1}D_1 = B\widehat{C}D$.

Similarly $C_1\widehat{D_1}E_1 = C\widehat{D}E$.

Also $A\widehat{B_1}C_1 = A\widehat{B}C$ (corresp. $\angle$s, B_1C_1 and BC parl.)

and $E_1\widehat{A}B_1 = E\widehat{A}B$ (common $\angle$)

$\therefore A\widehat{E_1}D_1 = A\widehat{E}D$ (sum of $\angle$s of pentagon = 6 rt. angles)

$\therefore$ ABCDE and $AB_1C_1D_1E_1$ are equiangular.

Also since the triangles AB_1C_1, ABC ; AC_1D_1, ACD ; AD_1E_1, ADE are equiangular

$\therefore$ corresponding sides are in proportion:

$\therefore \dfrac{AB_1}{AB} = \dfrac{B_1C_1}{BC} = \dfrac{AC_1}{AC} = \dfrac{C_1D_1}{CD}$, etc.

$\therefore AB_1C_1D_1E_1$ is similar to ABCDE and side $AB_1 = HK$ (constr.).

2nd Method:

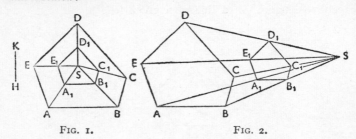

FIG. 1.   FIG. 2.

Construction: Draw $A_1B_1 = KH$ and parl. to AB, inside ABCDE (Fig. 1), or outside ABCDE (Fig. 2).

Join AA_1, BB_1 and produce them to meet at S.

Join SC, SD, SE.

Through B_1 draw B_1C_1 parl. to BC; through C_1 draw C_1D_1 parl. to CD; through D_1 draw D_1E_1 parl. to DE.

Join E_1A_1.

Then $A_1B_1C_1D_1E_1$ is the required figure.

Outline of Proof:

Since A_1B_1 is parl. to AB, $\triangle$s SAB, SA_1B_1 are equiangular. Similarly $\triangle$s SBC and SB_1C_1, $\triangle$s SCD and SC_1D_1, $\triangle$s SDE and SD_1E_1 are equiangular.

From similar triangles $\dfrac{SA_1}{SA} = \dfrac{SE_1}{SE}$

$\therefore$ E_1A_1 is parl. to EA.

Figs. ABCDE and $A_1B_1C_1D_1E_1$ are equiangular (corresp. sides parl.), also corresponding sides are proportional (from sim. $\triangle$s)

$\therefore$ $A_1B_1C_1D_1E_1$ is similar to ABCDE and $A_1B_1 = HK$.

S is called the **homothetic centre** or **centre of similarity**.

(3) To describe a rectilineal figure similar to one rectilineal figure and equal to another given rectilineal figure.

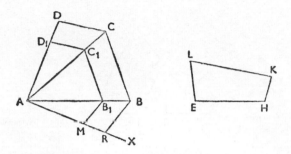

Given: Rectilineal figures ABCD and EHKL.

Required: To describe a rectilineal figure similar to ABCD and equal to EHKL.

Construction: Construct squares equal in area to ABCD and EHKL.

From AX, a str. line making any angle with AB, cut off AR, AM equal respectively to the sides of these squares.

Join RB and through M draw MB_1 parl. to RB, to cut AB in B_1.

On AB_1 construct a figure $AB_1C_1D_1$ similar to ABCD. Then $AB_1C_1D_1$ is the required figure.

Proof: $AB_1C_1D_1 : ABCD = AB_1{}^2 : AB^2$ (sim. polygons prop. to sqs. on corresp. sides)

and $AB_1{}^2 : AB^2 = AM^2 : AR^2$ ($AB_1 : AB = AM : AR$)

∴ $AB_1C_1D_1 : ABCD = AM^2 : AR^2$.

But $EHKL : ABCD = AM^2 : AR^2$ (constr.)

∴ $AB_1C_1D_1 : ABCD = EHKL : ABCD$

∴ $AB_1C_1D_1 = EHKL$, and is similar to ABCD.

(4) To construct a rectilineal figure similar to a given rectilineal figure and equal to a given fraction of it in area.

1st Method:

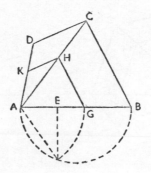

Given: Rectilineal figure ABCD.

Required: To construct a rectilineal figure, similar to ABCD and equal to $\frac{1}{3}$ABCD in area.

Construction: From AB cut off AE equal to $\frac{1}{3}$AB.
Find G in AB such that AG is a mean proportional between AE and AB.
On AG construct AGHK similar to ABCD.
Then AGHK is the required figure.

Proof: $\dfrac{AE}{AG} = \dfrac{AG}{AB}$ (constr.)

$\therefore AG^2 = AE.AB = \frac{1}{3}AB.AB$ (constr.)
$\qquad\qquad = \frac{1}{3}AB^2$

$\therefore \dfrac{AG^2}{AB^2} = \dfrac{1}{3}.$

AGHK is similar to ABCD (constr.)

$\therefore \dfrac{AGHK}{ABCD} = \dfrac{AG^2}{AB^2}$ (sim. polygons are prop. to sqs. on corresp. sides)

$\qquad\qquad = \frac{1}{3}$

$\therefore$ AGHK is similar to ABCD and equal to $\frac{1}{3}$ABCD.

2nd Method:

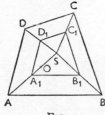

FIG. 1.

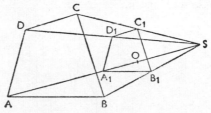

FIG. 2.

Construction: Take any point S inside ABCD (Fig. 1), or outside ABCD (Fig. 2).

Join SA and SB.

From SA cut off $SO = \frac{1}{3}SA$.

Find a point A_1 in SA such that SA_1 is a mean proportional between SO and SA.

Through A_1 draw A_1B_1 parl. to AB to meet SB in B_1.

On A_1B_1 construct $A_1B_1C_1D_1$ similar to ABCD.

Then $A_1B_1C_1D_1$ is the required figure.

Proof: A_1B_1 is parl. to AB (constr.)

∴ $\triangle SA_1B_1$ is equiangular to $\triangle SAB$

∴ $\dfrac{A_1B_1}{AB} = \dfrac{SA_1}{SA}$ (corresp. sides prop.).

But $\dfrac{SO}{SA_1} = \dfrac{SA_1}{SA}$ (constr.)

∴ $SA_1{}^2 = SO.SA = \frac{1}{3}SA.SA$ (constr.)
$= \frac{1}{3}SA^2$

∴ $\dfrac{SA_1{}^2}{SA^2} = \dfrac{1}{3}$

∴ $\dfrac{A_1B_1{}^2}{AB^2} = \dfrac{1}{3}.$

But $A_1B_1C_1D_1$ is similar to ABCD (constr.)

∴ $\dfrac{A_1B_1C_1D_1}{ABCD} = \dfrac{A_1B_1{}^2}{AB^2}$ (sim. polygons are prop. to sqs. on corresp. sides)
$= \frac{1}{3}$

∴ $A_1B_1C_1D_1$ is similar to ABCD and equal to one-third of its area.

In a triangle, inscribe a square having two vertices on the base and one on each side.

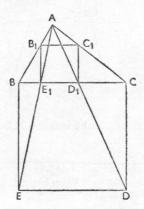

Given: △ABC.

Required: To inscribe in triangle ABC a square with two of its vertices on BC, and one on each of AB and AC.

Construction: On BC describe a square BCDE. Join AD, AE and let them cut BC in D_1 and E_1.
Through E_1 and D_1 draw E_1B_1 and D_1C_1 parallel to EB, to meet AB and AC in B_1 and C_1 respectively. Join B_1C_1.
Then $B_1C_1D_1E_1$ is the required square.

Proof: △s AB_1E_1, ABE ; △s AE_1D_1, AED ; △s AC_1D_1, ACD are similar △s

$$\therefore \frac{AB_1}{AB} = \frac{AE_1}{AE} = \frac{AD_1}{AD} = \frac{AC_1}{AC}.$$

$\therefore$ B_1C_1 is parl. to BC.
Also B_1E_1 is parl. to C_1D_1 (constr.)
$\therefore$ $B_1C_1D_1E_1$ is a parm. (opp. sides parl.).
But $E\hat{B}C$ is a right angle ($\angle$ of a sq.)
$\therefore$ $E\hat{B}_1C_1$ is a right angle
$\therefore$ $B_1C_1D_1E_1$ is a rectangle.

Also from similar $\triangle$s, $\dfrac{B_1E_1}{BE} = \dfrac{E_1D_1}{ED}$.

But BE = ED (sides of a sq.)

$\therefore$ $B_1E_1 = E_1D_1$

$\therefore$ $B_1C_1D_1E_1$ is a square.

Exercises 63

1. Draw a quadrilateral ABCD, given that AB = 2·5 in., $\widehat{A} = 95°$, $\widehat{B} = 120°$, BC = 1·5 in., CD = 4 in. Construct a quadrilateral $A_1B_1C_1D_1$ similar to ABCD, such that the ratio of each side of $A_1B_1C_1D_1$ to the corresponding side of ABCD is 2 : 3.

2. Inscribe a rectangle in a given triangle so that two vertices are on the base and one vertex on each of the other two sides, the sides of the rectangle being in the ratio 3 : 2.

3. Inscribe a square in a given semicircle so that two vertices are on the diameter and two on the arc.

4. In a given triangle ABC inscribe a triangle similar to another given triangle DEH.

5. Show how to draw a straight line, parallel to one side of a triangle, to divide it into two equal parts.

6. Draw a rectangle ABCD 4 in. by 3 in. Construct a similar rectangle of one-fifth the area.

7. Inscribe a regular octagon in a square.

8. Construct an equilateral triangle equal in area to a given triangle.

9. Construct a regular hexagon equal in area to a given square.

10. Construct a triangle whose sides are in the ratio 3 : 4 : 5, equal in area to a square of side 2 in.

REVISION PAPERS XLI–L

XLI

1. Twice the area of the square on the diagonal of a rectangle is equal to five times the area of the rectangle. Find the ratio of the sides.

2. Calculate **BD** and **DC** in terms of a, b, c.

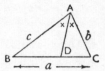

3. $BD = DC$.

$$\frac{CE}{EA} = \frac{1}{2}.$$

$$\frac{DF}{FE} = \frac{3}{2}.$$

Calculate $\dfrac{AG}{GB}$.

4. P is a point within the angle **BAC**. Show how to draw a straight line through P terminated by **AB** and **AC**, such that it is divided at P in the ratio $3 : 2$.

5. Two circles intersect at **A** and **B**, and tangents at **A** to the circles meet the circles again at **C** and **D**. Prove that $AB^2 = BC \cdot BD$.

CB and **DB** produced meet the circles again in **F** and **E** respectively. Prove that $\dfrac{AE^2}{AF^2} = \dfrac{BC}{BD}$.

XLII

1. ABCD is a quadrilateral. **DA**, **CB** produced meet at **F**; **BA**, **CD** produced meet at **E**. Show that the circles FCD, FBA, EAD, EBC all intersect at a point **P**, and that $\dfrac{PA}{PF} = \dfrac{PE}{PC}$.

2. Calculate **OQ**, **PQ**, **AQ**.

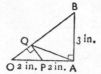

3. Calculate $\dfrac{BE}{EF}$ and $\dfrac{AF}{FC}$.

4. State and prove a construction for finding points **P** and **Q** in the sides **AB** and **AC** of $\triangle ABC$, such that **PQ** is parallel to **BC**, and quadrilateral **BPQC** is equal to $\frac{5}{9}$ of the triangle **ABC**.

5. Two triangles have one angle of the one equal to one angle of the other. Prove that their areas are in the ratio of the rectangles contained by the sides about the equal angles.

XLIII

1. **A** and **B** are fixed points. A point **P** moves so that $PA = 3PB$. Prove that **P** lies on a circle whose diameter is equal to $\frac{3}{4}AB$.

2. **ABCD** is a parallelogram, and **EF** is parallel to **AB**.
   If **ED** is a mean proportional between **AE** and **AD**, prove that **ME = BN**.

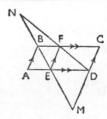

3. $\dfrac{BR}{RP} = \dfrac{1}{2}$.

Find the fraction that the quad. BRQC is of the triangle ABC.

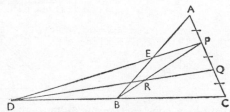

QR and CB produced meet in D, and DP cuts AB in E. Prove that

(1) BD = BC.
(2) AE = EB.

4. State and prove a construction for finding two points D and E in the sides AB and AC of △ABC, such that △ADE will be similar to △ABC, and AD + DE will be equal to a given length. If AB = 9 cm., BC = 6 cm. and AD + DE = 5 cm., what fraction of △ABC is △ADE?

5. Two circles with centres A and B intersect in C and D. A lies on the circle with centre B. AB produced meets the circle with centre B, in E. F is any point on this circle. AF cuts CD in G, and EF produced meets CD produced in H. Prove that CD is divided harmonically at G and H.

XLIV

1. CD is a chord perpendicular to a diameter AB in a circle with centre O. P is any point on the circumference of the circle, and PA and PB, produced if necessary, cut CD or CD produced, in E and H. Prove that CD is divided harmonically at E and H. If Q is the mid-point of EH, prove that $O\widehat{P}Q = 90°$.

2. If $\dfrac{BD}{DC} = \dfrac{4}{1}$, calculate $\dfrac{AB}{AC}$.

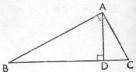

3. $\dfrac{AR}{RB} = \dfrac{3}{1}.$

$\dfrac{AQ}{QC} = \dfrac{1}{2}.$

What fraction of $\triangle ABC$ is $\triangle PQR$?

4. Construct a parallelogram ABCD in which AB = 2·5 in., AD = 1·5 in., and $\widehat{A} = 60°$. Show how to divide the parallelogram into three equal areas by lines drawn parallel to the diagonal BD.

5. AB is a diameter of a circle, and P and Q are the feet of the perpendiculars from A and B on the tangent at a point C. Prove that

$$\dfrac{\triangle APC}{\triangle ABC} = \dfrac{AC^2}{AB^2}.$$

Hence show that $\triangle ABC = \frac{1}{2}$quad. APQB.

XLV

1. ABCD is a semicircle on AD as diameter. P is a point on AC such that AB is a mean proportional between AP and AC. BP produced meets AD in Q. Prove that the angles at Q are right angles.

2. $\dfrac{AP}{PB} = \dfrac{m}{n}.$

Calculate ratio $\dfrac{\text{parm. BPQR}}{\triangle ABC}.$

3. ABCD is a rectangle and P is any point within it.

Prove that $\dfrac{EF}{GH} = \dfrac{AB}{AD}.$

4. Show how to construct a triangle ABC, having given that BC = 2 in.; $\dfrac{AB}{AC} = \dfrac{3}{2}$ and $\widehat{A} = 72°$.

5. Angle A of $\triangle ABC$ is bisected by AD which meets BC in D. Prove that $AB.AC = AD^2 + BD.DC$.

[*Hint*: Produce AD to meet the circumcircle in E, and prove $\triangle s$ ABD and AEC similar.]

XLVI

1. ABC is an equilateral triangle inscribed in a circle, and P is any point on the arc BC. AP cuts BC in Q. Prove that
   (1) △s APC and BPQ are similar.
   (2) △s ABP and CQP are similar.
   Deduce that PA = PB + PC.

2. $\dfrac{AB}{AC} = \dfrac{2}{1}$.

   $\dfrac{AD}{AE} = \dfrac{1}{3}$.

   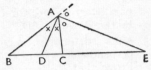

   Calculate $\dfrac{DC}{CE}$. Prove that $B\hat{A}C = 90°$.

3. P and Q are centres of circles which touch at A. BC is

   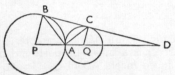

   a direct common tangent. Prove that
   (1) $B\hat{A}C = 90°$.
   (2) △BAD is similar to △ACD.
   (3) $DC.DB = DA^2$.

4. Prove that △XYZ is similar to △PQR.
   Hence find a construction for inscribing in a given triangle a triangle similar to a given triangle and similarly situated (i.e. with its sides respectively parallel to the sides of the given △).

   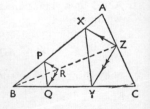

5. Triangle ABC is inscribed in a circle and D is any point on the side BC. E is a point on the arc BC of the circle such that $C\hat{A}E = B\hat{A}D$. Prove that $AB.AC = AE.AD$.

XLVII

1. P and Q are two points on the same side of a straight line AB, and C and D are the projections of P and Q on AB. PD and QC intersect at O, and ROE, the perpendicular from O to AB, meets PQ in R and AB in E. PQ, or PQ produced, meets AB in S. Prove that PQ is divided harmonically at R and S.

2.

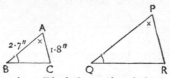

PQ − PR = 1·2 in. Find the ratio of the areas of △s ABC, PQR.

3.

D is the mid-point of BC. DE = DF. Prove GH parallel to BC.

4. A, B, C are three points in order on a straight line. Find a point P at which AB and BC each subtend an angle of 45°. Find also the locus of points at which AB and BC subtend equal angles.

5. △AXB is equilateral and C is the mid-point of AB. Equilateral triangles AYC and BZC are described on AC and BC, on the side of AB remote from X. Prove that XY and XZ trisect AB.

XLVIII

1. AD, BE, CF are the altitudes of △ABC.

Prove that $\dfrac{AF}{AE} = \dfrac{AC}{AB}$.

Deduce that $\dfrac{AF}{FB}\cdot\dfrac{BD}{DC}\cdot\dfrac{CE}{EA} = 1$.

2.

(a) What fraction is DGFEBC of the whole figure?

(b) What fraction is $\triangle$AED of the whole figure?

3. ABCD is a rectangle. BGH is perp. to the diagonal AC.

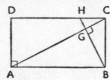

Prove that

$$CH.CD = CG.CA = CB^2.$$

Prove also that $\dfrac{CH}{CD} = \dfrac{BC^2}{AB^2}.$

4. Show how to divide a triangle ABC into three equal parts by straight lines drawn parallel to one of the sides.

5. ABC is a triangle inscribed in a circle and AD is the perpendicular from A to BC.

If AE is the diameter of the circumcircle of $\triangle$ABC, prove that $AB.AC = AD.AE$.

Hence show that $R = \dfrac{abc}{4\triangle}$ where the symbols have the usual meaning.

XLIX

1. A and B are two fixed points 2 in. apart. If P is a point which moves so that $\dfrac{AP}{PB}$ is constant, prove that the locus of P is a circle. Draw the locus when (1) $\dfrac{AP}{PB} = \dfrac{1}{2}$;

(2) $\dfrac{AP}{PB} = \dfrac{3}{2}.$ What is the locus when $\dfrac{AP}{PB} = 1$?

2.

a, b, c are the sides of the $\triangle ABC$. Prove that

$$AD^2 = bc\left[1 - \frac{a^2}{(b+c)^2}\right].$$

3. $\dfrac{AB}{AC} = \dfrac{2}{1}$. Calculate the value of the ratio $\dfrac{BD}{DC}$.

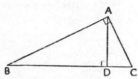

If $AB = 4$ in. and $AC = 2$ in., find BD and DC.

4. Show how to construct a triangle ABC, having given that angle $\hat{A} = 63°$, $\dfrac{AB}{AC} = \dfrac{3}{2}$, and the radius of the circumscribing circle is 1·3 in.

5. AB is a diameter of a circle, and AD and BE are perpendiculars from A and B to the tangent at a point C. Prove that AD.BE = DC.CE.

Show also that $AC^2 = AB.AD$. Find the corresponding value for BC^2, and deduce that AD + BE = AB.

L

1. The bisector of $\hat{A}$ of $\triangle ABC$ meets BC in D, and perpendiculars from B and C to the bisector meet it in H and K respectively. Prove that

$$\frac{AB}{AC} = \frac{DH}{DK}.$$

Hence prove that KH is divided harmonically at D and A.

2. ABCD is any quadrilateral whose diagonals intersect at O.

E and F are centroids of △s AOB and BOC. Find the value of the ratio $\dfrac{EF}{AC}$.

Hence prove that, if G and H are the centroids of △s COD, DOA, EFGH is a parallelogram.

3. $\dfrac{BD}{BC} = \dfrac{1}{3}$.

What fraction of △ABC is △BHK?

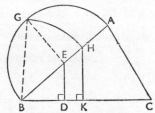

Hence find a construction for drawing a line perpendicular to one side of a triangle, to cut off a given fraction of the triangle.

4. Show how to construct triangle ABC when BC = 2 in., $\dfrac{AB}{AC} = \dfrac{2}{1}$, and △ABC = 2 sq. in.

5. ABCD is a quadrilateral inscribed in a circle. Prove that AB.CD + BC.AD = AC.BD. This is known as Ptolemy's Theorem.

[*Hint:* From C, draw CE to meet BD in E and making $D\widehat{C}E = A\widehat{C}B$. Prove first that AB.CD = AC.DE and find a similar expression for BC.AD.]

BOOK VI

PLANES AND SOLIDS

Representation

It is important to practise seeing a solid figure from a flat drawing. Study the following figures and try to see each in two ways as explained, and practise changing from one way to the other until you can do so readily. You should then be able to see a solid figure, i.e. a figure in three dimensions from a two-dimensional one, even when all the lines in the drawing are continuous.

I. *A Cube*

Try to see this as a cube standing on the base EFGH

(1) with AEFB the face nearest you,
(2) with DHGC the face nearest you.

II. *A Pyramid on a Triangular Base*

Try to see this as a pyramid, standing on the base BCD

(1) with AC the edge nearest you, and BD the line of the base farthest from you,

(2) with AC the edge farthest from you, and BD the line of the base nearest you.

III. *A Pyramid on a Square Base*

Try to see this pyramid in two ways, and state which line of the base is nearest you in each way.

[*Note:* (1) In some flat drawings representing solid figures certain lines are dotted to show in which of the two ways the solid is to be regarded. For example, the last figure might have been drawn in either of the following ways:

 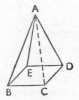

(1) BC the nearest side of the base.　　(2) ED the nearest side of the base.

(2) In drawings, a plane is represented by a parallelogram, and may be named either by a single letter as shown, placed near one of the vertices, or in the same way as the parallelogram.

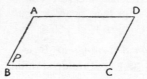

(3) A cuboid can be represented by drawing two overlapping rectangles in the position shown in Fig. 1 below, and then joining corresponding vertices as shown in Fig. 2. If some of the lines are dotted as shown in Fig. 3, it may be easier to see which face is intended to be the front face.

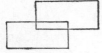

FIG. 1.　　FIG. 2.　　FIG. 3.

(4) A pyramid, a cylinder, and a cone may be represented as shown :

(5) To represent vertical lines in the solid, draw straight lines parallel to the side edges of the paper.

(6) To represent horizontal lines in the solid, draw straight lines in any direction on the paper.

AB, BC, CA, DE, EF, FD are horizontal lines.

DA, EB, FC are vertical lines.

(7) To represent parallel lines in the figure, draw parallel lines on the paper.

(8) To represent rectangles, draw parallelograms.

(9) To represent circles, draw ellipses.

(10) To represent triangles, draw triangles, right angles being represented by acute or obtuse angles generally, e.g. in the figure above, DAB, DAC, EBC, BEF are all representing right angles.]

Planes

A surface is said to be a plane surface or a **plane,** if, when any two points in it are joined by a straight line, this line lies wholly in the surface. Note that, although it is possible to find any number of pairs of points on the curved surface of a cylinder such that the straight line joining them lies wholly in the surface, this would not be true for **any** two points in that surface.

(1) Through one point any number of planes may be made to pass. The same is true also for two points, for we can think of a plane containing two points, **A** and **B**, rotating about **AB** as an axis into any number of positions. Two such positions are shown below:

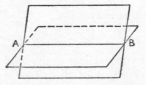

If we have three points not in a straight line, then there is one and only one plane which can pass through these 3 points, e.g. in the cuboid below, one plane passes through the 3 points **E**, **G** and **D** and may be referred to as the plane **DEG**.

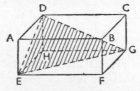

(2) This also means that one and only one plane can pass through two intersecting straight lines, or through a straight line and a point outside it. For example, in the figure above, **ED** and **EG** are two intersecting straight lines lying in the plane **DEG**. Also **EG** can be taken as a straight line, **D** a point outside it, and again these lie in the plane **DEG**.

(3) From the definition of parallel straight lines, it is clear that if two straight lines are parallel, they must lie in the same plane, e.g. in the figure, **AE** and **CG** are parallel and lie in the plane **AEGC**.

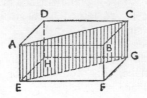

Exercises 64

1. Draw a figure to represent a cuboid and name the vertices as in the figure above. Sketch in the following planes. (Draw a new figure for each.)

(*a*) Through 3 points—B, E, G ; E, F, D ; D, H, F.

(*b*) Through 2 intersecting straight lines—HF and DF ; DE and EB ; HG and HD.

(*c*) Through a straight line and point outside it—EH and B ; AC and F ; HG and A.

(*d*) Through 2 parallel straight lines—DC and EF ; AD and FG ; DG and AF.

2. "A triangle is a plane figure bounded by three straight lines." What word is unnecessary in this definition ?

3. Why does a three-legged stool never rock and yet a four-legged one may rock ?

4. In the usual figure representing a cuboid, using 4 of the given

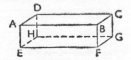

letters only for each plane, name all the planes that contain the lines (1) EB, (2) EG, (3) DF.

5. If in the cuboid (Exercise 4) X is the point of intersection of the diagonals of ABCD, and Y the point of intersection of the diagonals of EFGH, name the pairs of parallel lines in the figure determining the planes in which XY lies.

6. In the figure D, E, F are the mid-points of the sides BC, CA, AB respectively. Using only the letters X, A, B, C name

(1) the sets of three points that determine the plane in which (*a*) D lies, (*b*) E lies, (*c*) F lies ;

(2) the sets of two intersecting straight lines (intersecting at X) which determine the planes containing (*a*) XF, (*b*) XE, (*c*) XD.

Lines and Planes

A straight line and a plane may be related in the following ways :

(1) the straight line may lie entirely in the plane,

(2) the straight line may cut the plane in one point only,

(3) the straight line may be parallel to the plane in which case it has no point common with the plane.

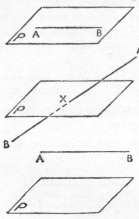

A **straight line** is said to be **perpendicular to a plane** when it is perpendicular to every straight line which meets it in that plane.

Such a line is called a **normal** to the plane. The point where the perpendicular meets the plane is called the **foot** of the perpendicular.

In the figure, if AB is a normal to the plane P, then AB is perpendicular to BC, BD, BE and BH, straight lines lying in P.

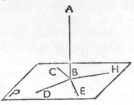

It can be proved that **if a straight line AB is perpendicular to each of two intersecting straight lines at their
point of intersection, it is perpendicular to the plane in
which the two lines lie.**

In the figure, if AB is perpendicular to both CB and BD it is

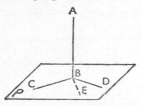

perpendicular to the plane P in which CB and BD lie.   Hence,
if, from B, any other line BE is drawn in plane P, the angle ABE
is a right angle.

This fact has been used previously in
this book, generally with reference to the
cuboid, e.g. in the cuboid ABCD, EFGH
AE is perpendicular to EH and EF.   It is
therefore perpendicular to the plane EFGH,
and hence $\widehat{AEG}$ is a right angle.

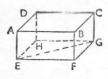

The Angle between a Straight Line and a Plane

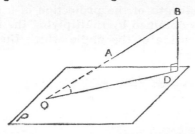

If there is a plane P and a straight line AB which is not
parallel to the plane, then AB (produced if necessary) must cut
the plane at one point, say O.   From B, draw BD perpendicular
to the plane.   Join OD.   Then $\widehat{BOD}$ is the angle which AB
makes with the plane P.

Projection of Straight Line on Plane

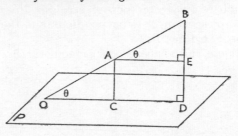

Let the straight line **AB** make an angle θ with the plane **P**.

Draw **AC** and **BD** perp. to **P**.

Then **CD** is the projection of **AB** on plane **P**.

Through **A** draw **AE** parl. to **CD** to meet **BD** in **E**.

$\quad$ B$\hat{\text{A}}$E = B$\hat{\text{O}}$D = θ (corresp. $\angle$s to parls. **AE** and **OD**).

$\quad$ A$\hat{\text{E}}$B = B$\hat{\text{D}}$C = rt. angle.

From the rt.-angled $\triangle$BAE

$$\frac{AE}{AB} = \cos \theta$$

$\quad \therefore$ AE = AB $\cos \theta$.

$\quad$ But **CD** = **AE** (opp. sides of rect.)

$\quad \therefore$ **CD** = AB $\cos \theta$.

Hence the length of the projection of a straight line on a plane is obtained by multiplying the length of the line by the cosine of the angle which the line makes with the plane.

The Three Perpendiculars

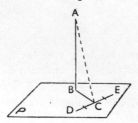

If a straight line AB is perpendicular to the plane P, and if from B, the foot of the perpendicular, a straight line BC is drawn perpendicular to DE any straight line in the plane P, then the straight line AC is perpendicular to DE.

This can be proved by cutting off CD = CE and proving the congruence of three pairs of triangles:

(1) $\triangle$BDC $\equiv$ $\triangle$BEC   whence   BD = BE
(2) $\triangle$ABD $\equiv$ $\triangle$ABE   whence   AD = AE
(3) $\triangle$ADC $\equiv$ $\triangle$AEC   whence   A$\widehat{C}$D = A$\widehat{C}$E, i.e. AC is perp. to DE.

(This might have been proved by using the theorem of Pythagoras.) It is left to the student to prove that if AB is perp. to the plane P and AC is perp. to DE then BC will be perp. to DE.

Worked Examples

(1) The figure represents a cuboid. Find the angle between EC and the plane ABCD, and also the angle between EC and BC.

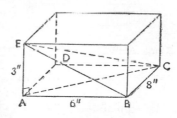

(a) From any point in EC we must draw a perpendicular to the plane ABCD. The point E will suffice because E$\widehat{A}$C is a rt. angle

$\therefore$ E$\widehat{C}$A is the required $\angle$.

Now $\tan$ E$\widehat{C}$A $= \dfrac{AE}{AC} = \dfrac{3 \text{ in.}}{10 \text{ in.}}$ $\begin{bmatrix} AC^2 = 6^2 + 8^2 \text{ sq. in.} \\ = 100 \text{ sq. in. by} \\ \text{Pythagoras' Th.} \end{bmatrix}$

$\qquad = \cdot 3$
$\qquad \therefore$ E$\widehat{C}$A $= 16° \ 42'$.

(b) E$\widehat{B}$C is a rt. angle

$\therefore \tan$ E$\widehat{C}$B $= \dfrac{EB}{BC}$

$\qquad = \dfrac{\sqrt{45} \text{ in.}}{8 \text{ in.}}$ $\begin{bmatrix} EB^2 = 3^2 + 6^2 \text{ sq. in.} \\ = 45 \text{ sq. in. by} \\ \text{Pythagoras' Th.} \end{bmatrix}$

$\qquad = \cdot 8385$
$\qquad \therefore$ E$\widehat{C}$B $= 39° \ 59'$.

(2) A, BCD is a triangular pyramid, the base BCD being an equilateral triangle, side 6 in. The perpendicular from A to plane BCD passes through the circumcentre of △BCD. If the edge AB is 6 in. long, find the angle between AB and the plane of the base.

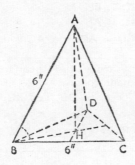 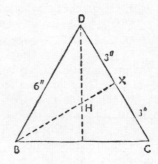

Since AĤB is a rt. angle, the angle required is AB̂H

$$\cos \hat{ABH} = \frac{BH}{AB} = \frac{BH}{6 \text{ in.}}$$

In equilateral △DBC the circumcentre H is the point of intersection of the medians (the centroid) and also the orthocentre

∴ $BX^2 = 6^2 - 3^2$ sq. in. from rt-angled △BDX

      = 27 sq. in.

∴ $BX = 3\sqrt{3}$ in.

      $BH = \frac{2}{3} BX$, since BX is a median and H is the centroid

      = $2\sqrt{3}$

∴ $\cos \hat{ABH} = \frac{BH}{6 \text{ in.}} = \frac{2\sqrt{3}}{6} = \cdot 5774$

∴ $\hat{ABH} = 54° \ 44'$.

EXERCISES 65

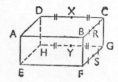

1. Using 4 and only 4 letters from the figure, name the planes which contain the following straight lines: BF, DC, AH, XY, RS, XR, DF.

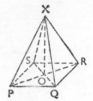

2. Using 3 and only 3 letters from the figure, name the planes which contain the following straight lines: PS, QO, XP, XO.

3. In the figure for Exercise 1, name the straight lines which are parallel to planes (a) HGCD, (b) BFGC, (c) DHFB.

4. In the figure for Exercise 1, name the straight lines which are perpendicular to the planes (a) ACHD, (b) AEFB, (c) ABCD.

5. In the figure for Exercise 1, at what point in the straight line EC does EC cut the plane DHFB ? At what point in DF does DF cut the plane AEGC ?

The figure represents a cuboid 12 in. × 9 in. × 8 in. Find the angles which the following lines make with the following planes :

6. DF and plane EFGH.
7. HB and plane AEHD.
8. EC and plane HGCD.
9. DX and plane EFGH.
10. AX and plane ABCD.
11. EY and plane EFGH.
12. FY and plane BFGC.
13. AX and plane AEHD.
14. XY and plane EFGH.

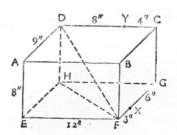

The figure represents a pyramid on a square base, such that the foot of the perpendicular drawn from the vertex to the base is the centre of the square.

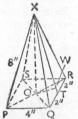

Find the angles between the following lines and planes.

15. XP and plane PQRS.
16. XT and plane PQRS.
17. XO and plane XQR.

(By the Three Perpendiculars, OW, the perp. from O to the plane XQR cuts the median XT at W. Note that XOT is a rt.-angled △ with OW perp. to the base.)

18. OT and plane XQR.

The figure represents a pyramid on an equilateral triangle as base. The perpendicular from the vertex passes through the circumcentre of the base.

Note that AB = AD = AC ($AB^2 = AH^2 + BH^2$
$= AH^2 + DH^2$
$= AD^2$).

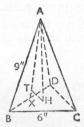

Find the angles between the following lines and planes.

19. AB and plane BCD.
20. AX and plane BCD.
21. HA and plane BAD.

(By the Three Perpendiculars, HT, the perpendicular from H to the plane BAD cuts the median AX at T.)

22. The figure is the plan of the roof of a house, **EF** being the ridge. If **EF** is 16 ft. above the plane **ABCD**, calculate the angle which **EB** makes with the plane **ABCD**.

[*Hint:* If **X** is the foot of the perpendicular from **E** to the plane **ABCD**, find **BX** from the rt.-angled △**BXY**.]

23. A tower **AB**, 100 ft. high, subtends an angle of 45° at a place **P** due east of the tower and in the same horizontal plane as **B** the foot of the tower. A place **Q** in the plane is 75 ft. south of **P**. Find the angle which **AQ** makes with the horizontal.

24. **ABCD** is a horizontal rectangle with **AB** = 8 in. and **BC** = 6 in. **X**, **Y** are two points 2 in. vertically above **D**, **C** respectively. **Q** is the mid-point of **XY**. Find the inclination of **BQ** to the horizontal.

25. **ABC** is an equilateral triangle, the length of each side being 5 in. **X** is a point, not in the plane of the triangle but 8 in. from each of the vertices of the triangle. **XO** is drawn perpendicular to the plane of **ABC**. Find
    (1) length of **XO**,
    (2) the angle which **XA** makes with the horizontal.

26. **ABC** is a horizontal isosceles triangle with **Â** = 90° and **AB** = **AC** = 8 in. **X** and **Y** are points vertically above **A** and **B** respectively, such that **AX** = 12 in. and **BY** = 8 in. **D** is the mid-point of **BC**. Find the inclination of (1) **XY**, (2) **XB**, (3) **XD** to the horizontal.

27. The figure represents two horizontal rectangles symmetrically placed as shown. If the plane **EFGH** is 10 ft. vertically

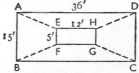

above the plane **ABCD**, find the inclination of **BF** to the horizontal.

Relation between Planes

[*Note:* Planes and straight lines are generally regarded as extending without limit.]

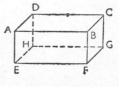

(1) If two planes do not meet they are said to be parallel.

In the cuboid represented in the figure, AEFB and DHGC are parallel planes.

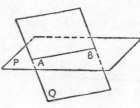

(2) If two planes intersect they do so in a straight line.

Planes P and Q intersect in the straight line AB.

In the figure for the cuboid above, the planes AEFB and AEHD intersect in the straight line AE, and the planes DEG and EFGH intersect in the straight line EG.

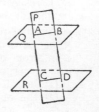

(3) If a plane intersects two parallel planes the lines of section are parallel.

AB and CD cannot meet because they are in parallel planes Q and R. Also AB and CD are in the same plane P.

∴ AB and CD are parallel.

EXERCISES 66

1. In the case of the cuboid, lettered as shown above, state the lines of intersection of the following planes:
   - (*a*) FBCG and DBFH.
   - (*b*) DHFB and AEGC.
   - (*c*) EHBC and ADGF.
   - (*d*) EFDC and ABGH.
   - (*e*) DHF and ABCD.
   - (*f*) BFG and DHGC.

2. State all the pairs of parallel planes in the above figure.

3. In the figure, D, E, F are the mid-points of AB, BC, CA respectively. State the lines of intersection of the following planes:
   - (*a*) XAE and XBC.
   - (*b*) DEF and XAC.
   - (*c*) XFD and ABC.
   - (*d*) ADX and AXE.

4. Draw a figure to represent the cuboid ABCD, EFGH.
   In the figure, name the four planes which cut the two
   parallel planes ABCD and EFGH and in each of the four
   cases name the two parallel lines of section.
   Repeat this for each of the other two pairs of parallel
   planes.

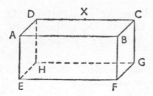

The above figure represents a cuboid.

5. Consider a plane section through A, D and F. What other
   point lies in this section ? Name the section. What
   kind of figure is the section ?

6. If X is the mid-point of DC, consider a plane section
   through A, X and E. Find the point in HG through which
   this section must pass. What kind of figure is the section ?
   Name the two pairs of parallel planes cut by the section,
   and in each case the parallel lines in which the section cuts
   these parallel planes.

7. Consider a plane section through A, X and G. Through
   what point in EF must this section pass ? Give a reason
   for your answer.

8. Let PQ be any line in the plane ABCD parallel to DA and
   cutting DC and AB at P and Q respectively. Consider
   a plane section through PQ and cutting the cuboid so that
   it cuts the face BFGC in a line RS. What do you know
   about the line RS ? Draw the section.

9. Let LM be any line in the plane ABCD, not parallel to AD,
   and cutting DC and AB in L and M respectively. Consider
   a plane section through LM and cutting the cuboid so that
   it cuts the face BFGC in a line NK. What kind of figure
   is the section ?

10. Consider a plane section through H, F, and X. What line
    in the figure will it cut, and at what point ? What kind of
    figure is the section ?

The figure represents a cube.

11. Consider the plane section through P, Q, R and S, the midpoints of AD, EF, FG, DC respectively. Where does the section cut AE and GC? Draw the section. What kind of figure is it?

12. Consider the plane section through A, C, and F. What kind of figure is it?

Angle between Two Planes

When two planes meet they form an angle called a **dihedral angle**.

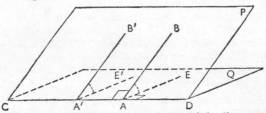

The two planes P and Q cut in the straight line CD. Any point A is taken in CD.

In plane P the straight line AB is drawn at right angles to CD.

In plane Q the straight line AE is drawn at right angles to CD.

B$\widehat{A}$E is the angle between the planes.

It is the angle through which the plane Q would need to be rotated about CD for it to coincide with the plane P.

No matter where point A is taken in CD it can be shown that the size of the angle BAE is the same, e.g. B'$\widehat{A}$'E' = B$\widehat{A}$E.

Hence, to find the angle between two planes, we find the line of intersection, and then draw two straight lines, one in each plane, from any point in the line of intersection and perpendicular to it. The angle formed by these two straight lines is the required angle.

If the dihedral angle is a right angle the planes are perpendicular to one another, e.g. in the figure P and Q are perpendicular to each other.

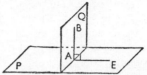

Exercise 1.—The following figure represents a cube ABCD, EFGH. Find the angle between the planes DEG and EFGH.

EG is the line of intersection of planes DEG and EFGH.

O (the point of intersection of the diagonals of the square EFGH) is a point in this line.

OH, in the plane EFGH, is at right angles to EG, since the diagonals of a square cut at right angles.

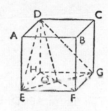

OD, in the plane DEG, is at right angles to EG, by the Three Perpendiculars (DH is perp. to plane EFGH and HO is perp. to EG).

Hence the angle formed by OH and OD, i.e. HÔD, is the angle between the planes.

To calculate the size of the angle HOD*, △ DHO is a right-angled triangle for DĤO = a rt. angle

$$\therefore \tan H\hat{O}D = \frac{HD}{OH}.$$

Let each edge of the cube be 1 unit in length.
HD = 1 unit, HO = ½ diagonal HF

$$= \tfrac{1}{2}\sqrt{2}\left[\begin{array}{l} FH^2 = HE^2 + EF^2 \\ \quad = 1 + 1 \text{ sq. units} \end{array}\right]$$

$$\therefore \tan H\hat{O}D = \frac{1}{\tfrac{1}{2}\sqrt{2}} = \sqrt{2} = 1\cdot4142$$

$$\therefore H\hat{O}D = 54° \ 44'$$

∴ the angle between the planes is 54° 44'.

* It may be found helpful to draw the section OHD separately.

Exercise 2.—A rectangular solid is 10 in. long, 5 in. broad and 8 in. high. It rests on a horizontal plane, and is cut by a plane which passes through an edge 5 in. long in the top face, and makes an angle of 30° with that face. Find the dimensions of the section.

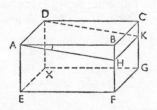

The figure ABCD, EFGX represents the solid, and AHKD is the section.

AD is the line of intersection of the planes ABCD and AHKD.
A is a point in AD and AB is in plane ABCD and is at right angles to AD.

Also AH is in plane AHKD and is at right angles to AD
∴ BÂH is the angle between the two planes
∴ BÂH = 30°
(CD̂K is also 30°).

HK and AD are parl. (sections of parl. planes by plane AHKD) and AH and KD are similarly parl.
∴ AHKD is a parm.

But DÂH is a rt. angle ∴ AHKD is a rectangle.
△ABH is a rt.-angled △.

$$\therefore \quad \frac{AB}{AH} = \cos 30° = \frac{\sqrt{3}}{2}$$

$$\therefore \quad \frac{10 \text{ in.}}{AH} = \frac{\sqrt{3}}{2}$$

$$\therefore \quad AH = \frac{20 \text{ in.}}{\sqrt{3}} = \frac{20\sqrt{3} \text{ in.}}{3} = 11·55 \text{ in.} \quad \text{Also AD} = 5 \text{ in.}$$

∴ the dimensions of the section are 5 in. and 11·55 in.

Exercise 3.—ABCD, EFGH is a cube each edge of which is 2 in. long. X is the mid-point of AD, and Y is the mid-point of AE. Find the inclination of the plane XYG to the plane AEHD.

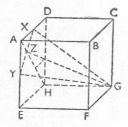

Join XY, YG, XG. Join AH to cut XY in Z. Join ZG.
XY is the line of intersection of the planes AEHD and XYG.
ZH is in the plane AEHD and is perp. to XY [diagonals AH and DE of square cut at rt. angles, and XY is parl. to DE].
ZG is in the plane XYG and is perp. to XY by the Three Perpendiculars (GH is perp. to plane AEHD and HZ is perp. to XY).

$\therefore$ X$\hat{Z}$G = G$\hat{Z}$Y

$\therefore$ G$\hat{Z}$H is the angle between the planes AEHD and XYG.
Also G$\hat{H}$Z is a rt. angle since GH is perp. to plane AEHD

$\therefore$ tan G$\hat{Z}$H $= \dfrac{GH}{ZH} = \dfrac{2 \text{ in.}}{\frac{3}{4} \text{ diag. AH}} = \dfrac{2 \text{ in.}}{\frac{3}{4} . 2\sqrt{2} \text{ in.}}$

$$= \dfrac{4}{3\sqrt{2}} = \dfrac{2\sqrt{2}}{3} = \cdot 9428$$

$\therefore$ G$\hat{Z}$H $= 43° \ 19'$.

[*Note:* It may be found helpful to draw separately the various planes as shown below.]

Exercise 4.—The figure represents a pyramid on a square base. BD and EC intersect at O, and AO is perpendicular to the plane BCDE. If BC = 4 in. and AB = 8 in., find the angle between the faces ABC and ACD.

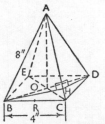

It can readily be proved that the faces ABC, ACD, ADE, ABE are congruent isosceles triangles, for △s AOB, AOC, AOD, AOE are all congruent (2 sides and incl. ∠).

Planes ABC and ACD intersect in the straight line AC. If perpendiculars are drawn from B and D to AC, they will meet at the same point H on AC, since

△s BCH and DCH are congruent (2 ∠s and corresp. side)

∴ the angle between the planes ABC and ACD is BĤD.

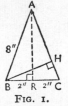

FIG. 1.

FIG. 2.

Fig. 1.

△ABC is an isosceles triangle. If R is the mid-point of BC, then AR̂B = 90°,

$$\therefore \ \sin \widehat{BAR} = \frac{BR}{BA} = \frac{2}{8} = \cdot 25 \quad \therefore \ \widehat{BAR} = 14° \ 29'$$

$$\therefore \ \widehat{BAC} = 2\widehat{BAR} = 28° \ 58'.$$

$$\frac{BH}{BA} = \sin \widehat{BAC} = \sin 28° \ 58' = \cdot 4843$$

$$\therefore \ BH = 8 \times \cdot 4843 = 3 \cdot 8744 \ \text{in.}$$

Fig. 2.

△BHD is an isosceles triangle

∴ BD² = BC² + CD² = 32 sq. in.

∴ BD = √32 in. = 4√2 in.

∴ BO = 2√2 in.

or $\dfrac{BO}{BC}$ = sin 45°

$\qquad = \dfrac{1}{\sqrt{2}}$

∴ BO = 4 × $\dfrac{1}{\sqrt{2}}$ = 2√2 in.

Sin B$\hat{\text{H}}$O = $\dfrac{BO}{BH}$ = $\dfrac{2\sqrt{2}}{3\cdot874}$ = ·7300

∴ B$\hat{\text{H}}$O = 46° 53′

∴ B$\hat{\text{H}}$D = 2B$\hat{\text{H}}$O = 93° 46′

∴ angle between faces ABC and ACD = 93° 46′.

EXERCISES 67

1. The figure represents a cube. Name the angle between the following planes and find the size of each.

   (a) EFGH and AEHD.
   (b) ABCD and HGCD.
   (c) EBCH and EFGH.
   (d) EFGH and EFCD.
   (e) HFBD and AEGC.

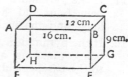

2. The figure represents a cuboid. AB = 16 cm., BC = 12 cm., BF = 9 cm. Name the angle between the following planes and find the size of each.

   (a) FGD and AEHD.
   (b) BFG and AEGC.
   (c) DEC and BCA.
   (d) DHB and AFB.
   (e) ABG and HGC.
   (f) HFBD and AEGC.

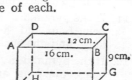

3. If the cube in Exercise 1 is cut by a plane passing through EH and making an angle of 45° with the base, find the dimensions of the section.

4. Repeat Exercise 3 if the angle is 60°. Find the area of the section.

5. If the cuboid of Exercise 2 is cut by a plane passing through FG, what is the greatest angle this plane can make with the base if it is to cut the face AEHD?

6. The cuboid of Exercise 2 is cut by a plane passing through DC and making an angle of 25° with the face ABCD. Find the dimensions of the section.

7. A cuboid measures 4 in. × 2 in. × 2 in. It is cut by a plane passing through an edge of one of the square faces and through the centre of the opposite square face. Find the dimensions of the section and its area.

8. The figure shows the end view of a shed with a sloping roof. Find the angle which each side of the roof makes with the horizontal.

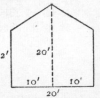

9. ABC is an isosceles triangle with $\hat{A}$ a right angle. AD is drawn perpendicular to the plane of the triangle. If AB = 6 cm., AD = 8 cm., find the angle which the plane DBC makes with the plane ABC.

10. A pyramid X, ABCD has a square base, each side 4 in., and is such that the vertex X is on the straight line through O, the point of intersection of the diagonals of the base, perpendicular to the plane of the square. If the height of the pyramid is 8 in., find the size of the angle which any triangular face makes with the base.

11. If the pyramid in Exercise 10 had a square base, each side being 6 in., and the edges XA, XB, XC, XD were all 10 in. long, find the inclination of plane XAD to the base.

12. If the pyramid in Exercise 10 had a square base, each side being 5 in. long, and XA was inclined at an angle of 50° to the base, calculate the angle which the face XAD would make with the base.

13. In the pyramid of Exercise 10, find the angle between the faces XAB and XBC.

14. In the pyramid of Exercise 11, find the angle between the faces XAB and XBC.

15. In the pyramid of Exercise 12, find the angle between the faces XAB and XBC.

16. ABCD is a rectangle. AC and BD intersect at O. OX is perpendicular to the plane ABCD. If AB = 8 in., BC = 6 in., OX = 12 in., find the angle between the planes XAB and ABCD, and the angle between the planes XBC and ABCD.

17. O, ABC is a pyramid on an equilateral triangle ABC as base, and the perpendicular from O to ABC passes through the circumcentre of ABC. Find the angle between OAB and the base, and the angle between OAB and OBC, if AB = 8 in. and OA = 10 in.

18. The figure is the plan of the roof of a house, EF being the ridge. If EF is 16 ft. above the plane ABCD, calculate the angle which plane AEB makes with ABCD, and the angle which plane BEFC makes with ABCD.

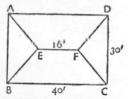

19. The figure is the plan of the flat roof of a house. The plane of EFGH is 10 ft. above that of ABCD. Find the

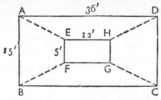

inclination of (1) plane AEFB, (2) plane BFGC to the horizontal.

20. ABCD, EFGH is a cube. X and Y are the mid-points of DH and HG respectively. Find the angle between the planes BXY and DCGH if AB = 3 in. Will this angle change in size when the length of AB is changed?

21. ABCD is a horizontal rectangle with AB = 8 in., BC = 6 in. AE is vertical and 5 in. long. Find the angle which plane EBD makes with the horizontal.

[*Note:* If AH is perp. to BD at H, then EH is also perp. to BD.]

22. ABC is a horizontal isosceles triangle with $\widehat{A} = 90°$ and AB = AC = 6 in. X, Y, Z are 3 points vertically above A, B, C respectively, such that AX = 14 in. and BY = CZ = 8 in. Find the inclination of (1) plane AYZ, (2) plane XYZ to the horizontal.

23. The figure represents a square board ABEF, each side 30 in. long, with the edge AB touching a horizontal table ABCD. The board is inclined at 20° to the table. Find the angles

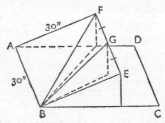

which BE, BG, BF make with the horizontal. Why could lines on the board, parallel to BE, be called lines of greatest slope ?

24. A, BCDE is a pyramid on a square base. AO, the perpendicular from A to the base, meets the base at O, the point of intersection of the diagonals. If BC is 6 in. and the face ABC is inclined at an angle of 50° to the base, calculate the inclination of AB to the base.

25. The figure in question 18 above is the plan of the roof of a house, EF being the ridge.

If AB = 24 ft., BC = 30 ft., EF = 16 ft., and the face AEB is inclined at 50° to the plane ABCD, find the inclination of BE to the plane ABCD.

Solid Figures—Areas of Surfaces and Volumes of Solids

The Cuboid

If a solid is bounded by three pairs of parallel plane faces and these six faces are all squares, then the solid is called a **cube**. If the six faces are all rectangles then the solid is called a **cuboid** or a **rectangular solid**.

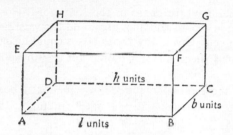

To find the surface area of a cuboid we could find the area of each rectangular face and add the results. But it is useful to express the surface area in a different way. We can speak of the face EFGH as the top face, the face ABCD as the bottom face and the other four surfaces as forming the lateral surface. Let the cuboid be l units long, b units broad, h units high.

Area of lateral surface = sum of areas of rectangles, ABFE, BCGF, DCGH, ADHE

$$= (lh + bh + lh + bh) \text{ units of area}$$
$$= (2lh + 2bh) \text{ units of area}$$
$$= (2l + 2b)h \text{ units of area}$$

∴ lateral surface = perimeter of base × height.

Total surface = area of ends + lateral surface
$$= (2lb + 2lh + 2bh) \text{ units of area}.$$

In the case of a cube, since the six faces are all equal squares, if side of square = l units of length,

total surface = $6l^2$ units of area.

Worked Example

A manufacturer receives an order for 240 dozen cubical closed boxes to be made of thin sheet metal. If the edge of the cube is 3 in. long, and 10 per cent of the metal is wasted in the process of manufacture, how many square feet of metal will he require?

If the manufacturer had used the same amount of sheet metal to manufacture boxes in the shape of a closed cuboid 6 in. long, 3 in. broad and 4 in. high, and the wastage now was cut to 5 per cent, how many dozen boxes could he have made?

(1) Area of sheet metal required for 1 cubical box
$$= 6 \times 3^2 \text{ sq. in.}$$

Area of sheet metal required for 240 dozen boxes
$$= 240 \times 12 \times 6 \times 3^2 \text{ sq. in.}$$
$$= \frac{240 \times 12 \times 6 \times 3^2}{144} \text{sq. ft.}$$

If x sq. ft. is the total area required, since 10 per cent of this is wasted in manufacture,
$$\therefore \frac{9}{10}x = \frac{240 \times 12 \times 6 \times 3^2}{144}$$
$$x = \frac{10 \times 240 \times 12 \times 6 \times 3^2}{9 \times 144}$$
$$= 1200$$

$\therefore$ area of sheet metal required = 1200 sq. ft.

(2) If boxes of the cuboid shape had been made, area of sheet metal at first
$$= 1200 \text{ sq. ft.,}$$
area wasted
$$= \frac{1}{20} \times 1200 = 60 \text{ sq. ft.,}$$

$\therefore$ actual area of metal in the boxes
$$= 1140 \text{ sq. ft.}$$
Total area of metal required for 1 box
$$= (2 \times 6 \times 3 + 2 \times 6 \times 4 + 2 \times 4 \times 3) \text{ sq. in.}$$
$$= 108 \text{ sq. in.}$$

∴ No. of boxes that could be made

$$= \frac{1140 \times 144}{108}$$

$$= 1520$$

$$= 126\tfrac{2}{3} \text{ dozen.}$$

EXERCISES 68

Find the total surface of the solids in Exercises 1 to 5.

1. Cube, edge 5 in.

2. Cube, edge 1 ft. 3 in.

3. Cube, edge 3·5 cm.

4. Cuboid, 6 in. by 4 in. by 3 in.

5. Cuboid, 5·2 cm. by 4·5 cm. by 6 cm.

6. The surface of a cube is $10\tfrac{2}{3}$ sq. ft. Find the length of one edge in inches.

7. The outside surface of a closed rectangular box is 184 sq. in. If the box is 8 in. long and 5 in. broad, find its height.

8. The outside dimensions of a closed box, made of wood $\tfrac{1}{2}$ in. thick, are 21 in. × 17 in. × 15 in. The box including the lid is lined with silk. How many square feet of silk will be required for a dozen boxes assuming there is no wastage of material?

9. From the four corners of a certain rectangular sheet of metal, equal squares are cut, and the remainder made into a rectangular open box by folding. If the box is 12 in. long, 6 in. broad, and total surface area is 180 sq. in., find the length and breadth of the original sheet of metal.

10. Find the number of closed rectangular boxes 8 in. × 5 in. × 5 in. that can be made from 1000 square feet of sheet metal, allowing a wastage of $12\tfrac{1}{2}$ per cent in the process of manufacturing.

11. The bottom of a lidless rectangular box is a square of side x in. If the height is 5 in. and the total external surface is 96 sq. in., find x.

Volume

Volume.—The **volume** of a solid is the amount of space it occupies. To measure a volume we must compare it with a volume taken as a unit. The unit volume is the volume of a cube whose edge is the unit of length. For example a cubic inch is the volume of a cube whose edge is 1 in., and a cubic centimetre is the volume of a cube whose edge is 1 cm.

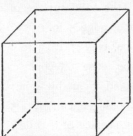

A centimetre cube, volume 1 cubic centimetre (1 c.c.)

An inch cube, volume 1 cubic inch (1 cu. in.).

Note that a solid may have a volume of 1 cubic in. and not be a cube.

To Find the Volume of a Rectangular Solid

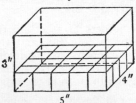

The figure represents a rectangular solid length 5 in., breadth 4 in., height 3 in. If a layer 1 in. thick is taken, it is clear from the figure that this layer can be divided into 20 blocks, each block being an inch cube,

∴ vol. of first layer = 20 cu. in.

In the whole rectangular solid there are three such layers

∴ vol. of rect. solid = 20 cu. in. × 3
$$= 60 \text{ cu. in.}$$
$$= 5 \times 4 \times 3 \text{ cu. in.}$$

Similarly for a rectangular solid with length a units, breadth b units, height c units

vol. of rect. solid = $a \times b \times c$ units of vol.

This is often expressed

vol. of rect. solid = length × breadth × height
or **vol. of rect. solid = area of base × height.**

In the case of a cube, since the length, breadth and height are all equal

vol. of cube = (edge)³.

Surface Area and Volume of Right Prism

The rectangular solid is a special kind of prism. If a solid is bounded by plane faces, two of them called ends being congruent figures in parallel planes, and the others called side faces are rectangles, then the solid is said to be a **right prism.**

Three examples of right prisms are shown below, a triangular prism, a square prism, and a prism on a pentagonal base

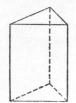 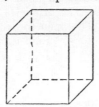 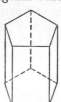

To find the surface area and the volume of a right prism, the same reasoning will apply as in the case of the rectangular solid.

Hence

(1) **Lateral surface of any right prism**
      = perimeter of base × height.
(2) **Total surface = area of ends + lateral surface.**
(3) **Volume of any right prism = area of base × height.**

Worked Examples

(1) The figure represents the vertical end of a hayrick. If the hayrick is 8 yds. long, find the volume of hay in cubic yards.

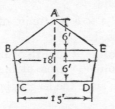

The hayrick is a right prism with **ABCDE** the end face

∴ vol. of hay = area of ABCDE × length.

Area of ABCDE = area of △ABE + area of trapezium BCDE

$= \frac{1}{2} \times 18 \times 6 + \frac{1}{2}(18 + 15) \times 6$ sq. ft.

$= 54 + 99$ sq. ft.

$= 153$ sq. ft.

$= 17$ sq. yd.

∴ vol. of hay = 17 × 8 cu. yd. = 136 cu. yd.

(2) The figure represents an open metal trough, the ends being equal vertical isosceles triangles with sides 1 ft. 3 in., 1 ft. 3 in., 1 ft. 6 in. The open top is a horizontal rectangle and the trough is 10 ft. long. Find the area of metal required to make the trough.

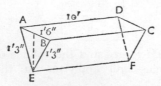

The trough is a right prism with **ABE** the end face.

Area of metal = twice area of △ABE + twice area of rect. EBCF.

Altitude of △ABE $= \sqrt{15^2 - 9^2}$ in.

$= 12$ in.

$\therefore$ area of metal $= 2 \times \frac{1}{2} \times \frac{3}{2} \times 1 + 2 \times \frac{5}{4} \times 10$ sq. ft.

$= 1\frac{1}{2} + 25$ sq. ft.

$= 26\frac{1}{2}$ sq. ft.

EXERCISES 69

In Exercises 1 to 4, find the total surface and the volume of the following right prisms :

1. 10 in. by 8 in. by 6 in.

2. Base, equilateral $\triangle$, side 4 in.—height 10 in.

3. Base, isosceles $\triangle$, equal sides 10 in., base 12 in.—height 18 in.

4. Base, regular hexagon, side 4 cm.—height 20 cm.

5. The volume of a cube is 1728 cu. in. Find its total surface in sq. ft.

6. The total surface of a cube is 384 sq. in. Find its volume in cu. in.

7. A closed wooden box in the shape of a rectangular prism is made of wood $\frac{1}{2}$ in. thick. If the external dimensions are 3 ft. $\times$ 2 ft. $\times$ 1 ft. 6 in., find the volume of the wood.

8. A manufacturer makes open metal containers in the shape of rectangular prisms 1 ft. 8 in. $\times$ 10 in. $\times$ 5 in. He replaces these by containers in the shape of a cube, the capacity of the container remaining the same as before. Assuming there is no waste in either case what percentage of metal does he save by the change ?

9. A swimming bath is 50 yd. long and 25 yd. broad. It is 3 ft. deep at the shallow end and 7 ft. deep at the deep end. Find the volume of water it can hold when full.

10. A room is 30 ft. long, 20 ft. broad and 15 ft. high. Allowing 250 cu. ft. of air space per person, how many persons can it accommodate ?

11. A rectangular tank is 6 ft. $\times$ 4 ft. $\times$ 1 ft. 6 in. Find the number of gallons of water it can hold when full. (1 cu. ft. $= 6\frac{1}{4}$ gal.)

12. A tank contains 1350 gallons of water. If the tank is a rectangular one 15 ft. long, 12 ft. broad and 6 ft. deep, what will be the depth of the water?

13. The figure represents the vertical end section of a wooden shed with a tiled roof. If the shed is 30 ft. long, find

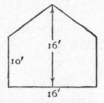

(*a*) the area of the roof, (*b*) the area of timber required for the ends and sides, (*c*) the cubic capacity.

14. The figure represents a lean-to shed placed against a brick

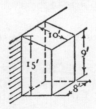

wall, and made entirely of wood. How much wood will be required? Answer in square feet.

15. The figure is the cross-section of an open trough with vertical ends. The top is a rectangle 5 ft. by 1½ ft. Find

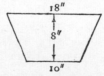

the area of the material required to make it, and the cubic capacity.

16. A rectangular tank is 3 ft. × 2½ ft. × 2 ft. It is half full of water. A cube, edge 12 in., is placed in the tank and rests on the bottom. What will be the rise in the level of the water?

The Right Pyramid

If a solid is bounded by plane faces, of which one, called the base, is any rectilineal figure, and the others are triangles with a common vertex, then the solid is called a **pyramid**.

If the perpendicular from the vertex of the pyramid to the base passes through the centre of the base (i.e. the point equidistant from the vertices of the base), then the pyramid is said to be a **right pyramid**. Three right pyramids are represented below.

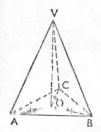
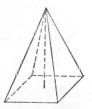
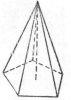

If the pyramid is bounded by four triangular faces, it is called a **tetrahedron,** and, if the four triangles are all equilateral triangles, it is called a **regular tetrahedron.**

It is important to notice that the edges of a right pyramid which join the vertex of the pyramid to the vertices of the base are all equal, because they are the hypotenuses of congruent right-angled triangles, e.g. in the tetrahedron above △s VOA, VOB, VOC are congruent ∴ VA = VB = VC.

Surface Area and Volume of Pyramid

The slant surface of any pyramid is the sum of the areas of the triangular faces. In the case of the right pyramid on a regular base, a convenient expression for the slant surface can be obtained as follows:

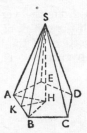

S, ABCDE is a right pyramid, the base being a regular pentagon.
SH is the perpendicular from S to the base.
SK is perpendicular to AB.
H is the circumcentre of ABCDE
$\therefore$ AH = BH.
But $SA^2 = SH^2 + AH^2$
and $SB^2 = SH^2 + BH^2$.
Since $AH^2 = BH^2$
    $\therefore SA^2 = SB^2$
    $\therefore SA = SB$
$\therefore$ $\triangle$SAB is an isosceles triangle and all the slant faces are congruent isosceles triangles
$\therefore$ SK, the perp. from S to AB, bisects AB.

[*Note:* SK is called the **slant height** of the pyramid, for the distance of S from the base of each isosceles triangle is constant.]

$\therefore$ Slant surface = sum of areas of $\triangle$s SAB, SBC, SCD, etc.
               $= \frac{1}{2}AB.SK + \frac{1}{2}BC.SK + \ldots$
               $= \frac{1}{2}(AB + BC + CD + \ldots)SK$
               $= \frac{1}{2}$ (perimeter of base) $\times$ slant height.
   Total surface = slant surface + area of base.

Volume

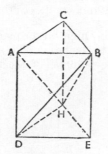

Consider the triangular right prism ABC, DEH. This can be regarded as split up into two pyramids, one with vertex B and base △DEH, the other with vertex B and base ADHC. This second pyramid B, ADHC can itself be regarded as made up of two triangular pyramids, one with vertex B and base ADH, the other with vertex B and base ACH. (It will be seen that none of the three triangular pyramids is a right pyramid.)

∴ △r prism ABC, DEH = pyr. B, DEH + pyr. B, ADH
$$+ \text{ pyr. B, ACH.}$$

It can be proved that pyr. B, ADH and pyr. B, ACH have equal volumes, since they are on equal bases and have the same altitude.

Also another name for pyr. B, ACH is H, ABC, and pyr. H, ABC = pyr. B, DEH, since they are on equal bases ABC and DEH and have the same altitude,

∴ vol. of each pyramid = $\frac{1}{3}$ vol. of △r prism.

Hence the vol. of the pyramid B, DEH is one-third the vol. of the prism on the same base and of the same height.

But the vol. of the prism = area of base × height

∴ **vol. of pyramid** = $\frac{1}{3}$ **area of base × height.**

Since a pyramid such as that shown on page 437 can be regarded as made up of a number of triangular pyramids with the same height

∴ **vol. of any pyramid** = $\frac{1}{3}$ **area of base × height.**

WORKED EXAMPLE

A right pyramid 8 in. high on a square base, edge 12 in., is cut by a plane parallel to the base and 2 in. from it.   Find the total surface, and the volume, of the frustum.

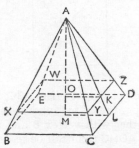

The frustum is the solid included by the base BCDE and the plane XYZW.

XY and BC are parallel because they are the lines of section of two parallel planes by the plane ABC.

Similarly YZ and CD are parallel.   Also △s ABC, ACD, etc., are congruent isosceles triangles.

∴ △s AXY, ABC, AYZ, ACD are similar

∴ $\dfrac{XY}{BC} = \dfrac{AY}{AC} = \dfrac{YZ}{CD}$.

But BC = CD   ∴ XY = YZ.   Also $X\hat{Y}Z = 1$ rt. angle since $B\hat{C}D$ is a rt. angle

∴ XYZW is a square.

Draw AM perp. to plane BCDE to meet XYZW in O.

Then AO is perp. to XYZW.

Draw AL perp. to CD, to cut YZ in K.

Then since ACD and AYZ are isos. △s, CL = LD and YK = KZ.

Join OK and ML.

△s AOK and AML are similar because they are equiangular

∴ $\dfrac{OK}{ML} = \dfrac{AO}{AM} = \dfrac{6}{8}$ ∴ $\dfrac{OK}{6 \text{ in.}} = \dfrac{3}{4}$ ∴ OK = $4\frac{1}{2}$ in.

∴ XY = 2OK = 9 in.

Also $AL^2 = AM^2 + ML^2$ (Pythagoras' Th.)

$\qquad = 8^2 + 6^2$ sq. in.

$\qquad = 100$ sq. in.

$\therefore AL = 10$ in.

$\dfrac{AK}{AL} = \dfrac{AO}{AM} \quad \therefore \dfrac{AK}{10} = \dfrac{6}{8} \quad \therefore AK = 7\frac{1}{2}$ in.

$\qquad\qquad\qquad\qquad \therefore KL = 2\frac{1}{2}$ in.

(1) *Total Surface*—

Area of top and bottom faces $= XY^2 + BC^2$

$\qquad\qquad\qquad\qquad = 9^2 + 12^2$ sq. in.

$\qquad\qquad\qquad\qquad = 225$ sq. in.

$\qquad$ Area of side faces $= 4 \times$ area of trap. CDZY

$\qquad\qquad\qquad\qquad = 4 \times \frac{1}{2}(9 + 12) \times 2\frac{1}{2}$ sq. in.

$\qquad\qquad\qquad\qquad = 105$ sq. in.

$\qquad \therefore$ Total surface $= 330$ sq. in.

(2) *Volume*—

Vol. of frustum $=$ vol. of pyr. A, BCDE $-$ vol. pyr. A, XYZW

$\qquad = \frac{1}{3} . 12^2 \times 8 - \frac{1}{3} . 9^2 \times 6$ cu. in.

$\qquad = 384 - 162$ cu. in.

$\qquad = 222$ cu. in.

EXERCISES 70

In Exercises 1 to 4, find the total surface and the volume of the right pyramids :

Base	*Height*
1. Square, edge 6 in.	1 ft.
2. Equilateral $\triangle$, side 5 cm.	20 cm.
3. Octagon, side 3 in.	10 in.
4. Regular hexagon, side 4 cm.	8 cm.

5. Find the slant height, the total surface and the volume of a regular tetrahedron, edge 6 in.

6. A right pyramid on a square base is 16 in. high, and is cut by a plane, parallel to the base and 4 in. from it. If the side of the square base is 8 in. long, find the volume of the frustum between the base and the plane.

7. The base of a right pyramid is a rectangle, 6 in. × 4 in. and the slant height is 5 in. Find the total surface and the volume.

8. A, BCDE is a right pyramid on a rectangular base. If BC = 8 in., CD = 6 in., AE = 13 in., find the height of the pyramid, its total surface, and its volume.

9. The roof of a tent, total height 13 ft., is a right pyramid on a square base, a side of the square being 10 ft. If the rest of the tent is in the shape of a square prism 8 ft. high, the edge of the square being 10 ft., find
   (a) the total area of canvas required,
   (b) the cubic capacity of the tent.

10. A vessel contains water to a depth of 1 ft. The vessel is an inverted right pyramid, the base being a square of edge 4 ft., and the depth of the vertex below the base 8 ft. Find the volume of the water.

Surface and Volume of Right Circular Cylinder

All cylinders referred to in the book are right circular cylinders.

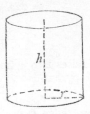

Consider a right prism standing on a regular polygon as base. If the number of sides in the polygon is increased indefinitely, the greater the number of sides the more nearly does the polygon become a circle, and the prism a right circular cylinder.

Hence the rules that apply to the right prism may be applied to the cylinder.

Let radius of base = r units of length
and height of cylinder = h units of length.

(1) Curved surface of cylinder = perimeter of base × height
$$= 2\pi r \times h \text{ units of area}$$
$$= 2\pi r h \text{ units of area.}$$

(2) Total surface of cylinder = curved surface + area of ends
$$= 2\pi r h + 2\pi r^2 \text{ units of area}$$
$$= 2\pi r(h + r) \text{ units of area.}$$

(3) Volume of cylinder = area of base × height
$$= \pi r^2 h \text{ units of volume.}$$

[*Note:* If the curved surface of a right circular cylinder is developed, it forms a rectangle, whose length is the circumference of the base and whose breadth is the height of the cylinder. Hence area of curved surface of cylinder = $2\pi r h$.]

WORKED EXAMPLES

(1) Find the volume of metal in a cylindrical pipe 60 ft. long, the external and internal diameters being 4 in. and 3 in. respectively.

Let R in. and r in. be external and internal radii respectively.

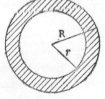

Area of cross-section = $\pi R^2 - \pi r^2$ sq. in.
$$= \pi(R^2 - r^2) \text{ sq. in.}$$
$$= \pi(R + r)(R - r) \text{ sq. in.}$$

If length of pipe = l in.

vol. of metal = $\pi(R + r)(R - r)l$ cu. in.

$$= \frac{22}{7}(2 + 1\tfrac{1}{2})(2 - 1\tfrac{1}{2}) \times 60 \times 12 \text{ cu. in.}$$

$$= \frac{22}{7} \times \frac{7}{2} \times \frac{1}{2} \times \frac{60 \times 12}{12 \times 12 \times 12} \text{ cu. ft.}$$

$$= \frac{55}{24} \text{ cu. ft.}$$

$$= 2\tfrac{7}{24} \text{ cu. ft.}$$

(2) 50 gallons of water are poured into a cylindrical tank, diameter of base being 4 ft. Find the depth of the water in inches, correct to $\frac{1}{10}$ in.

$$6\tfrac{1}{4} \text{ gal.} = 1 \text{ cu. ft.}$$

$$\therefore 50 \text{ gal.} = \frac{50}{1} \times \frac{4}{25} = 8 \text{ cu. ft.}$$

Let depth $= d$ in.
Vol. of cylinder $= \pi r^2 h$

$$\therefore \text{ vol. of water} = \pi.2^2.\frac{d}{12} \text{ cu. ft.}$$

$$\therefore \frac{22}{7} \times 4 \times \frac{d}{12} = 8$$

$$\therefore d = \frac{7 \times 12 \times 8}{4 \times 22}$$

$$= \frac{84}{11}$$

$$= 7.63$$

$\therefore$ depth of water $= 7.6$ in., to the nearest $\frac{1}{10}$ in.

EXERCISES 71

1. Find the total surface of a cylinder, height 40 cm., radius of base 14 cm.

2. Find the total surface of a cylinder, height 1 ft. 6 in., radius 7 in.

3. Find the volume of a cylinder, diameter of base 28 cm., height 25 cm.

4. Find the volume of a cylinder, diameter of base 1 ft. 2 in., height 15 in.

5. Find the area of the curved surface of a cylinder, radius of base 4.2 cm., height 10 cm.

6. If the area of the curved surface of a cylinder is 264 sq. in. and the height is 8 in., find the radius of the base.

7. If the total surface of a cylinder, 13 in. high, is 1056 sq. in., find the radius of the base.

8. If the volume of a cylinder is 77 cu. in. and the radius is $1\tfrac{3}{4}$ in., find the height.

9. If the volume of a cylinder is 1000 c.c. and the height is 50 cm., find the radius to the nearest millimetre.

10. Find the number of square feet of thin metal required to make 1000 cylindrical closed vessels, height = 8 in., diameter of base = 5 in.

11. A copper cube, edge 1 ft., is melted down and made into a cylindrical rod 1 yd. long. Find the radius of the circular end of the rod. Give answer to the nearest tenth of an inch.

12. Find the volume of a cylindrical ring, outer and inner diameters 4 in. and 3 in. respectively, the ring being $\frac{1}{2}$ in. thick.

13. Find the volume of copper required for a cylindrical pipe, internal diameter 7 cm., thickness of copper 6 mm., length 100 cm. Answer to the nearest c.c.

14. Find the weight of 1 mile of copper wire, diameter $\frac{1}{16}$ in., if 1 cu. ft. weighs 551 lb. Answer to $\frac{1}{10}$ lb.

15. A rectangle, 6 in. × 3·5 in., rotates about the 6-in. side as axis. Find the volume of the solid it generates.

16. A cylinder, 10 in. high, has a volume of 385 cu. in. Find the area of the section through the axis of the cylinder.

17. 50 gallons of water per minute flow through a cylindrical pipe, diameter $3\frac{1}{2}$ in. If the pipe is always full, find the speed of the water in miles per hour. Answer to nearest $\frac{1}{10}$ mile. (1 cu. ft. = $6\frac{1}{4}$ gal.)

18. 500 gallons of water flow into a cylindrical tank, diameter of base 5 ft. Find the depth of the water in feet, to the nearest tenth of a foot.

19. A cylindrical vessel, diameter of base 4 in., height 5 in., is used to fill a second vessel of the same shape, diameter of base 10 in., height 15 in. Find the least number of times the first vessel must be used.

20. A cylindrical can, 8 in. high, is made with the same capacity as a rectangular can, 8 in. high, base 7 in. × $5\frac{1}{2}$ in. Find the difference in the area of sheet metal required in the two cases, if both cans are closed cans.

Surface and Volume of Right Circular Cone

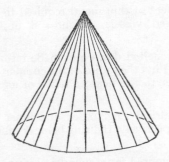 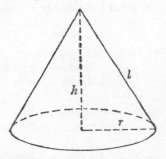

Consider a right pyramid standing on a regular polygon as base. If the number of sides in the polygon is increased indefinitely, the greater the number of sides the more nearly does the polygon become a circle, and the pyramid a right circular cone.

Hence the rules that apply to the right pyramid may be applied to the cone.

Let slant height of cone $= l$ units of length,
         height of cone $= h$ units of length
and radius of base $= r$ units of length.

(1) Curved surface of cone $= \frac{1}{2}$ (perimeter of base) $\times$ slant height
$$= \frac{1}{2}(2\pi r) \times l \text{ units of area}$$
$$= \pi r l \text{ units of area.}$$

(2) Total surface of cone $=$ curved surface $+$ area of base
$$= \pi r l + \pi r^2 \text{ units of area}$$
$$= \pi r(l + r) \text{ units of area.}$$

(3) Volume of cone $= \frac{1}{3}$ area of base $\times$ height
$$= \frac{1}{3} \pi r^2 h \text{ units of volume.}$$

Worked Example

From a circle, radius 6 in., is cut a sector, the angle of the sector being 120°. The sector is now folded so that it becomes the curved surface of a cone. Find (a) the radius of the base, (b) the height, (c) the area of the curved surface, (d) the volume, (e) the vertical angle of the cone.

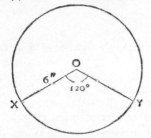 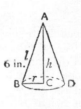

Length of arc XY = $\frac{1}{3}$ of circumference (since 120° = $\frac{1}{3}$ of 360°)

$$= \frac{1}{3} \times 2\pi \times 6 \text{ in.}$$
$$= 4\pi \text{ in.}$$

Hence circumference of base of cone = $2\pi r$, if r in. is the radius of the base,

$$\therefore 2\pi r = 4\pi$$

(a) $\therefore r = 2$.

From rt.-angled △ACB, $AC^2 = l^2 - r^2$

$$= 6^2 - 2^2 \text{ sq. in.}$$
$$= 32. \text{ sq. in.}$$

(b) $\therefore AC = \sqrt{32} = 4\sqrt{2} \text{ in.}$

(c) Area of curved surface $= \frac{1}{3}$ area of circle

$$= \frac{1}{3} \times \pi \times 6 \times 6 \text{ sq. in.}$$
$$= 12\pi. \text{ sq. in.}$$

(d)   Vol. $= \frac{1}{3}\pi r^2 h$

$$= \frac{1}{3}\pi . 2^2 . 4\sqrt{2} \text{ cu. in.}$$
$$= \frac{1}{3} . \frac{22}{7} . 4 . 4\sqrt{2} \text{ cu. in.}$$
$$= 23 \cdot 7 \text{ cu. in.}$$

(e) sin $B\widehat{A}C = \frac{2}{6} = \frac{1}{3}$ $\therefore B\widehat{A}C = 19° 28'$

$$\therefore B\widehat{A}D = 38° 56'.$$

EXERCISES 72

1. Find the total surface, and the volume, of the solid

formed by revolving the triangle right-angled at **B** about (1) **BC**, (2) **AB** as an axis.

2. Find the slant height, the total surface, and the volume of a cone, height 6 in., diameter of base 5 in.

3. Find the curved surface and the volume of a cone with slant height 6·8 cm. and radius of base 3·2 cm.

4. If the area of the curved surface of a cone is 165 sq. cm. and the radius of the base 5 cm., find the volume.

5. Find the total surface area of a cone of volume 770 cu. in., the diameter of the base being 7 in.

6. If the area of the base of a cone is 38·5 sq. in. and the volume is 462 sq. in., find the vertical angle.

7. A cone 12 in. high, whose base diameter is 20 in., is cut by a plane parallel to the base and at a distance of 6 in. from it. Find the volume of the part of the cone between the two planes (the frustum). Find also the area of the curved surface of the frustum, giving both answers to the nearest unit.

8. Find the curved surface and volume of the frustum of a cone formed when a cone of height 8 in. and diameter of base 8 in. is cut by a plane, parallel to the base and 6 in. from it.

9. The vertical angle of a cone is 60°, and the slant height 10 in. Find the volume.

10. Find the area of canvas required for a bell tent, 12 ft. high and 12 ft. in diameter.

11. Into a cylindrical vessel full of water, diameter 21 cm. and height 10 cm., is placed a cone of the same diameter and height. How much water will overflow?

12. The figure shows the cross-section of a funnel, which

consists of the frustum of a cone and a cylindrical pipe. Find the total volume.

13. Find the rise in the water level when a cone, height 9 in., base diameter 4 in., is placed in a cylindrical vessel, height 15 in., base diameter 12 in., the water completely covering the cone.

14. Find the volume of the conical vessel formed from a semi-circular piece of metal, diameter 26 in., the whole of the metal forming the curved surface of the vessel.

15. A sector of a circle, radius 18 cm., the angle of the sector being 100°, is folded to make the curved surface of a cone. Find the height and volume of the cone.

16. A filter paper in the form of a circle, diameter $12\frac{1}{2}$ cm., is folded in four, and opened out so as to form a hollow cone. Find the vertical angle of the cone.

17. The diameter of the two ends of the frustum of a cone are 6 in. and $1\frac{1}{2}$ in. If the height of the frustum is 4 in., find its volume.

18. A cone is 12 in. high. Where must a plane, parallel to the base, cut it, so that the cone is bisected?

The Sphere

A sphere may be regarded as a solid bounded by one surface which is such that all points on it are at the same distance from a fixed point. The fixed point is the centre of the sphere and the constant distance is the length of the radius. [The word sphere is sometimes used for the surface of the sphere, when no confusion can arise.]

If any straight line through the centre cuts the surface in two points A, B, then AB is a diameter of the sphere.

Every plane section of a sphere is a circle.

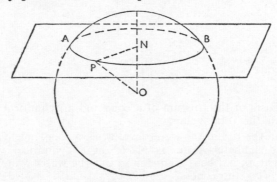

Let APB be any plane section of a sphere with centre O.

Take P any point on the bounding line of the section.

Let ON be the perpendicular from O to the plane section. Join OP, PN.

Then $O\hat{N}P$ = a rt. angle (constr.)

$\therefore$ $NP^2 = OP^2 - ON^2$ (Pythagoras' Th.).

But OP is a fixed length, the radius of the sphere, and ON is a constant length for all positions of P

$\therefore$ NP is a constant length; and N is a fixed point

$\therefore$ the locus of P is the circumference of a circle, centre N and radius NP.

Any plane section of a sphere, which contains the centre of the sphere, is a circle whose radius is equal to the radius of the sphere. This circle is called a **great circle**.

If we take any two points on the sphere (not the ends of a diameter), then one, and only one, great circle may be drawn through these two points, for the two points and the centre of the sphere determine a plane, and the section of the sphere by this plane is a circle which passes through the centre.

Surface and Volume of Sphere

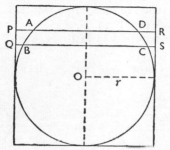

If we have a sphere and the circumscribing cylinder, it can be proved that the curved surface of the cylinder, intercepted by two planes perpendicular to the axis, is equal to the area of the belt of the sphere between the same planes, i.e. in the figure, the curved surface ABCD on the sphere is equal in area to the curved surface PQRS on the cylinder.

Hence if r units of length = radius of sphere

area of surface of sphere = area of curved surface of circumscribing cylinder

$= 2\pi r \times 2r$ [ht. of cylinder $= 2r$]

$= 4\pi r^2$ units of area.

To find the formula for the volume we may consider the whole sphere made up of a number of pyramids, the number being increased indefinitely,

∴ volume of sphere = sum of vols. of pyramids

$= \frac{1}{3}$ (sum of areas of bases) $\times$ height

$= \frac{1}{3} \times 4\pi r^2 \times r$ units of volume

$= \frac{4}{3}\pi r^3$ units of volume.

Worked Examples

(1) The figure represents the cross-section of a sphere placed in a conical vessel. Find the volume of water required to just cover the sphere.

From similar $\triangle$s ABC and DEC

$$\frac{DC}{DE} = \frac{BC}{AB}$$

$$\therefore \frac{DC}{1 \text{ in.}} = \frac{6 \text{ in.}}{3 \text{ in.}} \quad \therefore DC = 2 \text{ in.}$$

$$\therefore YC = 2 \text{ in.} + 1 \text{ in.} = 3 \text{ in.}$$

Also $\dfrac{YZ}{AB} = \dfrac{YC}{AC} = \dfrac{3 \text{ in.}}{3\sqrt{3} \text{ in.}} = \dfrac{1}{\sqrt{3}}$

$$AC^2 = BC^2 - AB^2 = 36 - 9 = 27 \text{ sq. in.}$$

$$\therefore \frac{YZ}{3 \text{ in.}} = \frac{1}{\sqrt{3}} \qquad \therefore YZ = \sqrt{3} \text{ in.}$$

Vol. of water = vol. of cone XCZ − vol. of sphere

$$= \tfrac{1}{3}\pi . YZ^2 . YC - \tfrac{4}{3}\pi 1^3 \text{ cu. in.}$$
$$= \tfrac{1}{3}\pi(\sqrt{3})^2 . 3 - \tfrac{4}{3}\pi \text{ cu. in.}$$
$$= \tfrac{1}{3}\pi[9 - 4] \text{ cu. in.}$$
$$= \tfrac{5}{3}\pi \text{ cu. in.}$$

(2) The figure represents the cross-section of a sphere floating in water, partly submerged.

Find the length of the water line on the sphere.

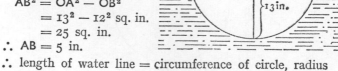

$$AB^2 = OA^2 - OB^2$$
$$= 13^2 - 12^2 \text{ sq. in.}$$
$$= 25 \text{ sq. in.}$$
$$\therefore AB = 5 \text{ in.}$$

$\therefore$ length of water line = circumference of circle, radius 5 in.

$$= 2\pi . 5 \text{ in.}$$
$$= 10\pi \text{ in.}$$

Exercises 73

1. Find the surface and volume of a sphere, radius = 6 in.
2. Find the surface and volume of a sphere, diameter = 14 cm.
3. The surface of a sphere is 616 sq. in. Find the radius.
4. The volume of a sphere is 440 c.c. Find the diameter.
5. The surface of a sphere is 38·5 sq. in. Find the volume.
6. A cube of lead, edge 10 in., is melted down and made into spheres, 2 in. in diameter. How many spheres can be made, allowing that 10 per cent of the lead is wasted?
7. A sphere, radius 3 in., is completely immersed in the water in a rectangular tank, length 6 in., breadth 5 in., depth 4 in. Find the consequent rise in level of the water.
8. The reading of the water level in a measuring glass is 14·6 c.c. A sphere is placed in the water and the reading is now 18·8 c.c. Find the radius of the sphere.
9. Find the volume of metal in a spherical shell, the inner and outer diameters being 8 in. and 1 ft. respectively.
10. How many spherical pellets, 0·2 in. in diameter, can be made from a sphere 6 in. in diameter, assuming that there is no waste?
11. Two metal spheres, radii 10 in. and 8 in., are melted and moulded into a single sphere. Find the radius of this sphere.
12. The volume of a sphere is 125 c.c. Find the area of the surface.
13. Find the radius of a sphere which circumscribes a cube whose edge is 4 in.
14. Find the internal diameter of a spherical iron shell, which weighs 500 lb. and has an external diameter of 2 ft., if 1 cu. ft. of iron weighs 480 lb.
15. A sphere, diameter 10 in., is placed in a cylinder full of water, the cylinder being 10 in. high and of diameter 10 in. Find the volume of water which is left in the cylinder.
16. Find the area of the zone of a sphere, diameter 10 in., bounded by two planes 2 in. apart.

17. A thin metal cap is part of a sphere of radius 1 ft. If its greatest depth is $\frac{1}{2}$ in., find the area of its surface.

18. A conical cap just covers three equal spheres (radius 1 in.),

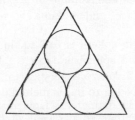

placed on a table as shown in the figure. Find the height of the cone and the diameter of its base.

19. A sphere of radius 2 in. is placed in a wire frame which is in the shape of an equilateral triangle, each side being 6 in. long. What is the depth of the lowest point of the sphere below the plane of the frame?

20. A sphere, radius 15 in., floats in water so that the highest point of the sphere is 5 in. above the water. Find the length of the water line on the sphere.

Latitude and Longitude

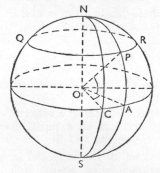

The earth is approximately a sphere, which rotates about its axis once every 24 hours. The ends of this axis are called the North and South Poles (marked N and S respectively in the figure).

The **equatorial plane** is the great circle to which the axis NS is normal, and the circumference of this great circle is called **the Equator**.

Parallels of latitude are the circumferences of small circles parallel to the equatorial plane.

Any number of great circles can be drawn having NS as diameter. Half the circumference of any one of these circles extending from the North Pole to the South Pole is called a **meridian of longitude,** or briefly a **meridian.**

(1) The **latitude** of a place P is its angular distance north or south of the Equator.

In the figure, NPAS is the meridian through the place P and cuts the equator at A. If O is the centre of the earth, $\hat{POA}$ (north) is the latitude of P. All places on the parallel of latitude QPR have the same latitude as P.

(2) The **longitude** of a place is its angular distance east or west of a standard meridian. It is the dihedral angle between the great circles containing the meridian of the place and the standard meridian (taken as the meridian of Greenwich).

In the diagram, NPAS is the meridian of the place P which cuts the equator at A. NCS is the standard meridian, cutting the equator at C. The planes containing these meridians intersect in the line NS, and OA and OC are straight lines, one in each plane, and both perpendicular to NS.

∴ AÔC measures the angle between these planes

∴ AÔC (east) is the longitude of P.

All places on the same meridian NPS have the same longitude as P.

The position of a place on the earth's surface is known if we know its latitude and its longitude.

Worked Example

Taking the radius of the earth as 4000 miles, find the distance between two places P, lat. 56° N. long. 10° E., and Q, lat. 56° N. long. 65° E.,

(1) measured along a parallel of latitude,

(2) measured along the great circle through P and Q.

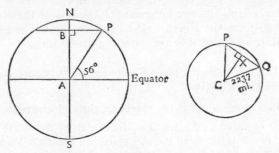

(1) The figure shows the section through place P and the Polar Axis NS. The parallel of latitude through P is the circumference of a circle radius BP.

$$\frac{BP}{AP} = \cos \widehat{BPA} = \cos 56°$$

$$\therefore BP = 4000 \cos 56°$$
$$= 4000 \times \cdot5592$$
$$= 2237 \text{ miles (to the nearest mile).}$$

Since place Q is on the same parallel of latitude, the distance PQ, measured along the parallel, is the length of the arc subtending an angle of 55° at the centre of a circle, radius 2237 miles.

$$\therefore \text{Distance } PQ = \frac{55}{360} \times 2 \times \frac{22}{7} \times 2237 \text{ miles}$$
$$= 2148 \text{ miles.}$$

(2) The length of the straight line PQ

$$= 2QX = 2 \times 2237 \times \sin 27\tfrac{1}{2}° = 2065 \text{ miles.}$$

This straight line subtends an angle at the centre of the earth.

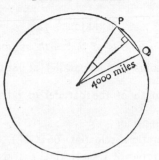

The figure shows that the

$$\text{sine of half of this angle} = \frac{\frac{1}{2}PQ}{\text{radius of earth}}$$

$$= \frac{1033}{4000}$$

$$= \cdot 2583$$

$$\therefore \tfrac{1}{2} \text{ of this angle} = 14° \ 58'$$

$$\therefore \text{ the angle} = 29° \ 56'$$

The distance from P to Q measured along the great circle, passing through P and Q, is the length of the arc of a circle, radius 4000 miles, subtending an angle of 29° 56' at the centre.

$$\therefore \text{ Distance} = \frac{29\frac{14}{15}°}{360°} \times 2\pi \times 4000 \text{ miles}$$

$$= 2089 \text{ miles.}$$

Note that this is less than the distance between the places measured along the parallel of latitude. The least distance between any two places is the distance measured along the great circle which passes through the places.

Exercises 74

(Take the radius of the earth as 4000 miles)

1. Find the radius of the parallel of latitude 40° N.

2. Find the length of the parallel of latitude 35° S.

3. Find the length of
   (a) the Arctic Circle (lat. 66½° N.),
   (b) the Tropic of Cancer (lat 23½° N.).

4. Due to the rotation of the earth, through how many miles per hour does a place move in latitude 56° N. ?

5. Find the area of the Tropical Zone and of the Antarctic Zone.

6. Find the distance measured along a meridian between the parallel of latitude 40° N. and the equator.

7. Find the distance of the Arctic Circle from the North Pole.

8. Two places on the parallel of latitude 50° N. differ in longitude by 25°. Find the distance between them measured along the parallel of latitude.

9. Find the distance between two places P and Q on the earth's surface, P lat. 30° N. long. 20° E., Q lat. 30° N. long. 160° E. measured
   (1) along the parallel of latitude,
   (2) along the great circle.

10. A place P is 3000 miles from the North Pole, measured along a meridian. Find the latitude of P.

11. A ship in latitude 40° S. sails due east for 100 miles. By how many degrees does her longitude change ?

REVISION PAPERS LI–LX.

LI

1. The figure represents a cuboid. Find the angles between
   (1) planes ACGE and BFGC,
   (2) planes ACGE and CGHD,

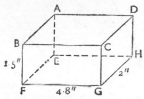

   (3) AF and plane EFGH,
   (4) AC and plane AEHD.

2.

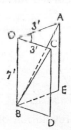

The figure represents a door, opened through AÔC, about the hinge OB. If AÔC = 70°, find AB̂C.

3. P, Q, R are three fixed non-collinear points. X is a point which moves so that it is always equidistant from P, Q, and R. Find the locus of X.

4. A cuboid measures 8 in. by 6 in. by 5 in. Find the total surface, the volume and the length of the diagonal.

5. A 15-in. cube of metal is melted down and made into a sphere. Calculate the diameter of the sphere, if 5 per cent of the metal is wasted in the process. Answer in inches, correct to 1 dec. pl.

LII

1. In the figure, **ABCD** represents a plane hillside, inclined at an angle of 30° to the horizontal plane **BCYX**. **BZ** represents a track up the hillside making an angle of 40° with the line

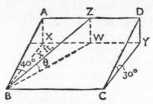

of greatest slope, **AB**. If **ZB** = x ft. and $Z\widehat{B}W = \theta$, write down an expression for **AB** in terms of x, and hence also for **AX**. Then express **ZW** in terms of x and θ, and hence prove that $\sin \theta = \sin 30° \cos 40°$. Find θ.

2. Find the area of the curved surface and the volume of the

solid formed by the revolution of $\triangle$**ABC** about **AD** as an axis.

3. What fraction of the earth's surface lies between the parallel of latitude 30° N. and the equator?

4. A, BCD is a tetrahedron on an equilateral triangle as base, with **BC** = 6 in. If **AB** = **AC** = **AD** = 8 in., find

  (1) the distance of A from the plane BCD,
  (2) the inclination of the edge **AC** to the plane BCD,
  (3) the angle between the faces **ABC** and **BCD**.

5. A right circular cone, height 10 in., base-radius 5 in., is placed in a cylindrical tank, base-radius 10 in. Water is poured in until the depth is 10 in. Find the volume of water poured in.

LIII

1. The figure represents an 8-in. cube. $BK = \frac{1}{4}BC$ and $EL = \frac{1}{4}EH$. Find $\widehat{KAL}$.

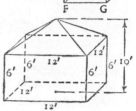

2. The figure represents a tent with 4 vertical canvas walls resting on horizontal ground, and a canvas roof in the shape of a regular pyramid on a square base. Find

   (1) the total area of canvas required,
   (2) the volume of air in the tent,
   (3) the angle which a face of the pyramid makes with the horizontal.

3. X and Y are two fixed points 6 in. apart. What is the locus in space of a point P which moves so that

$$XP^2 + YP^2 = 50 \text{ sq. in. ?}$$

4. The diagonals of a square ABCD, each side 4 in., intersect at O. OP is perpendicular to the plane ABCD and $OP = 2$ in. Find the angle between BP and the plane ABCD, and the angle between the face BPA and the plane ABCD.

5. A cylindrical hole, diameter 1 in., is bored through a metal cube, each edge 5 in. Find the volume of the metal that is left.

LIV

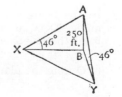

1. The figure represents a tower AB, 250 ft. high. X is due west of the tower, Y is due south of it. Find the distance XY, and the angle between the planes AXY and BXY.

2. The figure represents a triangle ABC, with YZ parallel to AB, and with $A\widehat{B}C$ a rt. angle, in two vertical positions.

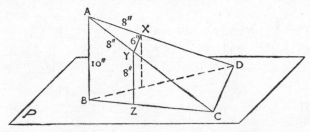

P is a horizontal plane. Calculate YC, BC, CD and the angle which plane ACD makes with the horizontal.

AX = AY = YZ = 8 in., XY = 6 in., AB = 10 in.

3. AB, AC, AD are three equal rods forming a tripod. Prove that, if AO is perpendicular to the horizontal plane BCD, O is the circumcentre of BCD. If AB = 7·5 in. and AO = 6 in., find the angle which AB makes with the plane BCD, and the inclination of ABC to the horizontal, if $\triangle$DBC is equilateral.

4. A and B are two places on the earth's surface, both in latitude 38° N., their longitudes being 24° W. and 33° E. respectively. Find the distance between them, measured along the parallel of latitude, taking the radius of the earth as 3960 miles.

5. A wooden sphere of radius 9 in. floats in water, with its lowest point 6 in. below the water level. Find the length of the water line.

LV

1. In the figure, ABCD is a vertical rectangle. BXYC is a horizontal rectangle. Find the length of XD and hence find $X\widehat{D}Y$. If DQ = ¼DX, find the distance of Q from the plane ABCD.

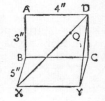

2. In the figure, the lowest point of the sphere is 4 in. below the plane containing the circular hole in which the sphere rests. The radius of the sphere = 10 in. Find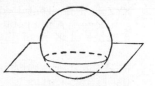

    (1) the radius of the hole,
    (2) the area of the surface of the sphere below the plane.

3. A door 3 ft. wide and 8 ft. high is opened through an angle of 50°. Calculate the angle between two positions of a diagonal.

4. A ship is in lat. 40° S. and long. 40° E. What is its shortest distance from the south pole?
If the ship travels due east until meridian 100° is reached, how long will she take if her speed is 18 miles per hour?

5. A lidless box in the shape of a square prism 8 in. high is made of thin wood. If the area of the wood is 420 sq. in., find the length of the side of the square base.

LVI

1. The figure represents a right circular cone, height 8 in., radius of base 6 in. If O is the centre of the base and BÔC = 60°, calculate

    (1) the area of △ABC,
    (2) the angle which plane ABC makes with the base.

2. The figure shows the plan of a hut with walls 10 ft. high,

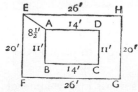

and a flat roof. Calculate the height of the roof above the ground, and the angle which AE makes with the horizontal.

3. XYZ is a horizontal equilateral triangle, each side being 5 in. long. A is a point 2 in. vertically above X. Find the distance of X from the plane AYZ.

4. Find the shortest distance between the following places on the earth's surface.

   A, lat. 4° N., long. 75° W.
   B, lat. 48° N., long. 75° W.

5. On a sphere of radius 6 in., a circle radius 2 in. is drawn. Find the distance of the plane of the circle from the centre of the sphere. Find also the area of the surface of the sphere enclosed by the circle.

LVII

1. QRS is in plane P. XS is perp. to P. Calculate XQ, the angle which XS subtends at R, and the angle between planes XQR and SQR.

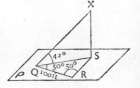

2. The figure shows a rectangular box standing on a square base ABCD and containing a square pyramid which just fits into the box as shown. If AC = 10 in. and AE = 12 in., find

   (1) AD,
   (2) OA,
   (3) AÔC,
   (4) inclination of OA to plane EFGH.

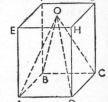

3. Find the slant surface and volume of the frustum of a pyramid, the ends being squares with sides 20 cm. and 36 cm. respectively, the thickness being 12 cm.

4. ABCD is a horizontal rectangle with AB = 4 ft., BC = 8 ft. X and Y are two points vertically above C and D respectively and CX = DY = 2 ft.
Find the inclination of plane ABXY to the horizontal.
Find the inclination of BY to the horizontal.

5. A spherical metal shell weighs 560 lb. Its external diameter is 2 ft. long. If 1 cu. ft. of the metal weighs 480 lb., find, correct to $\frac{1}{10}$ in., the thickness of the metal, assuming this to be uniform throughout.

LVIII

1. In the figure, planes P and Q represent respectively a wall and the floor of a room. A rod XY, 8 ft. long, is suspended

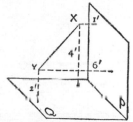

as shown. Find the angle which the rod makes with the wall and with the floor. The distances marked are the distances of the ends of the rod from the two planes.

2. ABCD is a rectangle in which AB = 9 in. and AD = 20 in. M and N are points in AD and BC respectively, such that AM = BN = 8 in. The rectangle is folded about MN until

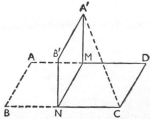

the plane A'B'NM is perp. to the plane NCDM. Calculate A'C, A'ĈM and the distance of B' from the plane A'CM.

3. Find the curved surface and the volume of the frustum of a cone, the radii of its ends being 2 in. and 5 in., and the slant thickness 5 in.

4. Two places on the earth's surface are on the parallel of latitude 54° N. If the shortest distance between them is 2000 miles, what is their difference in longitude ? [Radius of earth = 4000 miles, $\pi = \dfrac{22}{7}$.]

5. A triangle ABC with $\widehat{A} = 90°$, AB = 5 in., AC = 12 in., is situated so that the distances of A, B, and C from a plane P are respectively 8 in., 5 in., 10 in. Find the sides of $\triangle A'B'C'$, the projection of $\triangle ABC$ on plane P.

LIX

1. In the figure, $\triangle PQR$ is inclined at an angle of 40° to the horizontal plane Z. In $\triangle PQR$, PQ = 5 in., $P\widehat{Q}R = 52°$,

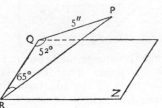

$P\widehat{R}Q = 65°$. Calculate the inclination of PQ and of PR to the horizontal plane.

2. ABC is an isosceles triangle with AB = AC.   D is the mid-point of BC and M, N are the mid-points of AB and AC respectively.   MN and AD meet in O.   The figure is folded as shown, until $\triangle A'MN$ is perpendicular to plane MBCN.

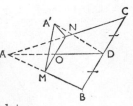

If AB = 10 in., BC = 12 in., calculate

   (1) inclination of A'B to plane MBCN,
   (2) inclination of plane A'BC to plane ABC.

3. From a circle of radius r in. is cut a sector, the angle of the sector being 60°. The remainder is folded, so as to form the curved surface of a cone. If $r' =$ the radius of its base, prove that $r' = \frac{5}{6}r$ in. If $r = 12$ in., find the height of the cone and its volume, both correct to the first decimal place.

4. What is the greatest distance of the surface of a sphere from the line joining two points on the sphere which subtend an angle of 75° at the centre, if the radius of the sphere is 10 in.? Answer correct to 2 dec. places.

5. A camera tripod is set up on level ground. If the legs are each 4 ft. long, prove that the angles which the legs make with the ground are all equal. If the height of the tripod is 3 ft., calculate this angle. If, further, the points of the legs in contact with the ground form the vertices of an equilateral triangle, find the length of the side of this triangle. Answer in feet correct to 2 dec. places.

LX

1. In the figure, isosceles $\triangle$ PQR is at right angles to plane A. $\triangle$s PQS and PRS are each at an angle of 45° to plane A, as

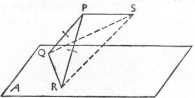

is also $\triangle$SQR. If RS = 3 in., calculate QR and PS. What is the inclination of QS to plane A?

2. The figure represents a 6-in. cube. X is the mid-point of

BF. Find the distance of X from the plane AFC. Answer in inches, correct to the 2nd dec. place.

3. The figure represents a solid figure bounded by a rectangular base 4 in. × 9 in., two congruent trapezia ABHE, DCHE, and

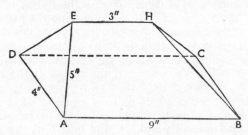

two congruent isosceles triangles AED, BCH. Calculate the height of EH above ABCD, the inclination of ADE and of ABHE to the plane ABCD.

4. A sphere circumscribes a cube, each edge of which is 6 in. Find the volume of the sphere and its curved surface.

5. The triangle ABC is right-angled at B and has AB = BC = 2 in. The plane of the triangle is at right angles to plane P and the side BC lies in the plane P. E is the mid-point of

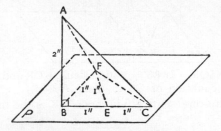

BC, and triangle BEF lies in the plane P. Find the lengths of AF, FC. Prove that $B\widehat{F}C = A\widehat{F}C = 90°$. Find the angle between the planes AFC and AFB, and between the planes AFC and BFC.

The following examination papers consist of questions set by several of the principal examining bodies. The source of each question is indicated in brackets after the question, as follows.

Scottish Leaving Certificate	(S.L.C.)
Glasgow University Bursary Examination	(G.U.B.)
Universities of Manchester, Liverpool, Leeds, Sheffield, Birmingham Joint Matriculation Board	(J.M.B.)
University of Cambridge, Local Examinations Syndicate	(C.L.E.)
University of Oxford, Local Examinations	(O.L.E.)
University of Bristol, Examination of the General Certificate of Education	(B.)
University of London, Matriculation Examination	(L.M.)

EXAMINATION PAPERS

PAPER 1

1. A triangle ABC is inscribed in a circle and the tangents at A and C to the circle intersect in T.   A line TX, parallel to AC, meets BC produced, at X.   Prove that the quadrilateral BATX is cyclic.   If TB and AC intersect at K, by consideration of angles which are equal to angle TXA, prove that XA is a tangent to the circle AKB.   (J.M.B.)

2. Points L, M are taken on the sides AB, BC of △ABC such that AL : LB = 2 : 3 and CM : MB = 4 : 5.   Through L, a straight line is drawn parallel to AM to meet BC at R. AM meets CL at P.

   (1) Write down the value of the ratio BR : BM.
   (2) Calculate the ratio MP : RL.
   (3) Calculate the ratio of the areas of the triangles CPM, CBL.   (C.L.E.)

3. ABCD is a square. The circle on the side BC as diameter is drawn. The line through A and the centre of this circle cuts the circle at P and Q (P being nearer A). The circle with centre A and radius AB cuts PQ at S between P and Q. Prove that

(1) AS = PQ ;
(2) AS² = AP . AQ ;
(3) AP² = AS . PS. (O.L.E.)

4. Two circles touch externally at a point A, and a straight line through A cuts the first circle at B and the second at C. The straight line BED is a tangent to the second circle at D and cuts the first circle at E. Prove that

(1) AD bisects EÂC.
(2) AD² = rect. AE, AC.
(3) rect. BA, DE = rect. AE, BD. (S.L.C.)

5. PQRS is a square of side 4 in. in a horizontal plane. LQ and MS are vertical lines above this plane, of lengths 2 in. and 1 in. respectively. The mid-point of LM is X and PX is produced to meet the vertical through R at the point N. Calculate (1) the length of RN ; (2) the angle LPM. (O.L.E.)

PAPER 2

1. OAB is a quadrant of a circle, O being the centre and OA and OB radii at right angles to each other. Q is the mid-point of the arc AB, and the tangent to the circle at Q cuts OA produced, at P, and OB produced, at R.

(1) Show how to use △OPR to draw a circle touching OA and OB and the arc AB.
(2) Prove that the radius of this circle is equal to AP.
(3) Draw accurately a circle of radius 2 in. divided into four quadrants, with a circle described, as in (1), in one of the four quadrants. (B.)

2. PQRS is a parallelogram in which PQ = 2QR. The bisectors of angles SPQ and SRQ meet SQ in X and Y respectively. Show that

(a) X and Y are points of trisection of SQ.
(b) PXRY is a parallelogram. (J.M.B.)

3. AB and CD are parallel chords of a circle. The tangent at A meets DC produced in Z. AD and BC intersect in X. Prove that △s ABC and CAZ are equiangular. If, further, the tangent at C meets AZ in Y, prove that the triangles AXC and CYZ are similar, and, hence or otherwise, prove that XY is parallel to DC. (S.L.C.)

4. ABCD is a parallelogram ; P and Q are points such that P and C are on opposite sides of AB, Q and A on opposite sides of BC, and the angles PAB, BCQ are right angles. If AP : AD = CQ : CD, prove that the angles PDA, CDQ are equal ; and that if, further, the angle PDQ is a right angle, then AP = AD. (G.U.B.)

5. V, ABCD is a pyramid, ABCD being a plane quadrilateral and VA = VB = VC = VD. Prove that A, B, C, D lie on a circle whose centre is the foot of the perpendicular from V on to the plane ABCD. If ABCD is a rectangle having AB = 8 in., BC = 6 in., and if

$$VA = VB = VC = VD = 13 \text{ in.,}$$

calculate

(1) the inclination of VA to the plane ABCD,
(2) the angle between the face VAB and the plane ABCD.
(J.M.B.)

PAPER 3

1. AM is a median of a triangle ABC. Through C, a parallel is drawn to AB, meeting AM produced, at E. Prove that M bisects AE, and that AB + AC is greater than 2AM. Prove also that in any triangle, the sum of the medians is less than the perimeter of the triangle. (L.M.)

2. In a triangle ABC inscribed in a given circle, AB > AC and AĈB is acute ; the circle which touches BA at A and passes through C, meets BC produced, in D, and AD meets the given circle in E. If the circle ACD meets BE in P, and BE produced, in Q, show that AP is a tangent to the circle PEC and AQ is a tangent to the circle QEC. (G.U.B.)

3. The bisectors of the angles A and B of an acute-angled triangle ABC meet in I.   XIY, perpendicular to AI, meets AB in X and AC in Y.   Find expressions for the angles of the triangle IYC in terms of A, B, C (the angles of $\triangle$ABC) and show that the triangles BXI and IYC are similar.   Prove that $BI^2 : IC^2 = BX : YC$. (S.L.C.)

4. (a) From a point P outside a circle, a tangent PT and a secant PAB are drawn.   The tangent touches the circle at T and the secant cuts the circle at A and B.   If PA = 2 in. and AB = 6 in. calculate the length of PT.

   (b) Two unequal circles cut each other at R and S.   From any point Q on RS produced, two secants QCD and QXY are drawn, one to each circle.   Prove that the points C, D, Y, X are concyclic.   Also prove that $QX.DY = QD.CX$. (J.M.B.)

5. (1) X is a place on the equator and Y is a place on the same meridian of longitude, due north of X.   If the distance XY measured along the meridian is 2000 miles, find the latitude of Y.

   (2) A ship sailing due west in Lat. 49° N. finds that after sailing a certain distance, her longitude has altered by 6°.   Find how far the ship has sailed.
     (Radius of earth = 3960 miles ; take π to be 3·142.) (C.S.C.)

Paper 4

1. O is a point inside a circle.   Chords AC and BD are drawn to pass through O and cut at right angles.   From O, a perpendicular ON is drawn to the line AB.   NO produced cuts CD at M.   Prove that OM = MC = MD.   Prove also that the angle OMD is equal to the angle subtended at the centre of the circle by the minor arc AD. (O.L.E.)

2. A straight line AB is bisected at O and OY is drawn perpendicular to AB.   On OY a point P is taken, and the line AP is produced to Q, so that $AP.AQ = 2AO^2$.   Prove that the angle AQB is a right angle. (L.M.)

3. Two circles intersect in A and B.   The tangent at A to one circle meets the other circle in C, and the tangent at B to the circle ABC meets the first circle in D.   Prove that

(1) DA is parallel to BC.

(2) AB is a mean proportional between DA and BC.

Prove also that if a line is drawn through B to cut the circle ABC in L and the circle ABD in M,

$$\frac{AB}{AL} = \frac{AD}{AM}.$$

(S.L.C.)

4. The internal bisectors of the angles A, B of a triangle ABC meet the opposite sides in D and E respectively, and EF is drawn parallel to CB to meet AD in F. Prove that

$$\frac{\triangle DEF}{\triangle DEA} = \frac{a}{c+a}$$ and find the ratio of $\triangle DEF$ to $\triangle ABC$.

(G.U.B.)

5. A tripod having its three legs OA, OB, OC each 4 ft. long, stands on level ground with its ends forming an equilateral triangle ABC whose sides are of length 2 ft. 6 in. P is the point on the ground, vertically beneath O. Calculate

(1) the length of PA (you may use the fact that PA, PB, PC bisect the angles of $\triangle ABC$),

(2) the angle which OA makes with the horizontal,

(3) the length of OP,

(4) the angle which the plane OAB makes with the horizontal. (C.S.C.)

PAPER 5

1. P is a point on the circumcircle of $\triangle ABC$. The feet of the perpendiculars from P to BC, CA, AB are L, M, N respectively. Prove that L, M, N are collinear.

If PL, PM, PN meet the circumcircle again in Q, R, S respectively, prove that $\triangle$s ABC and QRS are congruent.

(O.L.E.)

2. The sides AB, BC, CA of triangle ABC are of lengths 7, 24, 25 units respectively. Show that the triangle is right-angled.

The internal bisector of $B\widehat{A}C$ meets BC at X; find the length of BX.

If I is the incentre of $\triangle ABC$, and IY is the radius drawn perpendicular to AB, prove that IY : XB = AI : AX and determine the length of the radius of the inscribed circle.

(S.L.C.)

3. The tangent is drawn at A to the circumcircle of $\triangle$ABC. BR and CS are drawn perpendicular to this tangent. AD is the perpendicular from A to BC. Prove that

$\triangle$ARB is similar to $\triangle$CDA and that BR.CS = AD².

(J.M.B.)

4. ABCD is a rectangle having AB greater than BC. BP is drawn perpendicular to AC and produced to cut CD at E. Prove that

(1) CE.CD = CB².
(2) CE : CD = CB² : AB².

(L.M.)

5. A hillside facing south has a uniformly sloping surface in the form of a plane which makes an angle of 10° with the horizontal. A straight road is made up the plane in a north-easterly direction (i.e. on a bearing of 045° measured in the horizontal plane). Find the inclination of the road to the horizontal. (C.L.E.)

PAPER 6

1. ABCD is a square ; L and M are the mid-points of BC and CD respectively. AM, DL meet at O. Prove that ABLO is a cyclic quadrilateral. Prove also that if BO is joined, BO = AB. (L.M.)

2. Two circles with centres B and C are such that the circumference of each passes through the centre of the other. CB produced meets the first circle at D. The circles intersect at P and Q. Prove that

(1) $\widehat{PBQ}$ = 120°.
(2) $\triangle$PDQ is equilateral.
(3) PQ is a tangent to the circle DBQ.

(S.L.C.)

3. ABCD is a cyclic quadrilateral. O is any point on the circumference of the circle ABCD, and P, Q, R, S are the feet of the perpendiculars from O to the lines AB, BC, CD, DA respectively. Prove that OP.OR = OQ.OS.

(G.U.B.)

4. ABCD is a rectangle in which the length of AB is a and the length of AD is b and $a > b$. The foot of the perpendicular from C on the diagonal BD is L; the foot of the perpendicular from D on the diagonal AC is M. Prove that the length of LM is $\dfrac{a^2 - b^2}{a^2 + b^2}.a$. (O.L.E.)

5. A square tent standing on horizontal ground has vertical sides 12 ft. long and 5 ft. high, surmounted by a roof in the form of a regular pyramid on a square base with sides 12 ft. long. If the vertex of the pyramid is 8 ft. above the ground, find

    (1) the volume of air in the tent,
    (2) the length of one of the sloping edges of the roof,
    (3) the angle each sloping face of the roof makes with the horizontal,
    (4) the total area of canvas in the walls and roof.

    (C.S.C.)

PAPER 7

1. A, B, C, D are four points in a straight line in that order. X is a point at which AB and CD subtend equal angles. Prove that the circles XBC, XAD have a common tangent at X. (L.M.)

2. DBA is an isosceles triangle right-angled at A. P is a point within the triangle DBA, and RPA is a second isosceles triangle right-angled at A, and such that P and R are on opposite sides of AD. Prove that $B\widehat{P}A = D\widehat{R}A$. BP is produced to meet DR at S. Prove that BS is perpendicular to DR. Squares ABCD and APQR are completed. Prove that $B\widehat{S}C = 45°$, and hence or otherwise, prove that C, S, Q are collinear. (S.L.C.)

3. The tangent at A to the circumcircle of any triangle ABC cuts BC in D, the bisector of the angle BAD cuts BC in E, and the bisector of the angle DCA cuts DA in H. Prove that HE is parallel to AB. (G.U.B.)

4. In triangle ABC, BC is fixed and the ratio AB : AC is constant. Prove that, in general, A lies on a circle S. What is the exceptional case?

If S cuts AB, AC again at P, Q, prove that the circles APC and ABQ meet again at O, the centre of S, and that OP and OQ are equally inclined to BC. (B.)

5. The top of an open cubical box is the square ABCD; its base A'B'C'D' stands on a horizontal table, the edges AA', BB', CC', DD' being vertical and of length 3 in. A thin rod of length 6 in. is placed in the box. The lower end of the rod is in the corner A' and the rod is supported by the rim of the box at the opposite corner C. Find by drawing and measurement, or by calculation, the distance of the upper end of the rod from

(1) the table,
(2) the corner A. (O.L.E.)

PAPER 8

1. From a point P outside a circle, secants PAB and PCD are drawn. The line through A, parallel to BD, cuts PD at E; the line through B, parallel to AC, cuts PD, produced if necessary, at F. Prove that

(1) the points A, B, E and F are concyclic;
(2) the tangent from P to the circle passing through A, B, E, F is equal in length to the tangent from P to the given circle. (S.L.C.)

2. If three parallel lines AP, BQ, CR are cut by two straight lines at A, B, C and P, Q, R respectively, prove that $\dfrac{AB}{BC} = \dfrac{PQ}{QR}$. C and D are any points on the circumference of a circle on AB as diameter, and the perpendiculars from A and B to CD meet it in E and F. Prove that CE = FD. (G.U.B.)

3. The tangent at A to the circumcircle of triangle ABC meets BC at D. The bisectors of the angle BAC meet BC in E and F. Prove that D is the mid-point of EF.

(B.)

4. The triangle ABC is equilateral and D, E, F are the middle points of BC, CA, AB respectively. If X be a point inside the triangle, prove that

$$XA^2 + XB^2 + XC^2 = XD^2 + XE^2 + XF^2 + \tfrac{3}{4}BC^2.$$

(J.M.B.)

5. An equilateral triangle ABC has sides 3 in. long. A point D, not in the plane of the triangle, is 4 in. from each of the points A, B, C. Find

   (1) the distance of D from the plane ABC,
   (2) the angle DA makes with the plane ABC,
   (3) the angle between the planes ADB and ABC.

(C.L.E.)

Paper 9

1. Two circles intersect at P and Q. The tangent at P to one of them meets the second in R, and A is the mid-point of PR. If AQ meets the first circle in S and the second in T, show that A is the mid-point of ST, and that PR is the tangent at R to the circle QRS. Show also, that, if PS cuts the second circle in B, RS is the tangent at S to the circle BSQ.

(G.U.B.)

2. Two triangles ACB, ADB have the same base AB. CD meets AB in X. Prove that

$$\frac{\triangle ACB}{\triangle ADB} = \frac{CX}{DX}.$$

Hence, or otherwise, show how to find a point O inside a triangle ABC such that

$$\triangle AOB : \triangle BOC : \triangle COA = 3 : 9 : 1.$$

(O.L.E.)

3. If I is the incentre of $\triangle ABC$, and I_1 the ex-centre opposite to A, prove

   (1) that the circle I_1BC passes through I,
   (2) that, if the circle cuts AB and AC (produced if necessary) at E and F respectively,

$$AE = AC \text{ and } AF = AB.$$

(B.)

4. Two circles, centres A and B, intersect at points P and Q and any line through P cuts the circles at points R and S respectively. Prove that the triangles QRS and QAB are equiangular. (Consider both the case where R and S are on the exterior arcs and that where one of the points is on the interior arc.)

   (1) If QR = k.QA what relation does RS bear to AB ?
   (2) Show how to find two positions for the line RS so that RS = AB.
   (3) Prove that the greatest possible length of RS is 2AB and indicate how you would construct RS so that RS is of any desired length less than 2AB.

   (S.L.C.)

5. P and Q are two points on a geographical globe of diameter 20 in. They both lie on the parallel of latitude 50° N. P has longitude 90° W. and Q has longitude 90° E. A piece of string AB, has one end, A, on P ; the other end, B, just reaches Q when the string is stretched over the north pole. Calculate the length of the string.
If, instead, the string, with the end A still on P, is laid along the parallel 50° N., running east from P, calculate the longitude of the point reached by the end B.

   (O.L.E.)

PAPER 10

1. ABCD is a cyclic quadrilateral. AB and DC meet in E ; the circle with centre E and radius EC cuts AB in H, and HC, BC meet AD in K, L respectively. Prove that CL = KL.
   (G.U.B.)

2. ABCD is a trapezium, AD being at right angles to AB and DC. AD is 10 in. long, DC is 8 in. long, and the diagonals BD and AC cut at right angles. Prove that the triangles ABD and ADC are similar, and calculate the length of AB.
   (O.L.E.)

3. If **D** is the middle point of the side **BC** of a triangle **ABC**, prove that $AB^2 + AC^2 = 2(AD^2 + BD^2)$.

A point is such that the sum of the squares on the lines joining it to four fixed points is constant ; prove, by successive applications of the above result, that the locus of the point is a fixed circle, assuming all the lines to lie in the same plane. (J.M.B.)

4. **D** is the middle point of the side **BC** of a triangle **ABC**. A line through **D**, parallel to the external bisector of the angle **A**, cuts **AB**, **AC**, or these sides produced at **P**, **Q** respectively. Prove that **BP** = **CQ** and that each is equal to half the difference of **AB**, **AC**. (L.M.)

5. The edges **OA**, **OB**, **OC** of a rectangular box are of length 3, 4, 4 in. respectively. Calculate

   (1) the angle between the planes **ABC**, **AOC** (to the nearest minute),

   (2) the length of the perpendicular from **O** to the plane **ABC** (to three significant figures).

   (B.)

ANSWERS

Exercises 3

1. 2·54.   **2.** ·39.

Exercises 5

2. 360°.   **3.** 30°.   **4.** 720°.
5. 90°, 180°, 120°.   **6.** 90°, 7½°.   **7.** 12.45 p.m.
8. 3 o'clock, 9 o'clock.
9. 2 o'clock, 10 o'clock ; 4 o'clock, 8 o'clock ; 5 o'clock, 7 o'clock.
10. 180°.   **11.** 90°.   **12.** 45°.
13. 90°.   **14.** 45°.
15. 180°, 90°, 45°, 90°, 135°, 135°.
16. 160°, 110°, 100° 46′, 90°, 71° 23′, 60°, 1°.
17. 80°, 60°, 45°, 38° 45′, 30°, 22° 13′, 3°, 52° 46′.
18. 70°.   **19.** 90°.   **20.** 90°.
21. 45°.   **22.** 60°.   **23.** 140°.
24. 137° or 43° ; 58° or 122°.   **25.** $(180 - x)°$ or $x°$.
26. 60, 60° or 120°.   **27.** 45. 45° or 135°.

Exercises 6

12. 60°.   **13.** 69°.

Exercises 7

1. 115°.   **2.** 23°.   **3.** 34°.
4. 38° ; 25° ; 20° ; 30°.
5. 76°.   **6.** 30 ; 45°.   **7.** 132° or 48°.
8. 81° or 65° or 34°.   **9.** 45°, 60° or 75°.
11. $x = 45, y = 135$.   **12.** 134°.
13. 60°.   **14.** 58°.   **15.** 90°.
16. 68°.   **17.** 31.   **18.** 110.
19. 30°, 180°.   **20.** 249°.   **21.** $180° - x°, x°$.
22. 80°.   **23.** 26°.
24. $x = 20$; $y = 100$; $z = 120$.   **25.** 45°.
26. 50.   **27.** 24.   **28.** 39°, 41°.

Exercises 8

1. 1, 7, 3, 5 = 133°.   **2.** 4, 6, 2, 7 = 115°.
     2, 6, 4 = 47°.   1, 3, 5 = 65°.
3.   2, 6, 4 = $x°$.
     1, 7, 3, 5 = $180° - x°$.
4. 58° or 122°.   **5.** $x + y = 180$.
6. 30°.   **7.** 60°.   **9.** 65°.

Exercises 8 (*continued*)

10. $\widehat{ACD} = 45°$; $\widehat{BCA} = 20°$; $\widehat{B} = \widehat{D} = 115°$.
12. 80°. **13.** 20°. **14.** $x + y - z = 180$.
16. 60°. **20.** 85°. **21.** 60°, 75°.
22. $y° - x°$. **23.** 50°, 60°, 70°. **24.** 110°.
25. 58°, 82°. **26.** 60°. **28.** 38°, 98°.
29. 35°, 65°.

Exercises 9

1. 11 ft., 26·4 in., 110 yd. **2.** $31\frac{3}{7}$ in., 39·6 cm., 26·4 yd.
3. 4·9 in. **4.** 8·6 cm.
5. 88 in., 8800 in. or 244 yd. 1 ft. 4 in.
6. 28 in. **7.** 1·15 in., 2·77 in.
8. 90°. **15.** 6, 60°.

Exercises 10

1. 3·8 in., 71°. **2.** 8·4 in., 69°.
3. CA = 2·6 in., AB = 2·9 in. **4.** $a = 6·7$ cm., $b = 9$ cm.
5. B = 90°; A = 53°; C = 37°.
6. A = 52°; B = 38°; C = 90°.
7. 2·4 in., 41°. **8.** 8 cm., 37°.
9. $\widehat{ABC} = \widehat{ACB} = 51°$; $\widehat{BAD} = \widehat{CAD} = 39°$; $\widehat{ADB} = \widehat{ADC} = 90°$.
10. 60° each. **11.** 3·4 in., each. **12.** 60° each.
13. 2 cm.; 2 cm.; $\widehat{DAB} = 42°$; $\widehat{CAB} = 84°$.
14. C = 121°; $a = 3·0$ cm.: or C = 59°; $a = 9·2$ cm.
15. 14·7 cm. 31°. **16.** 3 cm. 72°. **17.** 69°.
18. 4 cm. 60°. **19.** 90°; 5·04 in. **20.** 30° each.

Exercises 11

1. 6 cm. **2.** 4·5 in. **3.** 30 cm.
5. 1·6 in. **6.** 6·75 cm. **7.** 6 in., 9 in.
9. 7 cm. **10.** 8 in. **11.** 9·6 cm., 6·3 cm.
14. 2·4 cm., 1·8 cm. **16.** 2·4 cm. **17.** 7·2 cm.
18. 90 ft. **19.** 24 ft. **20.** 1·2 in., 1·6 in.

Exercises 13

1. 90°, 45°, 45°. **2.** 72°, 72°, 36°. **3.** 120°.
4. 40° **6.** 40°, 50°, 90°.
7. 48°. **10.** 90°.

Exercises 14

2. 82°. **3.** 131°. **4.** 132°.
5. 35°. **6.** 20°. **8.** 28°.
9. 68°, 56°. **11.** 30°, 60°, 90°. **12.** 28°, 68°, 84°.
13. 11°. **16.** 100°. **19.** 72°.
22. 18. **23.** 57°. **24.** $22\frac{1}{2}°$.

EXERCISES 17

Answers to nearest degree and correct to 1 dec. pl.

1. A = 92°, B = 86°, C = 132°, D = 50°.
2. A = 121°, B = 63°, C = 39°, D = 137°, AD = 1·4 cm.
3. B = 73°, C = 89°, D = 122°.
4. AB = 4·1 cm., BC = 6·1 cm., A = 91°, C = 80°, B = 69°.
5. A = 117°, D = 69°, AB = 2·3 in., CD = 2·5 in., AD = 2·6 in.
6. D = 57°, CD = 6·3 cm., AD = 3·3 cm.
7. AD = 2·7 in., BC = 1·6 in., CD = 1·9 in., A = 77°, B = 103°, C = 111°, D = 69°.
8. A = 48°, CD = 4·0 cm., DA = 5·0 cm.
9. A = 90°, BC = 5·2 in., CD = 3·1 in.
10. A = 85°, B = 82°, AD = 3·6 in., DC = 3·7 in., C = 114°, D = 79°, BC = 2·6 in.
11. 2·7 in.
12. AB = 2·3in., AD = 2·0 in., AD̂C = 55°.
13. BC = 8 cm., CD = 5 cm., A = 48°.
14. Each 90°.   **15.** 3·2 in.
16. Each 6 cm., each 90°.   **17.** 2·5 cm.
18. 85°.   **19.** Two : 3·5 in. or 3·9 in.
20. Two.

EXERCISES 18

1. 109°, 109°.   **2.** CD = 6·7 cm. ; AD̂C = 53°.
3. 1·7 in.   **5.** A = 72°, B = 108°.
6. 2·3 in.   **7.** 4·3 in. each.   **8.** 2·9 in.
10. 90°.   **11.** 2·2 in.   **12.** 2·2 in.
13. 3·54 in.   **14.** 2·1 in.   **15.** 3·4 in.

EXERCISES 20

1. 47°, 86°.   **2.** 34°, 56°.
3. 124°, 62°.   **4.** 104°.

EXERCISES 21

1. 360°.   **2.** 54°.   **3.** 540°, 720°, 1080°.
4. 60°, 45°, 120°, 135°.   **5.** 150°, 162°.
6. 8, 10.   **7.** 20, 15.   **8.** Each 116°.
9. Each 130°.
10. 30°, 60°, 90°, 120°, 150°, 150°, 240°, 240°.
11. 6.   **12.** 6.   **13.** 72°, 60°, 45°.
16. 12, 6.   **17.** 36°.   **18.** 150°.
20. 72°, 144°, each remaining ∠ = 108°.

EXERCISES 22

25. AB = 8·9 cm. ;   BC = 10·3 cm. ;   CA = 6·8 cm.
26. AB = 9·5 cm. ;   AC = 7·7 cm.
27. BC = 9·9 cm. ;   CA = 8·6 cm.
28. CA = 5·6 in.   **29.** BC = 4·9 in.

Revision Papers I–X

I

1. 87.   5. 2·5 cm.

III

2. 115°.   4. 160°.

VI

2. 69°.

VII

1. 40°.   2. 1·2 in., 2⅔ in., 4½ in., 1·8 in.

VIII

2. 2⁵⁄₇ in., 12¼ in.

IX

2. 39°, 81°.

X

1. 44°.   4. 169°.

Exercises 25

1. 26·8 sq. cm.   4. 2·8 in.

Exercises 26

1. 26·8 sq. cm.   2. 5·6 in.   3. 2·4 in.

Exercises 27

4. 2·1 cm.   5. 4·2 cm., 3·5 cm.
6. 2·9 sq. in.   7. 2·6 sq. in.
18. 30°, 75°, 75°, 150°, 15°, 15°.

Exercises 28

1. 135 sq. in.   2. 108 sq. in.   3. 6·25 sq. in.
4. 9 sq. cm.   5. 6 sq. ft.   6. 10½ sq. ft.
7. 42 sq. cm.   8. 12 sq. in.   9. 14 sq. in.
10. 6²⁄₇ sq. in.   11. 1 sq. in.   12. 16½ sq. ft.
13. 1⅓ sq. ft.   14. 94 sq. in.   15. 84 sq. in.
16. (1) 47½ sq. ft.   (2) 13⁴⁄₉ sq. yd.   (3) 540 sq. ft.
    (4) 3¹⁵⁄₁₆ sq. ft.   (5) 526¾ sq. yd.   (6) 327⅞ sq. ft.
    (7) 38·5 sq. in.   (8) 18·865 sq. cm.   (9) 24 sq. cm.
17. 316⅔ ft.   18. 2·6 cm.   19. 13⅓ ac.
22. 3·0 in.   24. 3·5 cm., 2·8 cm.   25. 1·72 sq. in.
26. 3·70 sq. in.   27. 6·6 ac.   28. 6·45 ac.
29. 2·8 cm.   30. 24·8 in.   31. 1·32 in.
32. (1) 15, 112½ sq. m.   (2) 17, 250 sq. yd.
    (3) 1 ac. 2916 sq. yd.

Exercises 29

1. $k(a + b) \equiv ka + kb.$ **2.** $(2x)^2 \equiv 4x^2.$
3. $(x + 1)(x + 2) \equiv x^2 + 3x + 2.$
4. $(a + b)(c + d) \equiv ac + ad + bc + bd.$
5. $k(a - b) \equiv ka - kb.$
6. $(a + b)(c - d) \equiv ac - ad + bc - bd.$
16. $4x \times 2x \equiv 8x^2.$
17. $(x + y)(y + z) = xz + (x + y + z)y.$
18. $x(2x + y) = xy + 2x^2.$

Exercises 30

1. 15 in.   **2.** 8 cm.   **3.** 15·6 in.
4. 12·0.   **5.** 12 in.   **6.** 7 cm.
7. 1·6 in.   **8.** 13·3 in.   **9.** $n^2 + 1.$
10. $2n^2 + 2n + 1.$ **11.** $2xy.$ **12.** 5·1.
13. 4·8.   **14.** 6.   **15.** 5 in., $2\frac{2}{5}$, $1\frac{4}{5}$.
16. 7·2 in., 5 in.   **17.** 20 in., 15 in.   **18.** 17 ft.
19. 7·5 cm.   **20.** 16 in.   **21.** 7 ft.
22. 18 ft.   **23.** 4·8 in.   **24.** 5 in.
25. 15 cm., 210 sq. cm.   **26.** 84 sq. cm.
27. 7·81   **28.** 4·12, 3·61, 6·40.   **29.** 2·8 in., 3·5 in.
30. 7·21 in., 8·25 in., 6·40 in.   **32.** 7 ft.

Exercises 33

1. ·364; ·577; 1·00; 2·748.   **2.** 50°, 31°, 63°.
4. 2·89.   **5.** 2·97.   **6.** 3·86.
7. 2·55.   **8.** 9·42.   **9.** 9·53.
10. 53° 8′.   **11.** 22° 37′.   **12.** 38° 39′.
13. 33° 42′; 45°.   **14.** 67° 22′; 112° 38′.
15. 6·50 ft.   **16.** 16° 16′.   **17.** 46·2 ft.
18. 7·50 in.   **19.** 4·05 cm.
20. 2·10; 9·90; 28°.   **21.** $\frac{5}{12}$; $\frac{4}{13}$.

22. $\dfrac{1}{\sqrt{2}}$; 35°.

Exercises 34

1. ·423; ·731; ·891   **2.** 30°; 44°; 63°.
4. 2·80.   **5.** 2·60.   **6.** 5·73.
7. 4.   **8.** 3·21.   **9.** 3·38 cm.
10. 36° 52′.   **11.** 53° 8′.   **12.** 41° 49′.
13. 7·51 cm.   **14.** 73° 44′.
15. 27·96 yd., 82·9 yd., 18° 38′.
16. 21·21 cm., 21·21 cm., 14·85 cm.
17. 16° 16′; 6·72 cm.   **18.** 229 ft.
19. 23·49 ft.   **20.** 9·40 in., 3·42 in.

EXERCISES 35

1. ·8290 ; ·6157 ; ·3420. **2.** 75° 31′, 71° 20 49° 27′.
3. ·9397, ·7986, ·4695, ·2079. **4.** 4·096 cm.
5. 1·5 in. **6.** 2·676 in. **7.** 6·128 cm.
8. 1·4862 in. **9.** 36° 52′. **10.** 70° 32′.
11. 38° 41′. **12.** 19·66 cm. **13.** 51° 19′.
14. 8·612, 9·456, 42° 19′. **15.** 6·18 ft.
16. 67° 23′, 1·923 in. **18.** 2·418 ft.
19. 60°, 2·887 ft., 5·774 ft., 5·774 ft.
20. 3·214 cm., 3·830 cm., 28° 36′.

EXERCISES 36

1. 117°, 75°, 40° ; 75°, 35° ; 63°, 28°, 42° ; 21°, 42°.
2. (1) N. 40° E., 040° ; N. 25° W., 335° ;
   W. 32° S., 238° ; E. 40° S., 130°.
   (2) S. 40° W., 220° ; S. 25° E., 155° ;
   E. 32° N., 058° ; W. 40° N., 310°.
3. 350·1 ft. **4.** 259·8 ft. **5.** 565 yd.
6. 14·4 ft. **7.** 26·23 yd. **8.** 18·2 yd.
9. 541 ft. **10.** 87·2 yd. ; 60·6 yd.
11. 5·959 ml. ; 10 ml. **12.** 286 ft.
13. 1·972. 2·527 ml. **14.** N. 21° 48′ E. ; 5·39 ml.
15. 12·63 naut. ml. **16.** 6·6 ft. per sec.
17. 163·2 yd. 125·1 yd. west of B.
18. 209 yd., 340 yd., 161 yd. **19.** 25° E. of S. ; 26·6 ml.
20. 11·4 ch. ; 2·5 ch. ; 4·6 ch. **21.** 382 yd.
22. 128 ch. ; 59 ch.
23. 127·3 ch., 147·7 ch., 64·6 ch. **24.** 13·6 ml. 295°.
25. 10·3 ml. ; 1 hr. 14 min. after leaving A.

REVISION PAPERS XI–XX

XI

4. 7 ft. **5.** 2·6125 ac.

XII

1. 1·23 in., 1·64 in., 2·46 sq. in.
4. 114 ml. **5.** 3 sq. in.

XIII

2. 1·72 sq. in. **3.** $\frac{7}{16}$. **4.** 12·4 ac.

XIV

1. $\frac{1}{3}$. **2.** 3·12 cm., 2·65 cm., 1·40 cm., 3·76 sq. cm.
4. 20·1 m.p.h., N. 30° E.

XV

1. 5·16 in., 7·37 in., 4·63 in., 48° 6′, 23·89 sq. in.
2. $\frac{1}{2}$. **5.** 2820 yd., 1810 yd., W. 34° N.

XVI

1. 56° 19′.   **2.** 7½ sq. in.   **5.** 29·9 ml., N. 30° E.

XVII

2. 6·28 sq. cm.   **5.** 233 ft.

XVIII

2. 20·4 cm., 64° 56′.   **3.** ¾.

XIX

1. 6·403 in., 7·071 in., 25° 6′, 9·604 sq. in.
2. 26° 34′, 8·94 in.   **3.** 12·59 ft., 3° 12′.
5. 8 cm., 123° 53′, 56° 7′.

XX

1. 3·84 in., 5 in., 77° 19′, 57° 22′.   **2.** 3.
5. 21·62 m.p.h., 101°, 12·42 p.m.

Exercises 37

1. 3 in.   **2.** 30 in.   **3.** 7 cm.
4. 16 in.   **5.** 9 cm.   **6.** 10·5 in.
7. 4 cm.   **8.** 9·6 in.   **9.** 3·4 in.
10. 2 cm.; or 14 cm.   **11.** 1·4 in.
12. 4·47 in.   **13.** 5 in.   **17.** (1) 12, (2) 9·6.
18. 5 cm.; 4 cm.   **19.** 10·4 cm.   **20.** 5 cm.

Exercises 38

1. 67½°.   **2.** 60°.   **3.** 58°.
4. 60°, 92°.   **5.** 65°.   **6.** 78°.
15. 60°, 30°, 60°.

Exercises 40

1. AB̂D = 60°; DB̂C = 56°; AĈB = 39°; BD̂C = 25°; BD̂A = 39°.
2. 35°.   **3.** 107°.   **4.** 105°.
5. 68°.   **9.** 104°.   **10.** 89°.
11. AF̂B = (180 − x)°; AÊB = (180 − 2x)°; FB̂E = x°.

Exercises 43

4. $x = 90 − 2y$.   **5.** 121°, 59°.   **6.** 75°, 58°, 47°.

Exercises 44

2. 15 in.   **3.** 61.   **9.** 2·7 cm.
10. 7·2 cm.

Exercises 45

1. 100.   **2.** 100.   **6.** 56°, 57°, 67°.

EXERCISES 46

5. 12.   **6.** 6.

9. $BD = s - b$; $BE = s - c$; $CE = s - b$; $CD = s - c$.

12. 7·0 cm., 4·3 cm.

REVISION PAPERS XXI–XXX

XXI

1. 1·4 cm. or 6·4 cm.   **3.** 20°, 70°.

XXII

1. 4·8 cm., 1·8 cm. and 4·5 cm.

2. 30°.   **3.** 60°.

XXIII

1. 4·8 in.   **2.** 33°.

XXIV

2. $3y - 2x = 180$.

XXV

1. 15 cm. 9·64 cm.

2. Fig. 1.   28°, 34°, 118° ;   Fig. 2.   48°, 54°, 78°.

3. 34°, 66°.

XXVI

1. 9·6 cm.   **2.** 72°.   **3.** 60°, 92°, 120°, 88°.

XXVII

1. 2·83 in., 1·53 in.   **2.** 74°, 87°, 106°, 93°.

3. 118°, 113°, 110°, 88°, 111°.

XXVIII

1. 1·73 in., 3·46 in.   **2.** 5 in.

XXIX

5. 1 in.

XXX

2. 68°, 47°, 65°.

EXERCISES 49

1. Obtuse, right, obtuse, obtuse.

2. $AD = 2\frac{3}{4}$ cm. ; $AE = 3\frac{2}{3}$ cm.

3. 3·9 in.   **4.** 3·46 in. ;   1·73 in.

5. $x = \dfrac{c^2 - a^2 - b^2}{2a}$.

8. $BD = 10$ in. ; $CD = 24$ in. ; $\triangle ABC = 264$ sq. in.

9. $AD = 6$ in. ; $AE = 2\frac{2}{3}$ in.

EXERCISES 50

2. $2\frac{1}{4}$ in., $3\frac{3}{4}$ in.   **3.** 12 in.   **4.** 7·21 in.

5. $x = \dfrac{c^2 + a^2 - b^2}{2a}$; $y = \dfrac{b^2 + a^2 - c^2}{2a}$

6. (1) 5 in.   (2) 84 sq. in.
7. 5 in., $2\frac{5}{7}$ in., 3·9 in.

EXERCISES 51

1. 10 in.   **2.** 14 cm.   **3.** $x = 3·7$.
                                      $y = 3·3$.

4. 7·6 cm., 11·9 cm., 13·2 cm.
5. 14·4 in., 10·0 in., 17·1 in.

6. $\dfrac{\sqrt{2c^2 + 2b^2 - a^2}}{2}$, etc.

EXERCISES 52

1. 6 in.   **2.** $2\frac{1}{2}$ in., 6 in.   **3.** 7 in.
4. 3 in.   **5.** 5 in.
6. AT = 8 in. ; OA = 11·3 in.
8. $h = r - \sqrt{(r^2 - d^2)}$.

REVISION PAPERS XXXI–XL

XXXI

3. 10 in.

XXXII

3. 7·22 cm.   8·54 cm.

XXXIII

2. $x = 4$, $y = 2$.

XXXIV

2. 12 cm.   3 cm.

XXXV

2. 60 ml.   **3.** 72 sq. in.   **5.** 7 sq. in.

XXXVI

2. $7\frac{1}{2}$ cm.   **3.** $2\frac{1}{2}$ in.   17·32 sq. in.

XXXVII

1. 2·68 cm   **2.** 2·5 in.   81 sq. in.

XXXVIII

1. 3·87 cm.

XL

1. 12 ml.

Exercises 54

1. $\frac{5}{7}$, $\frac{5}{9}$, $\frac{1}{3}$.   **2.** $\frac{11}{24}$.   **3.** $\frac{41}{80}$.
4. $\frac{1}{3}$, $\frac{1}{4}$, $\frac{1}{12}$.   **5.** $\frac{8}{9}$.   **6.** $\frac{2}{3}$.

11. $\dfrac{xy}{(x+y)^2 - xy}$.   **15.** $4 : 1 : 12$.

Exercises 55

1. $4\frac{2}{3}$.   **2.** $x = 3\frac{3}{4}$.   **4.** $3 : 4$.
$\qquad\qquad\qquad\qquad y = 5\frac{1}{3}$.

9. $\frac{5}{7}$.   **10.** $2 : 1 : 2$; $3 : 2$.   **11.** $0{\cdot}921 : 1$.

Exercises 56

1. $1{\cdot}75$ in., $\cdot75$ in., $4{\cdot}38$ in., $1{\cdot}88$ in.
2. $\cdot63$ in., $\cdot83$ in., $1{\cdot}04$ in.
3. $6\frac{2}{3}$.   **4.** $5\frac{1}{3}$.   **8.** $4\frac{4}{5}$.
9. $2{\cdot}02$.   **10.** $2{\cdot}18$.

Exercises 57

1. $2\frac{1}{3}$.   **2.** $3{\cdot}53$.   **3.** $52\frac{1}{2}$.
4. BC $2\frac{2}{5}$ in., $1\frac{3}{5}$ in.; CA $1\frac{1}{7}$ in., $\frac{6}{7}$ in.; AB $1, 2$.
9. $1{\cdot}5$ in.   **12.** 5 cm., 6 cm.
13. $2 : 1$; $3 : 1$.   **14.** $\frac{1}{3}$.

Exercises 58

2. DH $= 1{\cdot}2$ cm.; EH $= 1{\cdot}68$ cm.
3. AB $= 2{\cdot}55$ in.; DH $= 1\frac{1}{3}$ in.
4. BD, AB.   **5.** $1{\cdot}35$; $\frac{3}{7}$.

Exercises 59

2. 1 in.

Exercises 60

2. $\frac{2}{3}$.   **3.** $\frac{2}{3}$.   **4.** $\frac{8}{15}$.
5. 8 in., 6 in., $4\frac{2}{3}$ in.

Exercises 61

1. 5 cm., $2\frac{3}{5}$ cm., $1\frac{4}{5}$ cm., $3\frac{1}{5}$ cm.
6. 4 cm., 9 cm.   **11.** $4\sqrt{2}$.   **12.** $3\sqrt{2}$.

13. $\cdot48$ in.   **14.** $\dfrac{3 \pm \sqrt{5}}{2}$.   **15.** $2 \pm \sqrt{2}$.

Exercises 62

1. $1\frac{1}{3}$ sq. cm.   **2.** $\sqrt{15}$ in.   **3.** 10 sq. in.
4. $\frac{1}{3}$.   **5.** $\frac{16}{49}$.   **6.** $\frac{25}{64}$.
12. 4 sq. cm., 12 sq. cm., $2{\cdot}4$ sq. cm.

Revision Papers XLI–L

XLI

1. 2 : 1.   **2.** $\dfrac{ac}{b+c}$; $\dfrac{ab}{b+c}$.   **3.** 1 : 1.

XLII

2. OQ = 1·6 in. ; PQ = 1·2 in. ; AQ = $\frac{4}{5}\sqrt{13}$ in.
3. 3 : 1.   1 : 2.

XLIII

3. $\frac{4}{9}$.   **4.** $\frac{1}{9}$.

XLIV

2. 2 : 1.   **3.** $\frac{7}{24}$.

XLV

2. $\dfrac{2mn}{(m+n)^2}$.

XLVI

2. 1 : 3.

XLVII

2. 9 : 16.

XLVIII

2. (a) $\dfrac{4m^2n^2}{(m^2+n^2)^2}$.   (b) $\dfrac{ad}{(a+b)(c+d)}$.

XLIX

3. 4 : 1.   BD = $\dfrac{8\sqrt5}{5}$ in., DC = $\dfrac{2\sqrt5}{5}$ in.

L

3. $\frac{1}{3}$.

Exercises 65

6. 28° 4′.   **7.** 44° 54′.   **8.** 31° 58′.
9. 30° 48′.   **10.** 32° 53′.   **11.** 33° 36′.
12. 18° 23′.   **13.** 54° 33′.   **14.** 47° 58′.
15. 69° 18′.   **16.** 74° 58′.   **17.** 14° 58′.
18. 75° 2′.   **19.** 67° 22′.   **20.** 78° 13′.
21. 11° 47′.   **22.** 39° 48′.   **23.** 38° 39′.
24. 15° 30′.   **25.** (1) 7·46 in.   (2) 68° 51′.
26. 26° 34′, 56° 19′, 64° 46′.   **27.** 37° 34′.

Exercises 67

1. (*a*) 90°, (*b*) 90°, (*c*) 45°, (*d*) 45°, (*e*) 90°.
2. (*a*) 60° 39′, (*b*) 53° 8′, (*c*) 36° 52′, (*d*) 36° 52′, (*e*) 53° 8′, (*f*) 73° 44′.
3. 2 in., $2\sqrt{2}$ in. **4.** 2 in., 2·31 in. Area = 4·62 sq. in.
5. 29° 21′. **6.** 16 cm., 13·24 cm.
7. 2 in., $\sqrt{17}$ in. 8·245 sq. in. **8.** 38° 39′.
9. 62° 4′. **10.** 75° 58′. **11.** 71° 40′.
12. 59° 19′. **13.** 93° 22′. **14.** 95° 40′.
15. 105° 2′. **16.** 75° 58′; 71° 34′.
17. 75° 24′; 66° 7′. **18.** 53° 8′; 46° 51′.
19. 39° 48′; 63° 26′. **20.** 43° 19′.
21. 46° 10′. **22.** 62° 4′, 54° 44′.
23. 20°, 17° 49′, 14°. **24.** 40° 7′. **25.** 25° 30′.

Exercises 68

1. 150 sq. in. **2.** $9\frac{3}{8}$ sq. ft. **3.** 73·5 sq. cm.
4. 108 sq. in. **5.** 163·2 sq. cm. **6.** 16 in.
7. 4 in. **8.** $137\frac{1}{3}$ sq. ft. **9.** 18 in., 12 in
10. 600. **11.** 4 in.

Exercises 69

1. 376 sq. in.; 480 cu. in. **2.** 133·9 sq. in.; 69·3 cu. in.
3. 689·1 sq. in.; 1018 cu. in. **4.** 563·1 sq. cm.; 831·4 cu. cm.
5. 6 sq. ft. **6.** 512 cu. in. **7.** 1 cu. ft. 139 cu. in.
8. $14\frac{2}{7}$ per cent. **9.** 56250 cu. ft. **10.** 36.
11. 225 gal. **12.** $1\frac{1}{5}$ ft.
13. 600 sq. ft.; 1016 sq. ft.; 6240 cu. ft. **14.** 344 sq. ft.
15. 1897 sq. in.; $3\frac{8}{9}$ cu. ft. **16.** $1\frac{3}{5}$ in.

Exercises 70

1. 175·4 sq. in.; 144 cu. in. **2.** 159·2 sq. cm.; 72·2 c.c.
3. 127·7 sq. in.; 144·9 cu. in. **4.** 128·1 sq. cm.; 110·8 c.c.
5. 4·1 in.; 43·3 sq. in.; 14·7 cu. in. **6.** $197\frac{1}{3}$ cu. in.
7. 74 sq. in.; 32 cu. in.
8. 12 in.; 206·4 sq. in.; 192 cu. in.
9. 390·7 sq. ft. $966\frac{2}{3}$ cu. ft. **10.** $\frac{1}{12}$ cu. ft.

Exercises 71

1. 4752 sq. cm. **2.** 1100 sq. in. **3.** 15400 c.c.
4. 2310 cu. in. **5.** 264 sq. cm. **6.** $5\frac{1}{4}$ in.
7. 8 in. **8.** 8 in. **9.** 2·5 cm.
10. $1145\frac{5}{6}$ sq. ft. **11.** 3·91 in. **12.** $2\frac{3}{4}$ cu. in.
13. 1433 c.c. **14.** 14·4 lb. **15.** 231 cu. in.
16. 70 sq. in. **17.** 1·36 m.p.h. **18.** 4·1 ft.
19. 18. **20.** 24 sq. in.

EXERCISES 72

1. $301\frac{5}{7}$ sq. cm.; $301\frac{5}{7}$ c.c. $452\frac{4}{7}$ sq. cm.; $402\frac{2}{7}$ c.c.
2. 6·5 in.; $70\frac{5}{7}$ sq. in.; $39\frac{2}{7}$ cu. in.
3. 68·39 sq. cm. 64·37 c.c.   **4.** 241 cu. cm.
5. 700 sq. in.   **6.** 88° 24′.
7. 1100 cu. in. 369 sq. in.   **8.** 105 sq. in., 132 cu. in.
9. 227 cu. in.   **10.** 253 sq. ft.   **11.** 1155 cu. in.
12. 121 c.c.   **13.** $\frac{1}{3}$ in.   **14.** 498 cu. in.
15. 17·3 cm.; 453 c.c.   **16.** 60°.
17. $509\frac{1}{7}$ cu. in.   **18.** 9·52 ft. from top.

EXERCISES 73

1. 453 sq. in. 905 cu. in.   **2.** 616 sq. cm. 1437 c.c.
3. 7 in.   **4.** 9·44 cm.   **5.** $22\frac{11}{24}$ cu. in.
6. 214.   **7.** $3\frac{27}{35}$ in.   **8.** 1·0 cm.
9. 5095 cu. in.   **10.** 27,000.   **11.** 11·48 in.
12. 598 sq. cm.   **13.** $2\sqrt{3}$ in.   **14.** 1·82 ft.
15. $261\frac{19}{21}$ cu. in.   **16.** $62\frac{6}{7}$ sq. in.   **17.** $37\frac{5}{7}$ sq. in.
18. Ht. 4·7 in. Diam. 5·5 in.
19. 3 in.   **20.** 70·28 in.

EXERCISES 74

1. 3064 ml.   **2.** 20590 ml.
3. 10020 ml.; 23050 ml.   **4.** 586 m.p.h.
5 $1\cdot844 \times 10^8$ sq. ml.; $1\cdot217 \times 10^8$ sq. ml.
6. 2794 ml.   **7.** 1640 ml.   **8.** 1122 ml.
9. 8467 ml. 7612 ml.
10. 47° N.   **11.** 12°.

REVISION PAPERS LI–LX

LI

1. (1) 22° 37′; (2) 67° 23′; (3) 36° 52′; (4) 22° 37′.
2. 26° 7′.
4. 236 sq. in.; 240 cu. in.; $5\sqrt{5}$ in.   **5.** 18·3 in.

LII

1. 22° 32′.   **2.** $56\frac{4}{7}$ sq. in.; 48·99 cu. in.
3. $\frac{1}{4}$.
4. (1) $2\sqrt{13}$ in.; (2) 64° 21′; (3) 76° 30′.
5. $2880\frac{20}{21}$ cu. in.

LIII

1. 86° 38′.
2. (1) 461·09 sq. ft.; (2) 1056 c. ft.; (3) 33° 42′.
3. Sphere of radius 4 in., centre at mid-pt. of XY.
4. 35° 16′, 45°.   **5.** $121\frac{1}{14}$ cu. in.

LIV

1. 341·2, 49° 23′.   **2.** 32 in., $10\sqrt{15}$ in., 30 in., 15° 39′.
3. 53° 8′, 69° 27′.   **4.** 3105 ml.   **5.** 53·31 in.

LV

1. $5\sqrt{2}$ in., $34°$ $27'$, $1\cdot25$ in.   **2.** (1) 8 in., (2) $251\cdot4$ sq. in.
3. $17°$ $4'$.   **4.** 3456 ml. ; $7\cdot355$ days.
5. 10 in.

LVI

1. (1) $28\cdot62$ sq. in. ; (2) $57°$.   **2.** 14 ft., $28°$ $3'$.
3. $1\cdot816$ in.   **4.** 3042 ml.
5. $4\sqrt{2}$ in. ; $12\cdot94$ sq. in.

LVII

1. $104\cdot7$ ft. ; $42°$; $49°$ $36'$.
2. $5\sqrt{2}$ in., 13 in., $45°$ $14'$, $67°$ $23'$.
3. 1615 sq. cm., 9664 c.c.
4. $14°$ $2'$, $12°$ $36'$.   **5.** $1\cdot2$ in.

LVIII

1. $38°$ $41'$, $14°$ $29'$.   **2.** 17 in., $28°$ $4'$, $7\cdot2$ in.
3. 110 sq. in., $163\frac{3}{7}$ cu. in.   **4.** $49°$ $46'$.
5. $A'B' = 4$ in., $B'C' = 12$ in., $C'A' = \sqrt{140}$ in.

LIX

1. $30°$ $26'$, $35°$ $38'$.   **2.** $29°$ $1'$, $45°$.
3. $6\cdot6$ in., $694\cdot9$ cu. in.   **4.** $17\cdot93$ in.
5. $48°$ $35'$, $4\cdot58$ ft.

LX

1. $2\sqrt{3}$ in., $\sqrt{3}$ in., $35°$ $16'$.   **2.** $\sqrt{3}$ in.
3. $3\cdot46$ in., $49°$ $6'$, $60°$.   **4.** $587\cdot9$ cu. in. ; $339\frac{3}{7}$ sq. in.
5. $\sqrt{5}$ in., $\sqrt{3}$ in. ; $90°$; $63°$ $26'$.

EXAMINATION PAPERS

1. (2) $\frac{3}{5}$, $\frac{2}{3}$, $\frac{8}{27}$.   (5) 3 in. ; $83°$ $47'$.
2. (5) $67°$ $23'$, $75°$ $58'$.
3. (4)(a) 4 in.
     (5) (1) $28°56'$ N.   (2) 272 ml.
4. (4) $\dfrac{abc}{(b + c)(a + c)^2}$.
     (5) 1. $1\cdot44$ ft.   2. $68°$ $51'$.   **3.** $3\cdot73$ ft.
          4. $79°$ $3'$.
5. (2) $5\frac{1}{4}$ in. ; 3 in.   (5) $7°$ $6'$.
6. (5) 1. 864 cu. ft.   **2.** 9 ft.   **3.** $26°$ $34'$.
         4. 401 sq. ft.
7. (5) 1. $3\cdot464$ in.   **2.** $4\cdot92$ in.
8. (5) 1. $\sqrt{13}$ in.   2. $64°$ $20'$.   **3.** $76°$ $30'$.
9. (5) $13\cdot96$ in. ; $34\cdot5°$ E.
10. (2) $12\frac{1}{2}$ in.
      (5) 1. $59°$ $2'$.   2. $2\cdot06$ in.